ERRATA

The European Vision of America

Number 2, line 28: *for* Lorenzo de Pier Francesco dei Medici *read* Lorenzo di Pier Francesco de' Medici

Number 6, column 6, line 26: *for* Los Casa's *read* Las Casas's

Number 7: This object will not be exhibited.

Number 14: See illustration for full inscription.

Number 15, column 2, line 12: *for* seventeenth century *read* sixteenth century

Number 16, line 35: *delete* and the oceans are enamelled blue. The enamelling is on the inside of the base, not the outside of the cup. Last item of literature, *for* col. 8600 *read* col. 860

Number 19, Biography of Mercator, column 2, line 1: *for* Biblioteca Civico *read* Biblioteca Civica

Page 57, line 25: *for* Tageses *read* Tagetes

Page 58, line 40: *for* Füch's *read* Füchs's

Number 28, column 3, line 40: *for* Anaimalium *read* Animalium

Number 41: Catesby biography, column 2, line 9, *for* engravings *read* etchings

Numbers 42, 43: *for* Engraving coloured by hand *read* Etching coloured by hand

Number 58, line 12: *for* 1610 *read* 1510

Number 61, line 15: *for* Villegegnon *read* Villegagnon

Number 70, line 46: *for* Vindodenensis *read* Vindobonensis

Page 100, line 28: *for* Marian *read* Merian

Number 86: *for* Jan van der Street *read* Jan van der Straet

Number 89, line 12: *for* anachronistic *read* anachoristic

Number 91 line 20: *for* an elongated Brazilian club *read* a feathered spear

Page 123 line 17: *for* Westwards he founde *read* Westwards be founde

Number 97: This object will not be exhibited.

Numbers 103, 104, 105: The impressions exhibited are uncoloured and not gilded.

Number 103, column 2, line 19: *should read:* The engraving exhibited shows the American attendants of the duc de Guise. There are hand-coloured copies of this work in the Bibliothèque Nationale, Paris, and the Bibliothèque Municipale, Versailles.

Number 109: This painting will be also exhibited in Cleveland.

Number 110: The cover and base are of carved horn, not of silver. The reference to an embossed base is incorrect.

Number 111: *The Credit should read* Dr. H. Popta-Gasthuis (on permanent loan to the Fries Museum, Leeuwarden)

Page 157, line 9: *for* Santa Domingo *read* Santo Domingo

Numbers 134, 135, 138: Not exhibited in Washington.

Number 144: This object will not be exhibited.

Number 170, line 14: *for* Mohican *read* Mahican

Number 183: *for* Pastel *read* Watercolour

Number 217: *for* terracotta *read* terra-cotta medallion in wooden frame

Numbers 219, 221: The illustrations of the obverses of the *Daniel Morgan Medal* and *Diplomatic Medal* are transposed.

Number 223, column 2, line 19: *for* van Hetsch *read* von Hetsch

Page 267, line 31: *for* Stevens *read* Stephens

Number 264, column 3: line 24, *for* begonias *read* bignonias

Number 279, line 9: *for* Mohicans *read* Mahicans

Number 281, column 2, line 15: *for* Montezume *read* Montezuma

Number 293: *for* engraving *read* etching

Number 326, column 2, line 13: *for* reckless *read* feckless

Page 376: Photograph credits. Nicholas Hlobeczy, Cleveland—27, 28, 29, 36-39, 42, 43, 63, 70, 204, 242, 243, 247, 248, 257, 276, 310, 322, 328, 329; National Gallery of Art, Washington, D.C.—340.

Page 377, line 45: *for* Museum Volkwang *read* Museum Folkwang

The European Vision of America

The European Vision of America

HUGH HONOUR

A special exhibition to honor the Bicentennial of the United States
organized by The Cleveland Museum of Art with the collaboration
of the National Gallery of Art, Washington,
and the Réunion des Musées Nationaux, Paris

EXHIBITION ORGANIZERS

William S. Talbot, The Cleveland Museum of Art
Irène Bizot, Réunion des Musées Nationaux

Published by The Cleveland Museum of Art

This exhibition was made possible by substantial grants from the National Endowment for the Humanities and the National Endowment for the Arts, Federal agencies.

A gift from Central National Bank has enabled the Cleveland showing to be open to the public without charge.

In Charge of the Exhibition

Gaillard Ravenel, Curator
National Gallery of Art

William S. Talbot, Associate Curator of Painting,
The Cleveland Museum of Art

Pierre Rosenberg, Conservateur au Département
des Peintures, Musée du Louvre

Exhibition Schedule

National Gallery of Art: December 7, 1975 through February 15, 1976

The Cleveland Museum of Art: April 28 through August 8, 1976

Grand Palais, Paris: September 17, 1976 through January 3, 1977

Cover illustration: *America* (detail), tapestry woven at the Beauvais Tapestry factory after Jean-Jacques-Francois Le Barbier the Elder (1738-1826), France, 1789-1791, silk and wool, 144 x 180 inches (366 x 457 cm.). Lent by Artemis S.A. Catalogue number 195.

Distributed by The Kent State University Press, Kent, Ohio 44242.

© 1975 by The Cleveland Museum of Art
University Circle, Cleveland, Ohio 44106
Typesetting by Dumar Typesetting, Dayton, Ohio 45404
Printing by The Meriden Gravure Company, Meriden, Connecticut 06450

Library of Congress Cataloging in Publication Data

Honour, Hugh.
   The European vision of America.
   Includes index.
   1. United States in Art. 2. Art, European—Exhibitions. I. United States. National Gallery of Art. II. Cleveland Museum of Art. III. Réunion des musées nationaux, Paris. IV. Title.
N8214.5.U6H57   709'.4'074   75-35892
ISBN 0-910386-26-9
ISBN 0-910386-27-7 pbk.

Contents

Foreword

After two hundred years of existence, the United States is quite properly being asked to examine and re-examine itself in addition to just celebrating its birthday. At nearly all institutions, particularly those concerned with the arts and humanities, months of meetings and debate have preceded the adoption of a "Bicentennial program" for that institution. And in almost all cases the thinking has involved the celebration or examination of unique and peculiarly American ways or achievements.

But in the twentieth century, and particularly with World War II and after, nations could no longer be islands unto themselves. Some of the most damaging and critical miscalculations have resulted from native pride combined with lack of profound knowledge about other people. Are not our confident self-evaluations usually self-serving? How might an objective observer see a given problem — or even an unobjective one — but at least an observer with a different viewpoint who would offer the proverbial second side of the question?

Such a proposition lies at the base of the exhibition, The European Vision of America. The idea was first proposed by Cleveland's Curator of Chinese Art, Wai-kam Ho, at a staff meeting some three years ago. Why not, when most art museums would be ransacking their galleries and storages for American material culture, select from the vast collections of Europe those visual images that would tell us what Europeans saw here and what they felt and thought about things for which Americans have traditional opinions? A single literary work obviously and properly pointed the way — de Tocqueville's *Democracy in America*, still one of the finest analyses and evaluations of the American political state. Why not transfer the intentions and methods of this French observer to the study of the visual images of the New World?

Initial planning and study confirmed the validity of the concept and the feasibility of mounting an exhibition to demonstrate it. The study also indicated that a distinguished specialist was required to do research, to seek works of art in very out-of-the-way locations, and to write a meaningful catalogue that would both elucidate the exotic mixture for the layman and make a scholarly contribution justifying the considerable expense and risk involved in mounting such an exhibition. Discussions were begun with Hugh Honour and his enthusiasm for the idea of the exhibition was reciprocated by our delight in finding a qualified scholar who understood the purposes of an art exhibition — the combination of visual delight with intellectual stimulation. The depth of his study, the success of his travels, and the grace of his prose is evident in the exhibition and its catalogue.

Now these are a reality; but we doubt that many can have any idea of how complex and enervating the task of completion was. Ninety cities, well over one hundred museums, libraries, and institutions, hundreds of letters, dozens of overseas calls and cables, as well as the inevitable conferences in Europe, Washington, and Cleveland, make up only the beginning of an endless litany. The generous and understanding patronage of both The National Endowments for the Arts and the Humanities was obtained and the exhibition could never have been achieved without their support, including the confidence given us by Miss Nancy Hanks and Dr. Ronald Berman, the heads of these two creative governmental agencies.

The institutional cooperation among the Réunion des Musées Nationaux de France, the National Gallery of Art, and The Cleveland Museum of Art, always good, was excellent in all the necessary matters involving administration, and the mechanics of transportation, insurance, printing, etc. We are particularly pleased that France, still our ally after two hundred years, is the place of exhibition abroad. The Réunion assembled all loans from France and after the showing in Paris will return the entire exhibition to the individual lenders.

One particular staff member of The Cleveland Museum of Art, Dr. William S. Talbot, Associate Curator of Paintings, deserves special mention, for next to Hugh Honour he was responsible for the success of this venture. His work involved all phases of scholarship and organization in connection with the European Vision of America, and he completed all tasks with intelligence, energy, and dispatch. We know that we speak for our guest curator, Mr. Honour, and for all of us in offering Dr. Talbot every thanks and congratulations for his crucial supporting work.

Without the lenders there would be no exhibition and to them go our thanks and the gratitude of every visitor. The burdens of correspondence, photography, insurance, preparation, and transport were heavy on all. That so many curators and librarians were willing to entrust their valuable objects to us encouraged greatly the realization of an exhibition which would justify that confidence.

Lenders are individually acknowledged elsewhere but we would like especially to thank Sir John Pope-Hennessy and John Gere of the British Museum; Lord Eccles, Chairman, British Library Board, and D. H. Turner, I. R. Willison, and Helen Wallis of that institution; R. S. Johnson-Gilbert, The Royal College of Surgeons of England; and C. M. Kauffman and R. J. Charleston of the Victoria and Albert Museum. We are also most grateful for the extensive and vital cooperation of Michel Laclotte, Pierre Rosenberg, and Maurice Serullaz of the Louvre; Etienne Dennery, Jean Adhémar, and M. Nortier of the Bibliothèque Nationale; Gérald Van der Kemp and Pierre Lemoine, Chateau de Versailles; and Reynold Arnould, Joachim Menzhausen and P. Arnold, Staatliche Kunstsammlungen, Dresden; Ulla Krempel, Bayerischen Staatsgemäldesammlungen, Munich; Musée National de la Coopération Franco-Américaine, Blérancourt; Ernst Mick, Deutsches Tapetenmuseum, Kassel; Heinrich Geissler, Staatsgalerie, Stuttgart; and Torben Monberg, Danish National Museum, Copenhagen. A particular debt of thanks is owed to Ruben Leitão, Director General of Cultural Affairs of Portugal.

In America we owe a special debt of gratitude to Clare Le Corbellier and Suzanne Boorsch of the Metropolitan Museum of Art; Herbert Sanborn, Milton Kaplan, and William Matheson of the Library of Congress; Christian Rohlfing of the Cooper-Hewitt Museum of Design; Elizabeth Roth of the New York Public Library; Dianne Pilgrim of the Brooklyn Museum and Goodhue Diament of Philadelphia. For their invaluable assistance we are particularly in the debt of William Bond, The Houghton Library, Harvard University; Richard Ludwig, Princeton University Library; Genevieve Miller, Howard Dittrick Museum of Historical Medicine, Cleveland; and Wesley Williams, Case Western Reserve University Library.

In organizing this exhibition we have had the inestimable assistance and counsel of Hubert Landais and Irène Bizot of the Réunion des Musées Nationaux and Danielle De Metz of the Musées Classés et Controllés.

Gaillard Ravenel, assisted by George Sexton were in charge of the exhibition including gallery design at the National Gallery of Art. Installation at The Cleveland Museum of Art was under the direction of William Ward.

Without the critical scholarship and dedicated efforts of two young art historians, Carol C. Clark and Kenneth Pearson, and the unflagging assistance of Martha Beall and Jean L. Cox, this exhibition simply would never have been realized.

Sherman E. Lee
J. Carter Brown
Emmanuel de Margerie

Author's Acknowledgments

I have incurred very many personal debts to friends and colleagues for help with this exhibition and I should like to take this opportunity of thanking them most warmly. First of all Dr. Sherman Lee and with him at Cleveland Dr. William S. Talbot for their enthusiastic and unfailing support, as also Mr. Henry Hawley and Mrs. Carol Clark. M. Pierre Rosenberg in Paris has been a constant fount of valuable information. To the generosity with which Prof. Detlef Heikamp and Dr. William C. Sturtevant allowed me to share their learning I owe a very great deal. In writing the catalogue I have had the constant encouragement and collaboration of Mr. John Fleming. Others to whom I am indebted for help in various ways include M. Jean Adhémar, Mr. Noel Blakiston, Mr. David Carritt, Mr. Ian Graham, Prof. Francis Haskell, M. André Kamber, Dr. Gerdt Kutscher, Mr. Alastair Laing, Dr. Hans Lüthy, Prof. J. R. Martin, Mrs. Georgina Masson, Mr. Terence Mullaly, Mr. Benedict Nicolson, Mme. Odile Nouvel, and Prof. Robert Rosenblum.

Hugh Honour

Introduction

"It needs to be painted by the hand of a Berruguete or some other excellent painter like him, or by Leonardo da Vinci or Andrea Mantegna, famous painters whom I knew in Italy," wrote Fernandez de Oviedo in the 1530s.[1] He was trying to describe an American plant so strangely unlike any to be seen in Europe that he was uncertain whether it was a species of tree or some monstrous anomaly of nature. Nearly three centuries later the great German explorer and scientist Alexander von Humboldt was still calling for painters capable of doing justice to America.[2] Both men were keenly aware of how different it all was from everything in Europe. And from their writings some sense can be gained of what Europeans felt at first sight of that "fresh green breast of the new world," when, for a transitory moment, as Scott Fitzgerald wrote, "man must have held his breath in the presence of this continent, compelled into an aesthetic contemplation he neither understood nor desired, face to face for the last time in history with something commensurate to his capacity for wonder."[3]

From the very beginning the American reality seems to have been too strange, too alien for most Europeans, and especially artists, to assimilate. In 1515 Albrecht Dürer drew in the margin of the Books of Hours he decorated for the Emperor Maximilian I an American Indian—a feathered figure of fantasy who looks like a snub-nosed German youth dressed up for some Nuremberg pageant, though his cap of short feathers and his feathered sceptre seem to have been drawn from genuine Tupinamba specimens that must have reached Germany by that date. Five years later Dürer saw the far more elaborate Aztec featherwork and richly decorated goldsmiths' work sent to Charles V by Cortés and "marvelled at the subtle *ingenia* of men in foreign lands."[4] But for once in his life he seems to have been without a pen or paint brush in his hand to make a visual record. Most of the objects were soon destroyed, and the same fate befell the masterpieces of gold sent from Peru to Spain in 1534. They were wondered at—but duly consigned to the melting pot just the same. Only a very few collectors seem to have valued Mexican works of art. The Hapsburgs in Austria and the Medici in Florence were quite exceptional in this respect—and even they seem to have admired them mainly as curiosities—though one may wonder why Tommaso dei Cavalieri, the friend for whom Michelangelo made so many of his finest drawings, included Mexican featherwork among the antique marbles in his collection in Rome. The conjunction must have been very odd.[5]

Had pre-Columbian objects arrived in Europe a century earlier, Aztec and Inca motifs might well have found their way into the repertory of late Gothic ornament alongside those derived from Oriental art. As it was, they reached Europe at a moment when artists, as well as scientists, were obsessed with their classical past and congratulating themselves on having

Numbers in brackets [ ] refer to catalogue numbers in the exhibition. The bibliographic notes for books and prints include the most important items whether or not they refer to the example exhibited. In listing the dimensions of an object, height precedes width and depth.

1

thrown off all traces of Gothic barbarism. The study of antiquity and the sciences were interdependent in the Renaissance, and the widening horizons opened up by scientific and geographical discoveries were scanned through classical lenses. Just as botanists earnestly tried to identify plants from the New World with those mentioned by Dioscorides and Pliny, so artists strove to fit America into a classical scheme of things artistically. An extreme example of this is provided by Peter Paul Rubens in his evocation of Potosí, painted in 1635, with classical gods and goddesses completely overshadowing the monkeys and parrots and the Peruvians emerging from the silver mines. The European visions of both the classical past and of America were, of course, partly, perhaps largely, wish-fulfillment dreams. But the former was static, the latter constantly developing. And whereas Europeans tended to regard Antiquity as their parent, to be revered, America was their child—the inheritor and repository of their own virtues and vices, aspirations and fears.

The recent discussion as to whether Europeans discovered or, as the Mexican historian Edmundo O'Gorman[6] argues, "invented" America—which may seem at first to be no more than a verbal quibble—serves as a reminder of the way in which the New World was revealed: not suddenly with the news of Christopher Columbus's landfall, but very gradually over the course of more than half a century. It was not until 1507 that Martin Waldseemüller charted a single landmass by joining up the various "islands" which had been explored on the far side of the Atlantic, not until 1522 that this continent's separation from Asia was established by the first circumnavigation of the globe, not until the 1550s that its discovery was hailed as "the greatest event since the creation of the world, excepting the incarnation and death of Him who created it."[7] But as early as 1493 Columbus's first letter had conjured up for Europeans an image very different from any that he had in fact seen in the Indies. Thus a myth preceded awareness of the reality of America in European minds.

Columbus believed he had reached the Spice Islands, which were well known to Europeans from the books of Marco Polo and especially "Sir John Mandeville," whose fantastic account of the marvels of the East had often been no less fantastically illustrated.[8] But the phrases in which Columbus described these islands recalled those used by Latin poets in their evocations of the Hesperides or Islands of the Blest, where eternal springtime reigned, and men lived as they did in the Golden Age, without toil or strife. His report may, therefore, have seemed to fuse two pre-existing ideas—those of a fabulous Orient and an idealised Europe—and so his islands could be visualised in familiar imagery.

The first readers of Columbus's letter included a Florentine sculptor and architect, Luca Fancelli, who had formerly worked under that great exem-

2

plar of Renaissance ideals, Leon Battista Alberti. Before the end of 1493 Fancelli informed his patron, the humanist Marquess of Mantua, of the letter, which told how the king of Spain had sent some ships across the ocean, where they had

> discovered certain isles, among others towards the East a very large isle which has very great rivers and terrible mountains and much fertile land, and is inhabited by handsome men and women, though they are entirely naked except for some who cover their genitals with a leaf made of cotton, and that the country is very abundant in gold, and the people generous with their possessions, and there is abundance of palms and more than six spices, and amazingly high trees, and that there are more islands of which five are named, and one of them is almost as large as Italy, and that the rivers bear gold, and that they have much copper but no iron, and many other marvels.[9]

Another Florentine artist in the same year illustrated this fabulous, hilly island, with its tall trees—including a palm—and naked people, in the woodcut frontispiece to the poem by Giuliano Dati, in which Dati translated Columbus's letter into the language and metre of a chivalric romance. Both artist and poet visualised the discovery as if it were a scene in *Orlando innamorato* or one of the other early Renaissance epics which were so often depicted on *cassoni* at this period [1]. And exactly the same design was used again some twelve years later on the title-page of the letters to Pier Soderini in which Vespucci described his voyages.

Amerigo Vespucci, like Columbus, believed that he had reached the shores of Asia, but his more vividly colourful letters gave much greater prominence to the extraordinary aspects of the land which was soon to be named after him. He thus provided greater scope for the imagination—and for his illustrators [3]. The general impression he gave may be deduced from a German woodcut of about 1505, which shows a group of Brazilian cannibals above an inscription summarising his report:

> The people are thus naked, handsome, brown, well-formed in body, their heads, necks, arms, privy parts, feet of women and men are slightly covered with feathers. The men also have many precious stones in their faces and breasts. No one owns anything but all things are in common. And the men have as wives those that please them, be they mothers, sisters or friends, therein they make no difference. They also fight with each other. They also eat each other even those who are slain, and hang the flesh of them in smoke. They live one hundred and fifty years. And have no government.[10]

This may seem the image of a very strange new world. Yet the nudity, free-love, longevity, and absence of both property and laws were all features of the Golden Age, while anthropophagy was known from both Mandeville and classical literature. In only one important respect did these people differ from the races of man previously described—in the use of feathers for such scanty garments as they wore.

The Indian in a feather head-dress—and usually a feather skirt, with which the European imagination had endowed him—made a prompt appearance in works of art. He figures in a very early sixteenth-century Portuguese painting as one of the Magi [4] and in another, slightly later, as the devil presiding over the torments of the damned [7]. In about 1512-16, Albrecht Altdorfer and Hans Burgkmair showed him marching in *The Triumph of the Emperor Maximilian I* [5], and he reappeared in two German drawings of about 1520, holding a Mexican shield in one of them.[11] He characterised the native population on maps of America. From the 1570s to the early nineteenth century, a woman decked in feathers symbolised the continent in innumerable allegorical paintings and sculptures, not to mention the title-pages of books and other prints, as well as decorations on ceramics, glass, silver, furniture, and textiles. From works of art the image passed into literature. Edmund Spenser in *The Faerie Queene* described

> paynted plumes in goodly order dight,
> Like as the sunburnt Indians do aray
> Their tawny bodies in their proudest plight.[12]

Francis Bacon speculated on why Indians wore feathers and concluded that it was because their ancestors had taken refuge from the Flood in mountains "and were invited unto it by the infinite flights of birds, that came up to the high grounds, while the waters stood below."[13] An idea of Indians derived from prints was clearly in John Milton's mind when he wrote in *Paradise Lost*:

> *Columbus* found th'*American* so girt
> With feathered Cincture, naked else and wilde
> Among the Trees on Iles and woodie Shores.[14]

As late as 1814 Alexander von Humboldt remarked:

> When we speak in Europe of a native of Guiana we figure to ourselves a man whose head and waist are decorated with the fine feathers of the macaw, the toucan and the humming-bird. Our painters and sculptors have long since regarded these ornaments as the characteristic marks of an American.[15]

While feather head-dresses and cinctures indicated the alien and exotic characteristics of the Indian, the nakedness of the rest of their bodies permitted their assimilation into the classically based European tradition. It may often have been simply for want of other models that artists depicted them with the proportions and poise of Greek and Roman statues. But travellers had also compared the Indians to these idealised nudes. The

4

Rhode Island Indians looked "very much like the antique," Giovanni da Verrazano wrote in 1524. And at a time when perfect physique was supposed to reveal qualities of soul, this heroic nudity had moral significance. The classical nudes stalking through the jungle in the illustrations to André Thevet's book on Brazil [61] may thus have inspired Pierre de Ronsard's description of the Tupinamba as being as free from malice as from clothes, still living "en leur age doré," though Thevet's text provided a far from favourable account of their way of life.[16] Michel de Montaigne had seen Brazilians in Rouen, but his belief in the superiority of "cannibales" to contemporary Europeans was perhaps strengthened by similar images[17] —epitomised some years earlier in Jan Mostaert's *West Indian Scene* [6]. In this, the first European painting of the New World, classically nude figures are shown in an Arcadian pastoral landscape invaded by Spanish troops, who seem to be on the point of converting an age of gold into one of iron. Similar confrontations of heroically nude Indians with steel-plated Spaniards were later to appear on page after page of Theodor de Bry's great collection of illustrated American travel literature [64, 65, 66, 67]. In this way, artists and especially book illustrators played a part of some importance in the diffusion of the "black legend" of Spanish atrocity—and also, of course, of the myth of the "noble savage."

The Indians were not invariably classicised, however. In 1528 Christoph Weiditz sketched with vivid immediacy and directness the Mexican jugglers and ball-players brought to Spain by Cortés (see photographs in the first gallery). The German mercenary Hans Staden did his amateur best to record the "wild, naked man-eating people" by whom he had been captured and almost cooked and eaten in Brazil [60]. In the 1580s John White made several watercolours of the Indians living near Roanoke Island, where the first "Virginia" colony was briefly established [9, 11]. And although he stressed their more attractive characteristics, he faithfully portrayed the strange ways in which they decked their hair, painted their bodies, and partly concealed their nakedness. Significantly, the book in which the watercolours were first published provided Shakespeare with hints for the more amiable traits in Caliban's character.[18] White also drew the strange fishes, reptiles, birds, and flowers he saw, recording them with the skill of a scientific illustrator [30-34]. He may, indeed, have been trained as a cartographer, for at this time map-makers were often required to depict the native inhabitants, birds, and beasts of the lands they charted (see section II).

Although it was the utter strangeness of American wild-life which struck the earliest explorers, few were able to describe its plants, birds, and beasts except by comparison with those already familiar to Europeans. Awareness that the flora and fauna of Central and South America were not

5

merely strange and unlike those in the Old World but were zoologically and botanically quite distinct thus dawned very slowly, and it was not until the 1740s that Georges Buffon announced the fact as a great discovery. The first arrivals in Europe were macaws, similar to but much larger and more gaudily coloured than the African parrots which had for so long been prized. They made a precocious appearance on the *Cantino Map* of 1502 (clearly distinguished from their Old World cousins)[19] and were soon incorporated in works of art, including the classical grotesques painted under the direction of Raphael in the *Logge* of the Vatican. Other American birds and animals more rarely attracted the attention of artists, but a turkey-cock figured in a cartoon for a tapestry by Bronzino before 1549[20] and a sculpture by Giovanni da Bologna of about 1567. The llama was neatly represented in an allegory of Peru on a medal by G. P. Poggini in 1562. American plants, which were destined to play a much more important part in the lives of Europeans than were American animals and birds, seem to have attracted little attention from artists, apart from those who illustrated travel-books (like Oviedo's of 1547, which includes the earliest print of a prickly pear) and, of course, the treatises of naturalists.

In the second half of the sixteenth century naturalists and illustrators— among whom Jacopo Ligozzi was artistically the most accomplished— began to reveal the extraordinary richness of American wild-life, gradually creating the image of a luxuriant landscape with gaudily coloured flowers and birds and strange beasts and reptiles. This new view found expression in Stradanus's drawing of Vespucci discovering America, which incorporates a pineapple plant, tapir, ant-eater, opossum, and sloth [86]. The study of American natural history was, however, haphazard and based on imported specimens, more often dead than alive. The pioneer ornithologist Pierre Belon derived his knowledge of American birds from carcasses brought back from Brazil by sailors [25]. The toucan he knew only by its beak. In 1571 a Spanish naturalist, Francisco Hernandez, led a scientific expedition to Mexico, but his findings remained unpublished for many years, and his vast collection of drawings was destroyed by fire in 1671.[21] Hence we see the importance of the work achieved by naturalists and painters employed by Count (later Prince) Maurits of Nassau in Dutch Brazil between 1638 and 1644. They provided the first full scientific and visual record of any part of the American continent, made generally available in the *Historia naturalis Brasiliae* (1648) by Willem Piso and Georg Marcgrave.

The artists employed by Prince Maurits included Frans Post and Albert Eckhout. The former specialised in landscapes of humid tropical greenery, often with diminutive figures of black slaves or Indians and, in the foreground, such animals as an armadillo or capybara [76, 79, 80]. Eckhout

6

painted still-lifes of Brazilian fruits and vegetables of gargantuan size and preternatural plumpness and juiciness [74]. But he is notable mainly for his life-size and almost disturbingly lifelike portraits of the Tapuya Indians. These are very remarkable indeed—quite without precedent in European art in their detached, objective observation of primitive people. In at least one painting—that of a Tapuya war dance—he broke completely free from all European conventions and stereotypes (see colour photographs in gallery 5). But all this seems to have gone over the heads of his contemporaries, for whom his almost scientifically accurate ethnological records were no more than exotic fantasies. Two of them were copied by Jan van Kessel in his fascinating allegory of America [109], and pictures by both Eckhout and Post (given by Maurits to Louis XIV in 1679) were used as the basis for the designs for tapestries woven at the Gobelins, in which the flora and fauna of America and Africa were freely mixed to satisfy a generalised taste for exoticism [114].

Van Kessel's painting brilliantly evokes the atmosphere of the *Wunderkammer,* those extraordinary private museums in which natural and artificial curiosities were displayed. Such hoards were first amassed in the early sixteenth century, mainly by princes, as a kind of humanist counterpart to mediaeval collections of holy relics.[22] And by the mid-seventeenth century they were very numerous, owned by both private individuals and learned institutions. In these collections, America was represented by dried flowers, insects, stuffed birds, fishes, reptiles, and other animals, and sometimes by such artifacts as hammocks, weapons, Mexican hardstone carvings, and featherwork. As collectors were naturally interested mainly in "prodigies" and sought out what seemed to them extraordinary, North American flora and fauna, which were similar to that of the Old World, tended to be neglected both by them and by writers on natural history, in favour of whatever was most strange and unusual. Thus a curiously bifocal vision of the New World came about, a vision in which everything which seemed odd if not anomalous to European eyes was gradually superimposed on that "Golden Age" idealisation of Europe which the first explorers had created.

The popular seventeenth-century taste for exoticism, initially inspired by the work of naturalists, was also an expression of a European feeling of superiority over the rest of the world—the belief summed up in Giovanni Botero's remark that Europe, though the smallest of the continents, "was born to rule over Africa, Asia and America."[23] Exotica gave a delicious yet reassuring *frisson* of pleasure because of their deviance from the European norm. Thus, feathered Indians quickly took their place alongside *chinoiserie* Mandarins and Pagods, delicately modelled or painted on porcelain, cast in ormolu or chased in silver, peeping out of rococo scrolls on gilt and enamelled snuff boxes, brandishing their tomahawks among wispy plants on embroidered silks, even serving as the richly gilded supporters of a ducal carriage. In allegories of the continents, of course, any suggestion of equality would have been quite out of place; Europe was always the presiding figure, sometimes graciously bestowing her gifts of civil government and religion on the other three and receiving their treasures as a just tribute. Giovanni Tiepolo's great Würzburg ceiling shows America, Africa, and Asia yielding their riches for the benefit of a Europe which alone indulges in the civilized arts of music, painting, and architecture. It was in such allegories that America and Americans were most frequently depicted in the art of the seventeenth and the first half of the eighteenth centuries.

In the hierarchy of continents, America occupied the lowest place, the last to have been discovered and also, some thought, the last to have been created. Emerging from the waters later than the other continents, it had not as yet completely dried out. It was "that unripe side of earth," as John Donne called it.[24] The ease with which its inhabitants had been subjugated seemed to prove their inferiority. And in the mid-eighteenth century the great French naturalist Georges Buffon declared that the wild-life of South America was not only different from, but inferior to, that of the Old World —with the notable exception of reptiles and insects, which were both larger and more venomous. This he attributed to

> the quality of the earth, the condition of the sky, the degrees of heat and humidity, to the situation, to the height of the mountains, to quantity of flowing and stagnant water, to the extent of the forests, and above all to the raw state of nature.[25]

This revelation of how far America had fallen short of being the best of all possible New Worlds—with its implications as to the impotence or inadequacy of the Creator—won immediate acceptance among the Enlightened. The argument was taken a stage further in 1768 by Cornelius de Pauw, who declared that in the unsalubrious climate of the American continent all mammals degenerated, not excepting Europeans who settled there; "It is without doubt a terrible spectacle to see one half of the globe so disfavored by nature that everything there is degenerate or monstrous," he wrote.[26] The allegorical figure of America with her alligator may thus have seemed to acquire a derogatory significance, especially when set beside Europe with her bull, Asia with her camel, and Africa with her lion.

Less than a decade after the publication of de Pauw's book, Europeans were, however, provided with a spectacle which seemed to contradict his theory, at least as far as American colonists were concerned. The interest aroused by the American Revolution was reflected in a wide variety of works of art, ranging from satirical prints to grandiose allegories, from battle scenes to portraits. In the allegories and even in the cartoons, America continued to be represented by the exotic feather-cinctured Indian,

8

often shown now in the company of such figures from classical mythology as wise Minerva and Mercury, the patron of commerce.[27] This might suggest that the exotic image of South America, which had been the first to form in the European mind, still dominated the view of the whole continent. On the other hand, engravings of idealised Mediterranean coast scenes by Claude Joseph Vernet were published as views of the ports of Boston and Philadelphia [167]. Prints of the events of the Revolution—especially the peep-show views published in Augsburg and Paris—gave the impression that New York hardly differed in appearance from European cities, with wide piazzas and tall stone-built houses and late baroque architectural monuments [201]. The old idea of America as an extension of Europe was thus brought up to date. Nor was this inappropriate, for the war in America was often seen as one between France and England. In several French allegories, including the tapestry which Louis XVI intended to give George Washington, the Bourbon Minerva confronts Britannia [195]. Others show France securing the freedom of the seas—for French trade—rather than the liberty of the Americans as the happy outcome of her intervention. American battle scenes commissioned for the French crown found a place beside those of victories in the Seven Years War [211, 212]. But outside court circles some Europeans seem to have read in the Revolution omens for the future of their own countries. A very popular print, *The Tea Tax Tempest,* likened the colonists' struggle for political independence to that of the Swiss in the thirteenth century and the Dutch in the sixteenth [202]. "It is impossible not to hope that this people may attain the prosperity of which they are susceptible," A. Turgot wrote in 1778. "They are the hope of the human race; they may well become its model."[28]

Interest was naturally aroused in the appearance of the leaders of the Revolution. A little earlier, American colonists travelling in Europe had occasionally been portrayed—but they were portrayed, not unnaturally, just as if they were English country gentlemen.[29] From 1776 onwards, however, there was a growing awareness that the citizen of the United States was different—in Crèvecoeur's famous phrase, "a new man, who acts upon new principles." Chief among them in European eyes was Benjamin Franklin, whose presence in Paris did so much to secure French support for their cause. With his battered fur hat, his home-spun coat, and fresh blanched linen, carrying a cane at a time when courtiers still wore swords, wearing his own white hair when frizzed and powdered wigs were still the fashionable rule, he looked the very image of "le bon Quaker." But he was much else besides—writer, scientist, and *philosophe.* Turgot linked Franklin's scientific achievements with his political ideals in a famous epigram illustrated by Jean-Honoré Fragonard [206]—"he snatched the lightning from heaven and the sceptre from tyranny." There was a lively demand for his portrait, etched and engraved, carved in marble, modelled in terracotta, wax, or porcelain, painted on canvas or even on tea-cups [207].[30]

The greatest French portrait sculptor of the day, Jean-Antoine Houdon, made several busts of him. In some, he showed Franklin wearing the simple clothes in which he appeared in Paris, in others with an antique toga, which had become, inconographically speaking, the "uniform" of the great men of all time [190]. But in none did he idealise his sitter's strong, forthright features. Similarly, he portrayed Washington in modern dress as well as with antique drapery or with his shoulders heroically nude [192]. This antique style of portraiture was widely popular at the time, but it may well have been thought peculiarly appropriate for these men, who seemed to have revived the ideals of ancient republicanism. The Irish painter James Barry allegorised the American Revolution as the resurrection of ancient democracy [200]. In 1788 the Italian dramatist Vittorio Alfieri dedicated his tragedy *Bruto Primo* to Washington, with the words: "Only the name of the liberator of America can stand on the opening page of the tragedy of the liberator of Rome." Thus, once again, America was assimilated into Europe's classical past, but this time with a great difference. In political thought, as in Neo-classical art, the return to antiquity was seen as a source of inspiration for the present and future, not as an escape route back to a mythical Golden Age. Houdon, in his great series of American portraits, presents us with Robert Fulton [193], John Paul Jones [191], and Joel Barlow [194] as, essentially, men of their own time—and the future. They have the straightforward directness and the "prodigious vitality" which seemed to many at the time to animate the whole nation.

As a result of the Revolution, the two images of America as an exotic land and as an extension of Europe became separated, the former being now associated mainly with the centre and South, the latter almost exclusively with the United States. As the latter played a far more prominent part in European life, it soon acquired the name formerly applied to the continent as a whole. William Blake's strange prophetic poem inspired by the Revolution is simply entitled "America" [224]. Goethe began his famous lines "To the United States" with the words: "America you are better off than our old continent." But to many European artists the vision of a primeval exotic south proved more attractive than that of the land of the future in the north.

Inaccessibility veiled Hispanic America in an aura of mystery, for the Spanish authorities did their best to exclude all foreigners and to impose restrictions even on Spaniards. The reports of the first explorers were therefore augmented rather than corrected by those of the few eighteenth-century travellers who contrived to penetrate the barriers—notably the astronomer Charles-Marie de la Condamine,[31] who painted a rather lurid picture of Peru, and John Byron, with his tall tales of Patagonian giants[32] — or visited the only slightly less inaccessible Portuguese Brazil and the Dutch and British enclaves in Guiana. Stories of cannibalism, which had been given such prominence by Vespucci and Hans Staden, were kept alive not only in travel literature but also in such influential novels as *Robinson Crusoe* and *Candide*. De Pauw in 1768 quoted Vespucci and Oviedo as incontrovertible sources, and in the debate on American degeneracy sparked off by his publication, his opponent, Pernety, replied with quotations from other sixteenth-century writers. Although he had never crossed the Atlantic, de Pauw was accepted as the main European authority on America by the *Encyclopédistes*. Pernety, who vaunted his first hand knowledge of the continent, had visited only the Falkland Islands and Terra del Fuego.

In 1799 Alexander von Humboldt and Aimé Bonpland obtained passports to visit Hispanic America. They found the reality still more extraordinary than the myth. "What a fabulous and extravagant country we're in!" Humboldt wrote to his brother soon after arrival. "Fantastic plants, electric eels, armadillos, monkeys, parrots: and many, many, real, half-savage Indians. What trees! Coconut palms, 50 to 60 feet high; *Poinciana pulcherrima* with a big bouquet of wonderful crimson flowers; pisang and a whole host of trees with enormous leaves and sweet smelling flowers as big as your hand, all utterly new to us. As for the colouring of the birds and fishes — even the crabs are sky-blue and yellow."[33] The fact that they found more than three thousand new species of plants in tropical America is enough to show how little the region had previously been investigated by competent naturalists.

Humboldt's discoveries were made known not only in the magnificently illustrated and beautifully produced volumes published at his own expense and intended mainly for the learned [243], but also in a travel book and a volume of essays, *Views of Nature*, which reached a much wider public, inspiring, among others, an even more influential naturalist, Charles Darwin.[34] Humboldt's writings encouraged others to explore South America, which became increasingly accessible as the Spanish Empire crumbled. It was also because of him that several German artists, most notably J. M. Rugendas, went there to paint the landscapes he had described with such infectious enthusiasm [252-256]. Yet, in the end, the achievements of nineteenth-century explorers served only to make the southern continent ever more tantalisingly mysterious in the eyes of Europeans (and, by now, of North Americans too) — a land where anything might be discovered: new species of plants, birds, animals, or reptiles, the ruins of ancient cities mouldering in the jungle (as depicted so powerfully by Frederick Catherwood [258, 259, 260]), or gold.

11

North America seemed to Europeans to possess few natural wonders comparable to those of the South, apart, of course, from Niagara. European depictions of North American landscapes and cities are usually the work of amateurs until well into the nineteenth century. The belief was widespread that the citizens of the United States were—rightly or wrongly—uninterested in the visual arts, and that their country was artistically uninteresting. There was an immense demand in Europe for books about the United States, but their writers concentrated on what the most notorious of them, Mrs. Trollope, called *The Domestic Manners of the Americans.* European concern with the problem of slavery—as often the expression of anti-American sentiments as of humanitarianism—created a demand for documentary prints but relatively few works of art, the outstanding exception being Joseph Turner's *Slave Ship* [315].

Artists seem to have been drawn ineluctably toward the one remaining exotic element in the North American scene—the Indian. He was the subject of all those works in which major nineteenth-century European artists essayed American themes—Goya, Girodet, Delacroix, Doré. But the Indian was no longer simply a picturesque figure. Like the American continent itself, he was at the same time familiar and alien, a projection of European dreams and fears. From the sixteenth century onwards, he had been associated with the Scythians as described by Cicero and the Germanii as described by Tacitus, or else with the Wild Men of the woods of mediaeval legend and poetry[35]—the embodiment of either the highest natural virtues uncorrupted by luxury (the noble savage) or of the basest human passions unrestrained by law and religion. The former view, though given its most notable literary expression by Montaigne and taken up in the early eighteenth century by Lahontan, was diffused mainly by missionaries, especially the Jesuits in Canada. The latter view was that generally held by laymen, who agreed with Thomas Hobbes that the life of "the savage people of America" was "solitary, poor, nasty, brutish and short."[36] This was an image which had scant appeal to artists, apart from Goya [290, 291]. In works of art the idealised image of the Indian prevails, especially in the late eighteenth century, when a "return to nature" was as important a tenet of Neo-classical doctrine as the "return to the Antique." Joseph Wright's *Indian Widow* [184] and J.-F. Le Barbier's *Canadian Parents* [181] are, above all, moral exemplars.

In the early nineteenth century the Indian began to take on the attributes of the Romantic hero—his solitariness, his depth of passion, his melancholy, and even his physical appearance—as in Anne Louis Girodet's *Burial of Atala* [265] and Eugene Delacroix's *Les Natchez* [274]. Belonging to a race frequently said to be on the point of extinction, he became a symbol of man's helplessness against the march of material progress. And as

12

"progress" was so closely identified with the American way of life, sympathy for him, as for the black slave, was allied, more often than not, to anti-American feelings. Significantly, the heroes of westward expansion are barely represented in European art, except in Jean François Millet's lithographs commissioned by an American publisher, who was, however, disappointed in them [301]. Conversely, most of the more notable images of Indians were painted by or for Europeans, like those of Arthur Jacob Miller. Charles Bird King's great series of officially commissioned portraits was limited to the Indian chiefs who had docilely signed treaties with the government. George Catlin's *Indian Gallery*, which illustrated the more savage aspects of Indian life, enjoyed far greater success in Europe than in America.

Indians dominated the European artist's view of America for most of the nineteenth century. The vision of the United States as a land of liberty and opportunity, which shone so brightly in the minds of the poor all over Europe, from Ireland to southern Italy, was very rarely reflected in European art. Emigration reached unprecedented heights in the mid-century— 1,880,000 passengers sailed to the United States from British ports alone between 1846 and 1855. Most visual images of emigration showed, however, only the sadness of farewell—or the horrors awaiting emigrants in the New World: the swamps, the matted woods where no birds sing, even Indian cannibals [327]!

But if it found no worthy artistic expression in Europe, American democracy continued to inspire the old continent, engulfed by alternating waves of revolution and repression. Its appeal was greatly strengthened by the abolition of slavery, and a medal commemorating Lincoln's life and work [332] was struck for a group of French republicans, several of whom were later to commission Frédéric Bartholdi's *Statue of Liberty* for New York harbour—now the symbol and personification of America all over the world but, originally, the embodiment of Europe's vision of America as the great hope for the future of the world as enlightened European liberals saw it.

In 1866 a group of Swiss radicals who wished to liberalize their own constitution planned to commission for the Parliament House at Bern a large picture celebrating the end of the Civil War, as a tribute from the only European republic to the United States. In order to gather material for this work, Frank Buchser went to Washington that same year, and, although he eventually abandoned his original project for Bern, he stayed in America until 1871. His paintings and still more numerous drawings of these years constitute the most extensive visual survey of the United States ever made by a European artist. They include portraits of the Civil War generals [336], prominent figures in literature and politics [335], street

13

scenes, domestic interiors, landscapes, and, inevitably, Indians [303, 304]. Abandoning nearly all the accepted European images of America, Buchser represented the country as he witnessed it, in the throes of momentous transition. He painted the Midwest on the point of being transformed by the rail-road, Indians rapidly losing their racial integrity, white society in the South recovering from defeat, a black population freed from slavery but barely emerging from destitution [320]. Like Alexis de Tocqueville, he recognised that the red man belonged to America's past, and that the future lay with the whites and blacks, whom he painted with a quite unusual understanding and sympathy. But, although his works were highly praised in the American press, he found few buyers for them on either side of the Atlantic. Most of those which now seem most interesting—because they depart from the stereotypes of America—were still in his studio when he died.

Edgar Degas went to America in the fall of 1872—some eighteen months after Buchser returned to Europe. His was, of course, a far greater talent, but his field of vision was curiously less wide so far as the United States was concerned. He came in order to visit his relations in New Orleans and, during his few months there, portrayed them and their friends in pictures which bring us vividly into the closed and sultry social milieu in which they lived.[38] He was the first major European artist, apart from Houdon, to visit the United States—and the last until the twentieth century.

The European visual image of America was created largely by artists who never went there. As the present exhibition shows, many of them were among the greatest—Burgkmair, Holbein, Rubens, Tiepolo, Goya, Delacroix. Similarly, the literary image of America was partly the creation of writers who never crossed the Atlantic—Tasso, Ronsard, Montaigne, Spenser, Shakespeare, Hobbes, Pope, Prévost, Rousseau, Goethe, Schiller, Blake, Wordsworth, Byron, Keats. This vision, conjured up from fact and fantasy, taking its form from Europe and only its colouring from America, accounts for several misconceptions which still survive. Yet it has its own artistic validity as the expression of European dreams of a terrestial paradise or of a Golden Age, an exotic world where everything is strange and bright, the setting for tales of adventure and for an ideal society.

The following notes are limited to references for specific points. Further biblio-graphical information on the works of art in the exhibition is supplied in the catalogue entries and, on more general topics, in the notes to my *New Golden Land* (New York, 1975). I should, however, like to acknowledge my general indebtedness to the following especially: Antonello Gerbi: *La Disputa del Nuovo Mondo*, Milan-Naples, 1955 (also available in an English translation by Jeremy Moyle as *The Dispute of the New World*, Pittsburgh, 1974); Durand Echeverria: *Mirage in the West*, Princeton, 1957; Howard Mumford Jones: *O Strange New World*, New York, 1964; Leo Marx: *The Machine in the Garden*, New York, 1964; J. H. Elliott: *The Old World and the New 1492-1650*, Cambridge, 1970.

1. Gonzalo Fernandez de Oviedo: *Historia General de las Indias,* Seville, 1535, quoted by H. Cermenati in *Annali di Botanica,* IV (1906), p. 329.

2. Alexander von Humboldt: *Ansichten von Natur*, Berlin, 1808, translated by E. C. Otté and H. C. Bohn, London, 1850, p. 229. In the second volume of *Kosmos* (Berlin, 1847), Humboldt suggested that the task had been partly achieved by Johann Mortiz Rugendas, Graf Clarac, Ferdinand Bellermann, and Eduard Hilde-brandt, cf. *Alexander von Humbolt und seine Welt,* exhibition catalogue, Schloss Charlottenburg, Berlin, 1969, p. 79.

3. F. Scott Fitzgerald: *The Great Gatsby* (New York, 1926), Harmondsworth, 1950, pp. 187-188.

4. For the identification of the feather cap and sceptre in Dürer's drawing on folio 41 recto of the Book of Hours of the Emperor Maximilian I, see William C. Sturtevant: "First Visual Images of Native America" in *Proceedings of the Inter-national Conference on First Images of America: The Impact of the New World on the Old,* Los Angeles, 1976. I am indebted to Dr. William C. Sturtevant for allowing me to read this paper before publication.
For Dürer and the Mexican goldwork and featherwork sent to Charles V by Cortés and seen by Dürer in Brussels in 1520, see H. Rupprich, ed.: *Albrecht Dürers schriftlicher Nachlass*, Berlin, 1956, vol. I, p. 155.

5. For Mexican objects imported into Europe in the sixteenth century, see K. A. Nowotny: *Mexicanische Kostbarkeiten aus Kunstkammern der Renaissance,* Vienna, 1960; F. Anders and D. Heikamp: "Mexikanische Altertümer aus süddeutschen Kunstkammern" in *Pantheon*, XXVIII (1970), pp. 205-220; D. Hei-kamp: *Mexico and the Medici,* Florence, 1972.
For Tommaso dei Cavalieri's Mexican featherwork, see D. Heikamp: "Pre-Columbian and Colonial Mexican Objects Preserved in Old Italian Collections or Described and Illustrated in the Italian Source Literature of the Sixteenth to the Eighteenth Century" in *Proceedings of the International Conference on First Images of America: The Impact of the New World on the Old,* Los Angeles, 1976. I am indebted to Dr. Heikamp for allowing me to read this paper before publication.

6. Edmundo O'Gorman: *The Invention of America,* Bloomington, 1961.

7. Francisco López de Gómara: *Primera Parte de la Historia General de las Indias,* Saragossa, 1552, dedication to Charles V, quoted by J. H. Elliott: *The Old World and the New,* Cambridge, 1970, p. 10.

8. On Columbus see S. E. Morison: *Admiral of the Ocean Sea,* Boston, 1942, and *idem: The European Discovery of America: The Southern Voyages,* New York, 1974.

9. *Raccolta di Documenti e studi pubblicati dalla R. Commissione Colombiana,* Rome, 1892, pt. III, vol. I, p. 165.

10. W. Eames: "Description of a wood engraving illustrating the South American Indians 1505" in *Bulletin of the New York Public Library*, XXVI (1922), pp. 755-760; Georg Leidinger: "Die älteste bekannte Abbildung südamerikanischer Indianer" in *Gutenberg Festschrift*, Mainz, 1925, pp. 179-181.

11. Attributed to Hans Burgkmair by Peter Halm in *Münchner Jahrbuch der bildenden Kunst*, 3 F, XIII (1962), pp. 125-129.

12. Edmund Spenser: *The Faerie Queene*, Book III (1589), canto xii, stanza 8.

13. Quoted by A. Gerbi: *La Disputa del Nuovo Mondo*, Milan-Naples, 1955, p. 70.

14. John Milton: *Paradise Lost*, London, 1667, book ix, lines 1116-1118.

15. Alexander von Humboldt: *Relation historique du Voyage aux régions équinoctiales du Nouveau Continent*, Paris, 1814, translated by T. Ross as *Personal Narrative of Travels to Equinoctial Regions of America*, London, 1852.

16. Pierre Ronsard: "Complainte contre Fortune," Paris, 1559, line 379, cf. E. Armstrong: *Ronsard and the Age of Gold*, Cambridge, 1968, p. 28.

17. Michel de Montaigne: *Essais*, Paris, 1580, chapter 31.

18. For Caliban's American background see the *Arden Edition of the Works of William Shakespeare: The Tempest*, ed. Frank Kermode, London, 1954, revised 1962, pp. xxv-xxxiv.

19. A Cortesão and A. Teixeira da Mota: *Portugaliae Monumenta Cartographica*, Lisbon, 1960, vol. I.

20. The tapestry, representing *Spring*, is in Palazzo Pitti, Florence, cf. D. Heikamp: *Mexico and the Medici*, Florence, 1972, pl. 10.

21. M. Cermenati, *Annali di Botanica*, IV (1906), pp. 341-348.

22. See J. von Schlosser: *Die Kunst- und Wunderkammern der Spätrenaissance*, Leipzig, 1908. Numerous collections of this kind are described in P. Skippon: "An Account of a Journey Made Thro' Part of the Low-Countries, Germany, Italy, and France" (1663) in *A Collection of Voyages and Travels*, London, 1752, vol. VI.

23. Giovanni Botero: *Relationi Universali*, Turin, 1601, quoted by R. Romeo: *Le Scoperte americane nella coscienza italiana del Cinquecento* (1954), Milan-Naples, 1971, p. 93.

24. "To the Countess of Huntington," line 1, in John Donne: *Complete Poetry and Selected Prose*, ed. J. Hayward, London, 1929, p. 149.

25. Quoted by A. Gerbi: *La Disputa del Nuovo Mondo*, p. 6.

26. Cornelius de Pauw: *Recherches philosophiques sur les Américaines* or *Mémoires intéressant pour servir à l'histoire de l'espèce humaine*, Berlin, 1768, p. 1.

27. On the allegorical figure of America in the Revolutionary period, see E. McClung Fleming: "The American Image as Indian Princess 1765-1783" in *Winterthur Portfolio*, II (1965), pp. 65-81.

28. Quoted by D. Echeverria: *Mirage in the West*, Princeton, 1957, p. 69.

29. Such portraits of American sitters include Peter Manigault by Allan Ramsay and Charles Cotesworth Pinckney of North Carolina by Zoffany (repr. *The Connoisseur*, CXLI [1958], pp. 268-269). Professor Sir Ellis Waterhouse has kindly informed me of those of Captain Benjamin Davies by Reynolds (private collection, Long Island) and a Mrs. Harrison by Francis Cotes (Colonial Williamsburg).

30. C. C. Sellers: *Benjamin Franklin in Portraiture*, New Haven and London, 1962.

31. Charles-Marie de la Condamine: *Relation abrégé d'un voyage fait dans*

l'Amérique méridionale, Maestricht, 1778.

32. *A Voyage round the World in his Majesty's ship the Dolphin, commanded by the Hon. Comm. Byron,* London 1768. See also Percy G. Adams: *Travellers and Travel Liars,* Berkeley and Los Angeles, 1962, pp. 19-43. A figure of a Patagonian giant according to Byron's dimensions was carved for the Grand Duke of Tuscany and is now in the Museo Etnologico, Florence.

33. Quoted by Douglas Botting: *Humboldt and the Cosmos,* London, 1973, p. 76.

34. On his journey to South America, Darwin wrote from HMS Beagle: "I formerly admired Humboldt, now I almost adore him." See D. Botting, *op. cit.,* p. 211.

35. See E. Dudley and M. E. Novak, ed.: *The Wild Man Within,* Pittsburgh, 1972.

36. Thomas Hobbes: *Leviathan,* London, 1651, p. 62. See also S. Landucci: I *filosofi e i selvaggi 1580-1780,* Bari, 1972.

37. For Arthur Jacob Miller and his Scottish patrons, see M. R. Porter and O. Davenport: *Scotsman in Buckskin,* New York, 1963.

38. John Rewald, James B. Byrnes, Jean Sutherland Boggs: *Edgar Degas: His Family and Friends in New Orleans,* exhibition catalogue, Isaac Delgado Museum of Art, New Orleans; May 2-June 16, 1965, p. 33 ff.

I
Savages and
Men of Ind

"They are well-built people of handsome stature," Columbus wrote in
1493 of the Indians he encountered on his first voyage. "In these islands I
have so far found no human monstrosities, as many expected; on the contrary, among all these people good looks are esteemed; nor are they negroes, as in Guinea, but with flowing hair."[1] They were to be distinguished
from Europeans only by their nudity, to which Columbus repeatedly referred—and as such they appear in illustrations to his published letter [1].
He returned to Europe with six of them, who were duly baptised and given
Spanish names. But surprisingly—or perhaps not so surprisingly—they
seem to have aroused very little interest. To contemporaries they were
simply another breed of Asiatics. Peter Martyr, the Italian humanist at the
Spanish court, never so much as mentions them in his letters of the time
about Columbus and his discoveries.[2] On the other hand, the Caribbeans
brought back by Columbus from his second voyage attracted some comment, for reasons which are clear from their description by Giambattista
Strozzi, a Florentine merchant in Cadiz: "dark skinned men with wide
faces like Tartars, with hair falling to their shoulders, tall and very agile
and proud; they eat human flesh, both children and castrati whom they
fatten up like capons and then eat. These men are called *Canabáli*."[3]

Asiatic islands rich in spicery were, of course, the objective of Columbus's voyage, as of those of the Portuguese in the opposite direction. It is
important to remember this all too easily forgotten fact. Verrazano wrote,
as late as 1524: "My intention on this voyage was to reach Cathay and the
extreme eastern coast of Asia, but I did not expect to find such an obstacle
of new land as I have found." So for many years the new discoveries in the
East and West were identified with each other, as by Sebastian Brant, for
example, in his satirical poem "Narrenschiff," of 1494,[4] or by the Antwerp
publisher who issued a decade later an illustrated broadsheet describing
conjointly Vespucci's voyages to America and Balthasar Springer's to
India.[5]

As a result, reports on South American Indians initially expanded the
Europeans' vision not of the New World but of the most easterly part of
the Old. A coppery-skinned Brazilian with his characteristic head-dress
appears as one of the three Wise Men from the East in an early sixteenth-
century Portuguese painting of the *Adoration of the Magi* [4]; several figures, some bedecked with feathers and others stark naked, represent the
"people of Calicut" in *The Triumph of the Emperor Maximilian I* [5], and
Jörg Breu the Elder in 1515 pictured the natives of Sumatra in the same
fashion.[6] Even as late as 1532, on a map which shows America as an independent continent, albeit one closer to Asia than to Europe, Hans Holbein
provided the inhabitants of the Spice Islands with American feather skirts
[18]. By a reverse process Asiatic characteristics were transposed to Amer-

ica—even to the extent of locating there some of those human monstrosities which Columbus had failed to find. According to Sir Walter Raleigh, almost a century later, men with no heads but with eyes, noses, and mouths in their chests—monstrosities known to Europeans since the Middle Ages as the Blemmyae, who were thought to live in India or Ethiopia—were to be found in the Ewaipanoma tribe on the Caura River in Venezuela.

The advance of Cortés into Mexico in 1519 brought, for the first time, news of people quite unlike any previously encountered by westerly voyagers. And the objects of gold and silver and featherwork which he sent to Charles V, and which Dürer saw in Brussels in 1520, revealed their riches, their accomplishment, and the strangeness of their art. Very shortly afterwards, in 1522, reports of the first circumnavigation of the world made clear how immense a distance separated South America from Asia. The Mexicans Cortés brought with him to Spain in 1528 seem to have created more of a stir than Columbus's Indians. They included ball-players and jugglers, who put on a show for Charles V in Valladolid. Some of the latter were sent on to Rome, where they juggled logs of wood with their feet before Pope Clement VII, who "thanked God that such countries had been discovered in his days." (See colour photographs in gallery.)

But American Indians raised a tricky theological problem. Their unashamed nakedness was difficult to explain. As early as 1520 Paracelsus wrote that he could not believe that the people who had been found "in out of the way islands" were "of the posterity of Adam and Eve." He doubted whether they had souls and proposed a theory of polygenesis to account for them.[7] Although no other writer of the sixteenth century is known to have committed such bold thoughts to paper, the famous Papal Bull of 1537, declaring the Indians to be "true men," may perhaps have been intended to scotch such heresies as well as to protect the Indians from exploitation by the Spaniards.

Two diametrically opposed views of the Indians were developed in the early sixteenth century. Colonial settlers and most travellers from Vespucci [3] onwards tended to regard them as little superior to brute beasts, living without "God, King or Law," devil-worshippers addicted to cannibalism and other "abominations" deserving the fate of Sodom. Their easy subjugation by the Spaniards was seen simply as the manifestation of God's curse on them. Bartolomé de Las Casas and a few other missionaries thought otherwise. To him the Indians were creatures of natural goodness, gentleness, obedience, and simplicity, living in peace and needing only the Christian faith to make them quite perfect. The former view seems to be reflected in a mid-sixteenth-century Portuguese painting of the devil dressed in Brazilian featherwork [7]. The other found artistic expression in Jan Mostaert's *West Indian Scene,* which might almost illustrate a passage

20

in which Las Casas likened the *Conquista* to the descent of "famished wolves, tigers or lions" on a flock of gentle sheep [6].[8] This was indeed the attitude which tended to prevail in works of art, as also in a poem by Ronsard and the still more famous essays by Montaigne, who praised the Indians' natural way of life and virtues:

> as for devotion, observance of the laws, goodness, liberality, loyalty, and plain dealing, it was of service to us that we had not so great a share of those virtues as they. For, by this advantage, they ruined, sold, and betrayed themselves.

The North American Indians brought from Newfoundland to Portugal in 1500 and to England in 1501 were regarded rather differently. Their country could not be likened to an earthly paradise, nor could they be associated with men of the Golden Age. Alberto Cantino, ambassador to the duke of Ferrara in Lisbon, "touched and examined these people." He noted the tattooing on their faces and seems to have been surprised to find that their speech, though unintelligible, "was almost human."[9] They had "the most bestial manners and habits, like wild men," he wrote, alluding to the fabulous wild men of the woods familiar from mediaeval legend. Newfoundlanders taken to London were said to be "clothid in bestys skinnys" and to have the manners of "bruyt bestis." Later in the century these northerners came to be much more favourably regarded. A couple brought back from Baffin Island by Sir Martin Frobisher in 1576 [10] were models of propriety. "Albeit they lived continually togither, yet did they never use as man and wife, though the woman spared not to do all neccessarie things that apperteyned to a good huswife," wrote George Best. "I think it worth the noting the continencie of them both; for the man would never shifte himselfe, except he had first caused the woman to depart out of the cabin, and they were both most shamefast least anye of their private parts should be discovered, eyther of themselves or any other body."[10] The Baffin Islanders further endeared themselves to the English by their love of sport. According to the chronicler of John Davis's 1585 voyage: "Divers times did they weave us ashore to play with them at football."[11]

Northern virtues were at first sight attributed also to Indians living further south, in the vicinity of the first English settlement on Roanoke Island. In his watercolours John White presented a very happy picture of them, not neglecting to indicate how the men "covereth their privities" while "virgins of good parentage . . . lay their hands often upon their Shoulders, and cover their brests in token of maydenlike modestye." Thomas Hariot's book describing their idyllic way of life was, of course, intended partly to attract settlers to the colony, and White's watercolours, too, are tinged with a slight "promotional" glow. This quickly faded, for in the very year in which the illustrated edition of Hariot's book appeared,

21

White returned to Roanoke and found not one of the colonists alive. Their fate was abundantly clear.

When Shakespeare wrote *The Tempest*—between 1610 and 1612—he was aware of both the good and the bad qualities ascribed to "Savages and men of Ind" and of the sad story of their relations with Europeans. "When thou cam'st first," Caliban says to Prospero:

> Thou strok'st me, and made much of me; wouldst give me
> Water with berries in't; and teach me how
> To name the bigger light, and how the less,
> That burn by day and night: and then I lov'd thee,
> And show'd thee all the qualities o' th' isle,
> The fresh springs, brine-pits, barren place and fertile:
> Curs'd be I that did so![12]

But Caliban proves to be an irredeemable "savage man," with all the lasciviousness and treachery of the Indians as described by the most hostile travel writers.

The alternative view was not altogether lost on Shakespeare, however. But the "Golden Age" vision of life among the American Indians, derived from Montaigne, was subsumed under a visionary ideal commonwealth for Europeans:

> I' th' commonwealth I would by contraries
> Execute all things; for no kind of traffic
> Would I admit; no name of magistrate;
> Letters should not be known; riches, poverty,
> And use of service, none; contract, succession,
> Bourn, bound of land, tilth, vineyard, none;
> No use of metal, corn, or wine, or oil;
> No occupation; all men idle, all;
> And women too, but innocent and pure:
> No sovereignty; . . .
> All things in Common Nature should produce
> Without sweat or endeavour: treason, felony,
> Sword, pike, knife, gun, or need of any engine,
> Would I not have; but Nature should bring forth,
> Of its own kind, all foison, all abundance,
> To feed my innocent people.[12]

In this section three examples of Mexican featherwork sent to Europe—probably by Cortés immediately after the *Conquista*—and the only surviving painting of Indians by Jacques Le Moyne de Morgues (Museum für Völkerkunde, Vienna, and New York Public Library) are shown in colour transparencies, as are a woodcut of Brazilians published in Germany about

1505 (Bayerische Staatsbibliothek, Munich) and the drawings by Christoph Weiditz of the Mexicans sent to Spain by Cortés in 1528 (Germanisches Nationalmuseum, Nuremberg).

1. S. E. Morison: *Christopher Columbus, Mariner,* London, 1956, p. 220, with comments on other translations of this passage.

2. *Epistolaria de Petro Martíre de Angleria,* ed. José López de Toro in *Documentos Ineditos para la Historia de Espana,* Madrid, 1953, vol. IX, pp. 236-237, 242-250. These letters are, however, dated from 14 May to 1 November 1493, i.e. from one to eight months after Columbus's return to Spain, and they may perhaps have been written later still.

3. *Raccolta di documenti e studi pubblicati dalla R. Commissione Colombeana,* Rome, 1892, Part III, vol. I, p. 166.

4. "Auch hat man sydt in Portogal / Und in Hyspanien uberal / Golt-inseln funden, und nacket lüt / Von den man for wust sagen nüt," quoted by J. A. Aboal Amaro: *Diez rares americanes del siglo XVI,* 1959.

5. M. E. Kronberg: *De Novo Mondo, Antwerp, Jan van Doesborch . . . A Facsimile of an Unique Broadsheet,* The Hague, 1927. The broadsheet is in the University Library, Rostock.

6. Götz Pochat: *Der Exotismus,* Stockholm, 1970, p. 156. The prints illustrate Ludovico Vartoman: *Die ritterliche Reise,* Augsburg, 1515.

7. Thomas Bendyshe: "The History of Anthropology" in *Memoirs of the Anthropological Society of London,* I (1863-64), pp. 353-354.

8. B. de Las Casas: *Brevissima relación de la destruciòn de las Indias,* 1552, quoted by G. Gliozzi: *La scoperta dei selvaggi,* Milan, 1971, p. 74.

9. H. P. Biggar: *Précurseurs de Jacques Cartier 1497-1534,* Canadian Archives Publications, No. 5, Ottawa, 1911, pp. 61-66.

10. George Best: *A True Discourse of the Late Voyage of Discovery for Finding a passage to Cathaya,* London, 1578, in R. Collinson: *The Three Voyages of Martin Frobisher,* Hakluyt Society, London, 1867, p. 145.

11. S. E. Morison: *The European Discovery of America: The Northern Voyages,* New York, 1971, p. 597.

12. The two passages from *The Tempest* are I:ii: 334-341 and II:i: 143-160.

1 *The Landing of Christopher Columbus, title page to Giuliano Dati:* La lettera dell isole che ha trovato nuovamente il Re di Spagna

Italy (Florence). Woodcut. 1493. Woodcut size 4⅝ x 4⁷⁄₁₆ inches (11.7 x 11.3 cm.). Provenance: Guglielmo Libri, from whom it was acquired 1848.

London, British Library.

This is possibly the first attempt by a European artist to visualize Columbus's landing in the West Indies. It appeared on the cover of a four-leaf pamphlet, of which only two copies survive, one dated 25 October 1493 and the other—exhibited here—26 October 1493 (both in the British Library, but the former lacking two leaves). The text is a sixty-eight stanza Italian poem, incorporating a translation of Columbus's first letter by Giuliano di Domenico Dati (d. 1524), a Florentine who had settled in Rome and was later to become bishop of S. Leone in Calabria. Dati told Columbus's story in the language and also the *ottava rima* metre of such recent Italian epics of chivalry as Luigi Pulci's *Morgante* and Matteo Boiardo's *Orlando Innamorato*. And the anonymous artist of the woodcut represented the scene as if it were an episode in one of the several early Renaissance romances which were illustrated at the same period by Florentine painters. The woodcut was copied with slight alterations for the 1495 edition of Dati's poem (copy in the Huntington Library, San Marino, California) and, in reverse, for the first edition of Vespucci's letters to Soderini, published in Florence, probably in 1505-06. Another very early representation of Columbus's landing is provided by the woodcut frontispiece of a Latin edition of his letter, without either date or place of publication but generally assumed to have been printed in 1493 in Basel (the only surviving copy is said to be in the New York Public Library, reproduced as *The Letter of Columbus on the Discovery of America. A Facsimile of the Pictorial Edition*, New York, 1892). This shows a hilly wooded island with naked people on it, labelled *Insula hyspana*, but the foreground is filled with a forty-oared galley of a type suitable only for Mediterranean coasting. Though schematically drawn, the ships in the Florentine woodcut are closer to the probable appearance of the *Santa Maria*.

CLalettera dellifole che ha trouato nuouamente il Re difpagna.

Literature: H. Harrisse: *Biblioteca Americana Vetustissima*, New York, 1866, p. 28; P. Kristeller: *Early Florentine Woodcuts,* London, 1897, no. 125; *Catalogue of books printed in the XV century now in the British Museum,* pt. vi, London, 1930, p. 683; Max Sander: *Le Livre à figures italien depuis 1467 jusqu'à 1530,* Milan, 1942, no. 2352; G. Pochat: *Der Exotismus während des Mittelalters und der Renaissance*, Stockholm, 1970, p. 148.

2 *Title page of Amerigo Vespucci:*
Be ora antartica per regem
Portugallie pridem inventa
Germany (Strassburg). Woodcut.
1505. Page size 7⅚ x 5⅚ inches
(18.5 x 13.5 cm.).
Washington, D.C., Library of Congress, Rare Book Division.

In May 1499 Amerigo Vespucci (1451-1512), who had been working in Seville for eight years as head of a banking house affiliated to that of the Medici in Florence, joined a transatlantic expedition under the captaincy of Alonso de Ojedo, landing on the South American continent in the region he named Venezuela. He returned to Spain in June 1500 and then went to Portugal. In May 1501 he joined an expedition sent by the king of Portugal, with Gonçalo Coelho as captain general, to investigate and establish his claim to the lands which Pedro Alvarez Cabral had discovered in 1500.

Back in Lisbon in September 1502, Vespucci described his adventures in a letter to his former employer, Lorenzo de Pier Francesco dei Medici, who was now Florentine ambassador in Paris. This provided the basis for Latin translations published under the title *Mundus Novus* in Paris in 1503 and in Venice, Augsburg, and Rome in 1504. The original letter is lost, but comparison between an early sixteenth-century manuscript, which appears to be a copy of it (Biblioteca Nazionale, Florence), and the printed versions suggests that the translators took considerable liberties with Vespucci's text, though he was probably responsible himself for magnifying his own importance in the expedition and exaggerating how far south it had sailed ("within 17.5 degrees of the Antarctic circle"). The letter provides a highly coloured description of the newly discovered lands and, especially, their inhabitants. Where Columbus had

been vague, Vespucci was specific—describing the Indians' sexual habits with salacious relish and providing a gruesomely vivid account of their cannibalism. But, like Columbus, he believed that he had reached the eastern coast of Asia, and he used the term "new world" simply to signify a region which had been unknown to the geographers of classical antiquity.

Vespucci's letter was very widely diffused; it was translated into five modern languages and printed in some thirty editions before 1515. The copy shown here is one of two surviving examples (the other is in the British Library) of what is generally described as the sixth edition, printed by Matthias Hupfuff in Strassburg in 1505. The text is taken from the edition printed by Euchario Silber in Rome in 1504 as *Mundus Novus*, augmented by a letter and a poem by Ringmann and at the end a statement on the authenticity of the letter by an apostolic notary who had been present at a public audience in the Vatican when the Portuguese ambassador informed Pope Julius II of

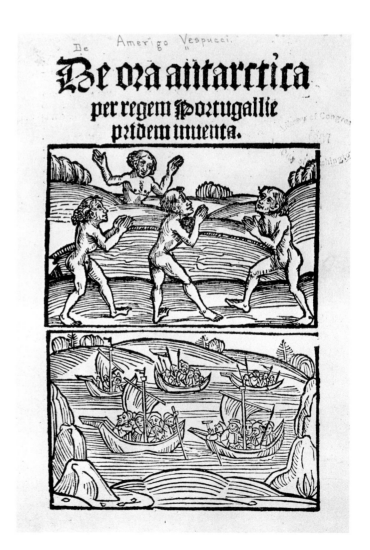

the newly discovered lands. The title generally used was, however, changed to *Be [De] Ora Antartica per regem Portugallie pridem inventa* (concerning the Antarctic coast discovered some time ago for the king of Portugal). Matthias Ringmann (1482-1511) was a humanist poet, who soon after 1505 went to St. Dié and may have been responsible for informing Martin Waldseemüller about Vespucci.

On the title-page there are two woodcuts by an anonymous artist. One shows four figures as the Indians are described in the letter: "all of them, of both sexes, go naked, covering no parts of their bodies, as they issued from their mothers' wombs and as they will eventually die. They have large well-built and proportioned bodies of a reddish colour which comes I think from their being exposed naked to the sun. They have abundant black hair. In walking and in their sports they are agile and they have handsome faces which however they disfigure, boring holes in their cheeks, lips and noses...." The lower woodcut shows five ships, three with sails (as enumerated in Vespucci's letter) and two without, perhaps intended to represent canoes.

Literature: H. Harrisse: *Biblioteca Americana Vetustissima,* New York-Paris, 1866, no. 39; G. Fumagalli: "Bibliografia delle opere concernenti Paolo Toscanelli ed Amerigo Vespucci" in A. M. Bandini: *Vita di Amerigo Vespucci,* Florence, 1898, pp. 99-128, no. 15; H. Vignaud: *Americ Vespuce. Sa bibliographie,* Paris, 1917, pp. 13, 15; *Mostra Vespucciana,* exhibition catalogue, Palazzo Vecchio, Florence, 1954-55, no. 67; R. Levillier in *Boletín del Istituto de Historia Argentina "Doctor Emiliano Ravignani,"* 2nd series, I (1956), pp. 17-18; G. Pochat: *Der Exotismus,* p. 149.

3 *Wild Naked People, Previously Unknown. Illustration to a German translation of Amerigo Vespucci's letters to Pier Soderini*

Germany (Strassburg). Woodcut. 1509. Page size 7½ x 5¹¹/₁₆ inches (19 x 13.4 cm.). Provenance: Adolphus Asher, Berlin, from whom it was acquired 1845.
London, The British Library.

The print illustrates an incident described by Vespucci in his account of his second voyage to America in 1501. While the ships were anchored off the coast of Brazil (probably near Cape San Roque), two men were sent ashore to parley with the natives but failed to return. Some days later a group of Indian women appeared on the beach, and a good-looking sailor was sent to charm them. While the women crowded round him, touching and admiring him, another came up behind him and knocked him senseless to the ground with a club. Immediately the women took him by the feet and dragged him off, while men with bows let fly a torrent of arrows towards the ships, until a few gunshots sent them fleeing to the mountains, where, Vespucci relates, "the women were cutting up the Christian, and on a large fire they had made, were roasting him in our sight, displaying the many pieces and eating them." This is one of the several colourful stories related by Vespucci in his letter to his boyhood friend Pier Soderini and first printed in Florence in about 1505-06. The publication seems to have had less success in Italy

than in northern Europe, where it was frequently reprinted in a Latin translation as part of Martin Waldseemüller's *Cosmographiae Introductio* from 1507. The volume exhibited is a unique copy of a German translation issued by J. Grüniger of Strassburg (who also published an edition of the *Cosmographiae Introductio*) in 1509 under the title: *Disz büchlin saget wie die zwē herrē Fernandus K. zü Castilien und herr Emanuel K. zü Portugal haben das weyte mör ersüchtet unnd funden vil Insulen unnd ein Nüwe welt von wilden nackenden Leüten, vormals unbekant* (this booklet tells how the two lords Fernandus King of Castille and lord Emanuel King of Portugal have searched the wide sea and found many islands and a new world of wild naked people previously unknown). The woodcuts, which appear only in this edition and are the first to illustrate precise incidents described by Vespucci, show, in addition to that exhibited, a group of Brazilians placidly conversing while one urinates and another chops up human limbs; three Europeans, one of whom politely raises his hat as he approaches a group of naked long-haired women among rocks; and the return of the voyaging fleet to Lisbon. The anonymous artist seems to have read Vespucci's text carefully, though he naturally pictured the Brazilians with European physiognomy.

Literature: H. Harrisse: *Biblioteca Americana Vetustissima,* New York, 1866, no. 62; G. Fumagalli: "Bibliografia delle opere concernenti Paolo Toscanelli ed Amerigo Vespucci" in A. M. Bandini: *Vita di Amerigo Vespucci,* Florence, 1898, no. 39; H. Vignaud: *Americ Vespuce. Sa bibliographie,* Paris, 1917, no. 122; *Mostra Vespucciana,* exhibition catalogue, Palazzo Vecchio, Florence, 1954-55, no. 89; *Short-title catalogue of books printed in the German-speaking countries . . . from 1455 to 1600 now in the British Museum,* London, 1962, p. 891. G. Pochat: *Der Exotismus,* p. 149.

4 *The Adoration of the Magi*
Portugal. Oil on panel. ca. 1505.
52⅞ x 32⅜ inches (134 x 82 cm.).
Provenance: Cathedral of Viseu.
Viseu, Museu de Grão Vasco.

The coppery-skinned figure in the centre of this panel is probably the first American Indian to be depicted in a European work of art. He carries an accurately rendered Tupinamba arrow (more heavily fletched than those of Europe) and he has a radial feather crown like those worn by several tribes of Brazilian Indians—though his shirt and breeches are European, presumably added to make him presentable in church. Africans and Asians were often included in paintings of the *Adoration of the Magi,* but this is the only known instance of an American appearing as one of the wise men who had seen Christ's "star in the east and are come to worship Him." The Portuguese discovered Brazil in 1500, when a fleet commanded by Pedro Alvarez Cabral, on the way to Calcutta, was blown off course, sighted Monte Pascoal, landed on the coast, and then sailed some

forty miles north to Porto Seguro (safe harbour). Cabral sent a storeship back to Lisbon to report the discovery to the king, and Pedro Vaz de Caminha, who sailed on it, wrote a detailed account of the very friendly Indians encountered on the shore. No attempt was made to follow up the discovery for some years, but from 1501 Portuguese ships occasionally visited the Brazilian coast to replenish supplies of water, food, and wood, on their way to or from India. It is more than probable that Brazilian artifacts and also Indians were taken to Portugal on one of them.

The panel is one of fourteen which form a polyptych painted for the high altar of Viseu cathedral. The whole series is dated between 1500 and 1506 on stylistic grounds and is clearly the work of several different painters. In 1630 it was attributed to Vasco Fernandes (ca. 1475-1541/2), who lived in Viseu from 1501 to 1541 and was one of the leading Portuguese painters of his day. He may well have contributed to the polyptych, but whether he painted *The Adoration of the Magi* is questionable. The polyptych has also been ascribed to Jorge Afonso, who is first recorded in 1508, when he was appointed court painter to King Manuel; but no documented works by him survive.

Literature: Forjaz de Sampaio: *Historia da Literatura Portuguesa Illustrada*, Paris-Lisbon, 1929, vol. I, p. 303; L. Reis Santos: *Vasco Fernandes e Os Pintores de Viseu do século XVI*, Lisbon, 1946, pp. 22-23, 65, 82-83, pl. v; *idem.*, *Vasco Fernandes*, Lisbon, 1962, pp. 8-9; *L'art portugais*, exhibition catalogue, Musée du Jeu de Paume, Paris, 1932, no. 12; *Os primitivos Portugueses 1450-1550*, exhibition catalogue, Museu de Arte Antiga, Lisbon, 1940, no. 228; *Portuguese Art 800-1800*, exhibition catalogue, Royal Academy, London, 1955-56, no. 145; G. Kubler and M. Soria: *Art and Architecture in Spain and Portugal and their American Dominions 1500-1800* (Pelican History of Art), Harmondsworth, 1959, pp. 331-332; G. Pochat: *Der Exotismus*, p. 171.

Hans Burgkmair the Elder

German, 1473-1531.

The leading painter of his day in Augsburg and, after Dürer, in all Germany, Burgkmair was the son of a painter and was probably trained on the Upper Rhine under Martin Schongauer. He visited North Italy, where he came under the influence of Lombard and especially Venetian Renaissance art. His paintings include both religious pictures and portraits. But he is probably better known for the many woodcuts after his drawings, in which his technical accomplishment, imaginative fantasy, and delight in decorative splendour are well displayed. His taste for the exotic is seen in the drawings he made of Africans and Asians to illustrate Balthasar Springer's account of a voyage to India, as well as in the "People of Calicut" in *The Triumph of the Emperor Maximilian I* (see below).

Meticulously rendered exotic birds and plants, including a dragon tree from the Canary Isles, appear in his St. John altarpiece of 1518 (Alte Pinakothek, Munich).

Hans Burgkmair the Elder (after)

5 *People of Calicut*

Woodcut. 1517-1518. Signed *H B* on the elephant's neck-piece. Three sheets, each 16³⁄₁₆ x 23¹⁄₁₆ inches (41 x 58.5 cm.).
Stuttgart, Graphische Sammlung, Staatsgalerie Stuttgart.

These sheets form part of a series of 137 woodcuts of an imaginary triumphal procession. The woodcuts were commissioned by the emperor Maximilian I and engraved after drawings, of which sixty-six were by Burgkmair and two by Albrecht Dürer (the rest

are attributed to Albrecht Altdorfer, Wolf Huber, and others). They purport to represent *Die Kalikutischen Leut* (the people of "Calicut" or Calcutta), but since they were made at a time when the West Indies were still thought to form part of Asia they freely mix Oriental and Occidental motifs. Thus while the elephant and its turbaned mahout, the garlanded cattle, and the sheep with fat tails are Asiatic, most of the figures wear the feather skirts and head-dresses of American Indians, a few are completely naked, several have clubs of a Brazilian type, one carries a large Brazilian macaw and another two ears of maize (the first to be represented in European art).

The emperor Maximilian I (1459-1519) devised the programme of *The Triumph* and dictated it to his secretary in 1512. There were to be two versions, one in miniature technique on vellum for the emperor's own collection (now in the Graphische Sammlung Albertina, Vienna), the other to be published as a series of woodcuts. In the former the "people of Calicut" were painted in the guise of American Indians, probably by Albrecht Altdorfer. The programme described this section of *The Triumph* as: "People of Calicut . . . a man of Calicut (naked, with a loincloth), mounted and carrying a verse inscription, wearing a laurel wreath; on the plaque shall be written these words: 'These people are subject to the previously shown praiseworthy crowns and houses.' Then shall come on foot the people of Calicut. They shall be wearing laurel wreaths." Verses were written for the banner carried by the mahout:

The Emperor in his warlike pride,
Conquering nations far and wide,
Has brought beneath our Empire's
    yoke
The far-off Calcuttish folk.
Therefore we pledge him with our
    oath
Lasting obedience and troth.

An inscription was also written for the other group:

One rank with shields and swords
One rank with spears.
Two ranks with English bows and
    arrows.
All are naked like Indians or dressed
    in Moorish fashion.
(Translations by S. Appelbaum)

It is no more than a coincidence that American Indians were to be brought beneath the yoke of the Holy Roman Empire under Maximilian I's successor, Charles V.

Wood blocks were cut as soon as the

drawings for *The Triumph* were completed, but several had still to be made when Maximilian I died in 1519, and none of them was provided with an inscription. The first set of prints made from them was published in 1526. The original blocks survived, and further sets of impressions were pulled from them in 1777, 1796, and 1883-84. The sheets exhibited are from the 1796 edition published in Vienna under the direction of the great connoisseur of prints, Adam Bartsch.

Literature: F. Shestag: "Kaiser Maximilian I Triumph" in *Jahrbuch der Kunsthistorischen Sammlungen des Allerhöchsten Kaiserhauses*, 1 (1883), pp. 154-181; L. Baldass: *Der Künstlerkreis Kaiser Maximilians*, Vienna, 1923; S. Appelbaum, ed.: *The Triumph of Maximilian I*, New York, 1964. *Hans Burgkmair, das graphische Werk*, exhibition catalogue, Städtische Kunstsammlungen, Augsburg, no. 204. William C. Sturtevant: "First Visual Images of Native America" in *Proceedings of the International Conference on First Images of America*, Berkeley, 1976.

Jan Mostaert

Dutch, ca. 1475-1555/6.

He was born and died in Haarlem, where he became the leading painter. In 1500 he is mentioned there as a master. But he must have travelled in Europe from 1490/95 to about 1510, if, as is said, he was court painter to the Regent Margaret for eighteen years and was in her retinue wherever her court went. Both in subject matter and style he was very versatile, and his work ranges from small devotional images to large altarpieces and portraits, of which several are very fine.

Jan Mostaert

6 *West Indian Landscape*

Oil on oak panel. ca. 1542.
34⅛ x 60³⁄₁₆ inches (86.5 x 152.5 cm.).
Provenance: Private collection, Scheveningen, 1909; Museum van Stolk, Haarlem, 1912; N. Beets, Amsterdam, 1928; J. Goudstikker, Amsterdam, 1936.
Haarlem, Frans Hals Museum, on deposit from the Dienst voor's Rijks Verspreide Kunstvoorwerpen.

This is the earliest known painting of the New World. It was discovered in 1909. The sixteenth-century painter and historian of Netherlandish art, Carel van Mander (1548-1606), who lived in Haarlem, mentions in his *Het Schilder-boeck* (Alkmaar, 1604) that he had seen an unusual painting in the house of Mostaert's grand-son. He describes it as follows: "A West Indies Landscape with many naked people, a curious protruding cliff, and strange constructions of huts and houses." Carel van Mander could well have known contemporaries of Mostaert in Haarlem. The painting exhibited was seen in a private collection in Scheveningen in 1909 by Edward Weiss, who identified it with that described by van Mander. Despite its great and unusual

historical interest, the painting was not discussed for some time, and speculation as to the precise location and significance of the scene depicted did not begin until 1931. (To van Mander, of course, the "West Indies" were not simply the islands but the whole New World.)

Edouard Michel proposed in 1931 that the conquests of Cortés in central Mexico were the subject of the painting and argued that it had been executed for the Regent Margaret of Austria in ca. 1523-25, just after the first news had reached Europe of the spectacular discoveries of gold in Aztec cities. This interpretation of the painting was widely accepted, notably by the historians of Netherlandish art M. J. Friedländer and G. J. Hoogewerff.

In 1948 Michel's Mexican interpretation was disputed by R. van Luttervelt, who pointed out that the painting contains no specifically Mexican features—either in topography or in costume—and he proposed that it depicted the exploits of Coronado in the American Southwest in 1540-42, mentioning in particular Coronado's skirmish with the Indians at Cibola, "the Seven Cities of Gold," an area between New Mexico, Arizona, and California, where the Spaniards believed large stores of gold and silver objects were to be found. Van Luttervelt also drew attention to the *arco naturale* in the middle distance, comparing it to the Window Rock in Arizona, and suggested that the landscape was based on sketches made in America and sent back to Europe.

In 1952 another interpretation was put forward by H. van de Waal (later supported by E. Reznicek), that the event depicted is the landing of Columbus on Goanin as described in the ship's journal of 13 January 1493. More recently, in 1970, Eric Larsen proposed that the scene is that of the invasion of Brazil by the Portuguese

army in about 1550, the Indians being identified as Tupinamba and the parrot on the tree stump in the foreground being interpreted as a direct reference to Brazil, then known as the "land of parrots." (The Spanish flag carried by the soldiers is, Larsen argues, a later addition.)

In the most recent discussion of the painting, James Snyder accepts van Luttervelt's identification in general, that the painting depicts some incident in Coronado's campaign and that the landscape is intended to represent New Mexico and Arizona, though questioning whether it is based on accurate topographical views. Snyder agrees with van de Waal that the landscape is much in the contemporary Netherlandish tradition and indeed can be paralleled in other works by Mostaert "where one finds the same *arco naturale* and the sprawling mountain

ranges delicately rendered under a bright blue sky filled with scallop-shaped clouds." Snyder suggests that the painting is "an imaginative reconstruction of what Mostaert believed to be some lost primitive society in the New World where man still lived much as he did in some Ovidian Golden Age." But he goes on to propose that the painting is based on contemporary accounts of Coronado's exploits, accounts now lost but which Mostaert may be presumed to have read or heard, similar to those known to us from Pedro de Castañeda's history of the campaigns published after Mostaert's death. The central incident depicted is, Snyder suggests, the stoning of Coronado in the first village of Cibola on 24 June 1540, when, according to Castañeda, the Indians hurled down rocks from the cliffs at the entrance to the village and Coronado

would probably not have survived had not two officers come to his rescue and warded off the advancing Indians. Snyder also points out that the most striking feature of Mostaert's landscape—the terraced cliff with horizontal striations—is described by Castañeda as a feature of Cibola. Castañeda also described the ladders reaching from one level to another and the simple huts or shrines built within them, with one at the top of the cliff for the elderly sentinel. He also mentions that these tribes were generally ruled by elders—in the painting both the sentinel and the leader of the advancing Indians are elderly, with long white beards. One of the more colourful figures described by Castañeda in connection with Coronado and the Zuni was a chieftain from Pecos nicknamed *Bigotes* or "Big Whiskers" by the Spanish. However,

Snyder admits that neither the village nor the natives correspond to those described by Castañeda, the Indians described by Castañeda being colourfully dressed, not nude. (Castañeda did describe a tribe of tall naked men who lived in large straw cabins built into the earth with part of the straw roof projecting above ground, as in Mostaert's painting, but these were encountered by one of Coronado's officers, Melchior Diaz, who left the company before they reached Cibola. Diaz left Coronado on the Sonora River and marched back to the West Coast of Mexico, then along the Gulf of California to the mouth of the Colorado River.)

A less specific interpretation may be preferred for what is, essentially, an imaginary scene of the *Conquista*, not untinged by the black legend of Spanish cruelty. Both Haarlem and Mexico belonged to Charles V's empire. Mostaert may well have known of Los Casa's denunciations of Spanish atrocities in the Indies and doubtless had personal experience of the behaviour of Spanish troops in the Low Countries. The landscape is a pastoral paradise very similar to the backgrounds of some of his religious paintings, while the naked Indians are lithe, athletic Europeans with very inappropriate beards. The painting is perhaps best understood and appreciated as a visual parable on the innocence and peace of unspoilt nature and the destructive urge of civilised man — a secular counterpart to Mostaert's painting of Eve banished from Eden with Cain killing Abel nearby (Clark Institute, Williamstown, Mass.). The theme was to echo down the ages in America.

Literature: C. van Mander: *Het leven der Doorluchtighe Nederlandtsche en Hoogduytsche schilders*, Alkmaar, 1604, p. 229; E. Weiss: "Ein neues Bild Jan Mostaerts" in *Zeitschrift für Bildende Kunst*, N.F. XX (1909/10), pp. 215-217; *Catalogue Museum Van Stock*, Haarlem, 1912, no. 408; M. Conway: *The Van Eyks and their Followers*, London, 1921, p. 422; E. Michel: "Un tableau colonial de Jan Mostaert" in *Revue Belge d'Archéologie et d'Histoire de l'Art*, I (1931), pp. 133-141; M. J. Friedländer: *Die Alt-Niederländische Malerei*, Berlin, 1932, vol. X, pp. 14, 23, 24, 120; G. J. Hoogewerff: *De Noord-Nederlandsche Schilderkunst*, The Hague, 1937, vol. II, pp. 493-495; G. Gluck: *Aus drei Jahrhunderten europäischer Malerei*, Vienna, 1933, p. 320; R. van Luttervelt: "Jan Mostaert's West-Indische landschap" in *Nederlands Kunsthistorisch Jaarboek*, II (1948-49), pp. 105-117; O. Kurz in *The Burlington Magazine*, XCII (1950), p. 239; H. van de Waal: *Drie eeuwen vaderlandsche geschied-uitbeelding, 1500-1800. Een iconologische studie*, The Hague, 1952, p. 91; G. J. Hoogewerff: *Het landschap van Bosch tot Rubens*, Amsterdam, 1954, p. 60; H. Baudet: *Het paradijs op aarde*, Assen, 1959, p. 36; E. K. J. Reznicek: "Episode uit de verovering van Amerika" in *Openbaar Kunstbezit*, jrg. 4 (1960), no. 19; L. van Puyvelde: *La peinture flamande au siècle de Bosche et Breughel*, Paris, 1962, p. 303; H. G. Franz: *Niederländische Landschaftsmalerei im Zeitalter des Manierismus*, Graz, 1969, p. 54; G. von der Osten and H. Vey: *Painting and Sculpture in Germany and the Netherlands 1500-1600*, Harmondsworth, 1969, p. 162; G. Pochat: *Der Exotismus*, pp. 177-180; E. Larsen: "Once more Jan Mostaert's West-Indian landscape" in *Mélanges d'archéologie et d'histoire de l'art offerts au professeur Jacques Lavalleye*, Louvain, 1970, p. 127; J. Snyder: "The Earliest Painting of the New World. The 'West Indian Landscape' by Jan Mostaert" in *Proceedings of the International Conference on First Images of America: The Impact of the New World on the Old*, University of California Press, forthcoming.

7 *Inferno*

Portugal. Oil on panel. ca. 1550.
47 x 85⅞ inches (119 x 217.5 cm.).
Lisbon, Museu Nacional de Arte Antiga.

Early in the sixteenth century a Portuguese artist had depicted a Brazilian Indian as one of the three wise men worshipping the Christ Child [4]. But here Brazilian featherwork is worn by the devil presiding over the torments of the damned and also by one of his assistants carrying the body of a tonsured priest on the right. By the mid-sixteenth century, when this *Inferno* was painted, the Indians had often been described as devil-worshippers. The panel is neither signed nor dated. Like many Portuguese works of the first half of the sixteenth century, it is strongly influenced by the art of the Low Countries. It has been attributed to Jorge Afonso (fl. 1508-1540), court painter to King Manuel and King John III, but no documented works by this artist survive.

Literature: *Os Primitives Portugeses 1450-1550*, MS. exhibition catalogue, Museu Nacional de Arte Antiga, Lisbon, 1940, no. 25; João Couto: "O Inferno — Painel Português do século XVI" in *Litoral* no. 2 (1944), pp. 179-184; *Portuguese Art 800-1800*, exhibition catalogue, Royal Academy, London, 1955-56, no. 92; *Arte Portugesa 1550-1950*, exhibition catalogue, Museu Nacional de Belas Artes, Rio de Janeiro, 1965, no. 18; L. Reis-Santos: *Jorge Afonso*, Lisbon, 1966, p. 8, pl. I; *Dicionario de Pintura Universal — Pintura Portugesa*, s.d. s.l. vol. III, p. 245.

L'Entrée du Roy nostre Sire faicte en sa ville de Rouen, Paris, 1550 (cf. Margaret M. McGowan: "Forms and Themes in Henri II's Entry into Rouen" in *Renaissance Drama,* I (1968), pp. 199-251). This carving has often been associated with this spectacle, but it may equally well have been carved slightly earlier or later for a merchant interested in the dye-wood trade. Many Brazilians were brought to Rouen in the sixteenth century—it was here that Montaigne in 1562 met those whose remarks he recorded in his famous essay *Des cannibales* (1580)—but the carver of this panel, far from recording their physical peculiarities, endowed the men with beards and moustaches, like Europeans. Stylistically the relief is similar to, though coarser than, two panels of the story of Phaeton which formerly decorated a house at 115 rue Gros Horologe, Rouen, and are now also in the Musée Départemental, Rouen.

Literature: De La Querière: "Des enseignes considérées comme le signe distinctif des Maisons particulières" in *Précis de l'Academie de Rouen*, Rouen, 1849, p. 286; Ferdinand Denis: *Une fête brésilienne célébrée à Rouen en 1550*, Paris, 1850; Camille Enlart: *Rouen*, Paris, 1906, pp. 10-11; J. H. Hyde in *Apollo*, IV (1926), pp. 232-233; *France et Brésil*, exhibition catalogue, Hotel de Rohan, Paris, 1955, no. 16; *Bois sculptés*, exhibition catalogue, Musée Dobrée, Nantes, 1964, no. 286.

8 *Brazilians Cutting and Carrying Brazil-Wood*

France. Carved oak. ca. 1550.
20⅝ x 85¼ inches (52 x 221 cm.).
Provenance: Removed from 17 rue Malpalu, Rouen, 1837.
Rouen, Musée Départemental des Antiquités.

This panel and another slightly smaller, showing figures loading a boat with logs, decorated a house which was demolished in 1837 in Rouen. It dates from the mid-sixteenth century, when Rouen was one of the main markets for the red dye-wood called brazil-wood, after which Brazil was named [17]. In 1550, when Henri II made a state visit to the city, a "Brazilian village" was created on the banks of the Seine, populated by some fifty Tupinamba Indians and rather more Frenchmen dressed (or undressed) and painted to resemble them—an occasion recorded in an illuminated manuscript (Bibliothèque Municipale, Rouen, MS. Y28 [1268]); in a published book with woodcut illustrations, *C'est la Deduction du sumptueux ordre, plaisantz spectacles et magnifiques dresses, et exhibes par les citoiens de Rouen . . .*), Rouen, 1551; and in Robert Masselin:

John White

English, fl. 1577-1593.

John White was the cartographer and draughtsman on Sir Walter Raleigh's 1585 expedition, which founded the first English colony on North American soil, named Virginia in honour of Queen Elizabeth. Nothing is recorded about White before this date, but it is almost certain that he was on Frobisher's 1577 expedition to the Northwest [10] and perhaps also on the expedition sent out in 1584 by Raleigh under Captains Philip Amadas and Arthur Barlowe. The 1585 expedition sailed from Plymouth with seven ships, under Sir Richard Grenville, on 9 April and, after victualling in the West Indies, reached Wococon (Ocracoke Inlet) on 26 June. After exploring the sounds, Grenville left for England on 25 August, leaving Governor Ralph Lane at Roanoke in charge of the first colony. John White's name does not appear among Hakluyt's list of 108 settlers, but there can be no doubt that he stayed with the colony from August 1585 until June 1586, when all its members returned to England. It was from Roanoke that he explored the neighbouring Indian villages of Pomeiooc, Aquascogoc, and Secoton. Both there and elsewhere he made the drawings which, with the comments of the expedition's mathematician and astronomer, Thomas Hariot, form an unrivaled record of North America as it appeared to Europeans in the sixteenth century—though some allowance should be made for the "promotional" aspect of their work.

The colonists failed to establish themselves and by the summer of 1586 were facing famine. Unexpectedly relieved by the arrival of Sir Francis Drake's fleet, on his return from plundering the West Indies [23], they returned to England in June. The following year Raleigh sent out another colony, this time under John White as governor, to establish "the Cittie of Raleigh in Virginia." White's instructions were to establish a settlement on Chesapeake Bay, but he went back to Roanoke. After the supplies had been landed he returned to England, leaving behind the colony, which included his daughter Elinor Dare and his granddaughter Virginia, the first child born of English parents in North America. He never saw them again—nor any other members of the colony. He was not able to return until 1590, and he found the colony abandoned. "We saw in the sand the print of the Salvages feet of 2 or 3 sorts troaden that night," he wrote. "We found the houses taken down ... Wee found five chests ... three were my owne, and about the place many of my things spoyled and broken, and my bookes torn from the covers, the frames of some of my pictures and Mappes rotten and spoyled with rayne, and my armour almost eaten through with rust." A storm blew up and, in spite of White's pleas for a search for any possible survivors of the colony, the captains refused to stay. Nothing more is known of White, though it is presumed that he retired to Munster near the great estate granted to Raleigh by the queen in 1586, since his letter to Hakluyt describing his last expedition is dated from "Newtowne in Kylmore" in 1598.

All White's surviving work is in the British Museum. None is signed, and the provenance goes no further back than 1788, but there can be little doubt about his authorship. These drawings—on seventy-six sheets, of which fifty-nine are connected with the Virginia venture—were formerly in an album, of which the title-page reads: *The pictures of sondry things collected and counterfeited according to the truth in the voyage made by Sr Walter Raleigh knight for the discouery of La Virginea. In the 27th yeare of the most happie reigne of our Souereigne lady Queene Elizabeth. And in the yeare of o^r Lorde God. 1585.* However, despite this it has been suggested—because of the uniformity of style and finish throughout and the inclusion of a number of drawings unconnected with Raleigh's expedition—that they were made after White returned from Virginia in July 1586 from sketches made on the expedition. Engravings after White's drawings were published by Theodor de Bry in 1590 in Part 1 of his *America* [64]. This contains Thomas Hariot's *Brief and true report of the new found land of Virginia,* and the frontispiece to the plates mentions "the true pictures and fashions of the people. ... Diligentlye collected and drawne by Ihon White who was sent thither speciallye and for the same purpose by the said Sir Walter Raleigh."

In addition to these seventy-six sheets of drawings, there are three drawings of insects pasted into the manuscript of Thomas Moffet's *Insectorum Theatrum* (British Library, Sloane MS.4014) which are presumably by White, who is referred to in the text accompanying that of West Indian fireflies as follows: "Hanc Cicindelam una cum icone a Candido pictore [the artist, White] peritissimo, qui diligentissime eam tam in Hispaniola quam in Virginiâ obseruauit, accepi."

An album containing copies of White's drawings, also now in the British Museum, was discovered in 1706-07, when it was still in the possession of White's descendants—being used as a copy book by the children. It was bought by Sir Hans Sloane, who gave it to the British Museum. Other copies of White's drawings are known. For a discussion of them and the originals, see P. Hulton and D. B. Quinn: *The American Drawings of John White 1577-1590,* London and Chapel Hill, North Carolina, 1964.

John White

9 *A Woman of Florida*

Pen and brown ink and watercolours over black lead, with blue body-colour, touched with gold and silver (?) (oxidised). ca. 1586. 10¼ x 5⅜ inches (26.1 x 13.5 cm.). Inscription: *Of Florida.* Provenance: Thomas Payne sale, Langford & Son, London, 3-4 March 1788, purchased by James Caulfield, 1st Earl of Charlemont; James-Molyneux, 3rd Earl of Charlemont sale, Sotheby 11 August 1865, lot 228, purchased by Henry Stevens, from whom purchased by the British Museum, 1866.
London, The British Museum.

Since there is no record of White's having been in Florida, this figure of a Timucuan Indian of the St. John's River region of Florida was presumably drawn after a lost original by Jacques le Moyne, artist to the French expedition to Florida in 1564, who died in Blackfriars in 1588 and had probably been living in London for some time previously. In 1588 White met Theodor de Bry, who had come to London to acquire Le Moyne's drawings in connection with his proposed publication, *America,* and obtained some of White's drawings of Virginia at the same time. An unsigned engraving in *America,* Pt. II, Pl. XVIII was probably after the same Le Moyne original that White used for this drawing.

Literature: D. B. Quinn, ed.: *The Roanoke Voyages, 1584-1590. Documents to Illustrate the English Voyages to North America,* Hakluyt Society, series II, vol. CIV, London, 1955, p. 462, no. 2; E. Croft Murray and P. Hulton: *Catalogue of British Drawings,* British Museum, London, 1960, p. 53, no. 62; P. Hulton and D. B. Quinn: *The American Drawings of John White, 1577-1590,* London and Chapel Hill, North Carolina, 1964, no. 113A; W. P. Cumming, R. A. Skelton, D. B. Quinn: *The Discovery of North America,* London, 1971, p. 208.

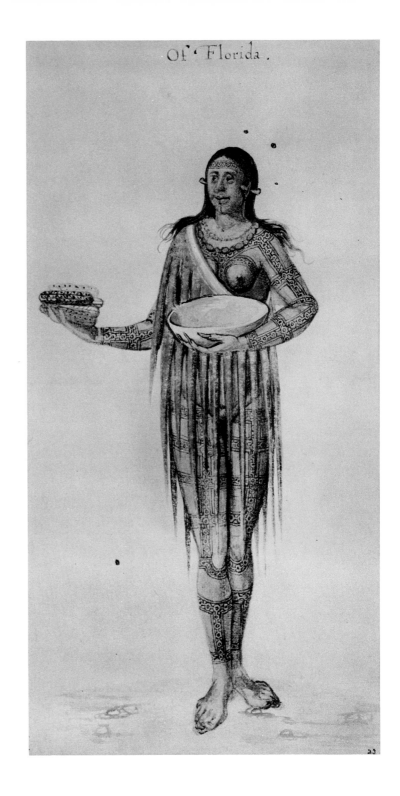

Of Florida.

John White

10 *An Eskimo Woman*

Pen and brown ink and watercolours over black lead, touched with white (oxidised). ca. 1577. 8¾ x 6½ inches (22.3 x 16.6 cm.). Provenance: As for [9].

London, The British Museum.

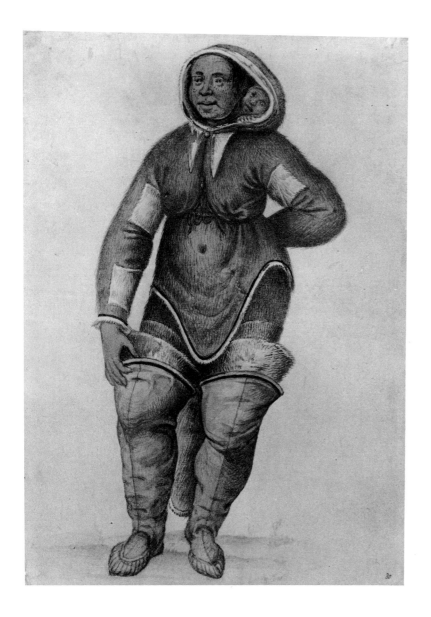

This drawing and one of an Eskimo man may well have been made in 1577 on Frobisher's second voyage to the Northwest, as was suggested by Dr. K. Birket-Smith in 1959. Another drawing, by or after John White (British Museum, 78 f.12.v.), depicts English sailors in a skirmish with Eskimo. That this represents an inci- dent on Frobisher's second voyage, perhaps that off Bloody Point on 1 August 1577, is strongly suggested by the relation between the Eskimo in the kayak and that (in reverse) in the woodcut frontispiece to the German and Latin editions of Dionysius Settle's account of Frobisher's last voyage, published in 1580. However, the draw- ing exhibited and its companion of an Eskimo man could have been made in England, for Frobisher brought back an Eskimo man and woman with a baby. Drawings of them were made in England. George Best's report of the second voyage says: "We shewed him [an Eskimo] ye picture of his Countrey- man, which yᵉ last yeare was brought into England (whose counterfet we had drawne, with boate, & other furni- ture, both as he was in his own, & also in english apparell)."

The Eskimo portrayed is a native of Baffin Island. A similar drawing of a native of the same region by Lucas de Heere (University Library, Ghent, MS. 2466) is inscribed: *Homme sauage amené des pais septentrionaux par M. Furbisher L'an 1576.* The Mongolian features of the Eskimo are emphasised, as they were by all the early voyagers, who, in search of Cathay, were ready to identify them as Asiatics "much like . . . to the Tartar nation, whereof I think he was," as Frobisher's asso- ciate, Michael Lok, wrote.

Literature: *Sir Walter Raleigh and Richard Hakluyt,* exhibition catalogue, British Museum, London, 1952, p. 13, no. 55; J. Andersen: "Kunster og Kolonisator. John Whites Tegninger fra Virginia" in *Bogrennen,* no. 10, (1955), p. 112; D. B. Quinn, ed.: *The Roanoke Voyages, 1584-1590,* p. 464, no. 3; K. Birket-Smith in *Folk* (Danish Ethnological Association), I (1959), pp. 25-27; E. Croft-Murray and P. Hulton: *Catalogue of British Drawings,* p. 54, no. 64; P. Hulton and D. B. Quinn: *The American Drawings of John White, 1577-1590,* no. 116A; W. P. Cumming, R. A. Skelton, D. B. Quinn: *The Discovery of North America,* p. 241.

John White

11 *A Festive Dance*

Watercolours over black lead, touched
with white; many details off-printed
on either side of a central fold. ca. 1585.
10¾ x 14⅛ inches (27.4 x 35.8 cm.).
Provenance: As for [9].
London, The British Museum.

The same dance is shown on a smaller
scale in White's drawing of the Indian
village of Secoton (British Museum
1906-5-9-1[7]), which is inscribed
below the dancing figures: *A Ceremony in their prayers wth strange
iesturs and songs dansing abowt posts
carued on the topps lyke mens faces.*

It seems to have been associated with
the green corn ritual. An engraving
after this drawing in Theodor de Bry:
America, Pt. I, 1590, Pl. XVIII is entitled
*Their danses which they vse att their
hyghe feastes,* with the following commentary by Thomas Hariot:

> At a Certayne tyme of the yere they
> make a great and solemne feaste.
> The place where they meete is a
> broade playne, abowt the which are
> planted in the grownde certayne
> posts carved with heads like to the
> faces of Nonnes covered with theyr
> vayls. Then beeing sett in order they
> dance singe, and use the strangest
> gestures that they can possibly

devise. Three of the fayrest Virgins,
of the companie are in the midds,
which imbrassinge one another doe
as yt wear turn abowt in their
dancinge. All this is donne after the
sunne is sett for avoydinge of heate.

Literature: L. Binyon: "The Drawings of
John White" in *Walpole Society,* vol. XIII,
1924-25, Pl. XXV; *Sir Walter Raleigh and
Richard Hakluyt,* exhibition catalogue,
British Museum, 1952, p. 27, no. 115; D. B.
Quinn, ed.: *The Roanoke Voyages, 1584-
1590,* p. 427, no. 41A; E. Croft-Murray
and P. Hulton: *Catalogue of British Draw-
ings,* p. 44, no. 39; P. Hulton and D. B.
Quinn: *The American Drawings of John
White, 1577-1590,* no. 42A; W. P. Cum-
ming, R. A. Skelton, and D. B. Quinn: *The
Discovery of North America,* p. 197.

John White

12 Indians Fishing

Watercolours touched with white and gold. ca. 1585. 13⅞ x 9¼ inches (35.3 x 23.5 cm.). Inscription: At the top, *The manner of their fishing.*; and on the canoe, *A Cannow.* Provenance: As for [9].
London, The British Museum.
Colorplate 1.

In this drawing White appears to have combined, from individual sketches, various fishes, marine creatures, and birds, not all of which are appropriate to the area (Cape Hatteras, North Carolina), as, for example, the West Indian Hermit Crabs and shells and the Hammer-headed Shark. The King-crab *(Limulus polyphemus)* is of special interest as one of the earliest known representations of this creature (see *Science*, XXVII [1908], p. 669). Other fish depicted include a Striped Mullet or Striped Bass, two Trigger fish, a Catfish, a barndoor skate, and a Spiny Box-fish. In the foreground is a horseshoe crab, with the tail of which the Indians pointed their fishing spears. A Brown Pelican and two Trumpeter Swans are shown in the upper left-hand corner. The engraving after this drawing in Theodor de Bry's *America*, Pt. I, 1590, Pl. XIII is entitled *Their manner of fishynge in Virginia.* It contains several additions and modifications, such as three fish weirs in the background, a different kind of fish-trap, and a White Cat-fish, a Garfish, a Diamondback Terrapin, and a West Indian Land Crab. In his commentary Thomas Hariot relates that

> They have likewise a notable way to catch fishe in their Rivers, for whear as they lacke both yron, and steele, they faste unto their Reedes or longe Rodds, the hollowe tayle of a certain fishe like to a sea crabbe in steede of a poynte, wehr with by

nighte or day they stricke fishes, and take them opp into their boates. They also know how to use the prickles, and prickes of other fishes. They also make weares, with setting opp reedes or twigges in the water, whiche they soe plant one within a nother, that they growe still narrower, and narrower, as appeareth by this figure. Ther was never seene amonge us soe cunninge a way to take fish withall, wherof sondrie sortes as they fownde in their Rivers unlike unto ours. Which are also of a verye good taste. Dowbtless yt is a pleasant sighte to see the people, somtymes wadinge, and going somtymes sailinge in those Rivers, which are shallowe and not deepe free from all care of heapinge opp Riches for their posteritie, content with their state, and livinge friendlye together of those thinges which god of his bountie hath given unto them, yet without givinge hym any thanks according to his desarte.

Literature: L. Binyon: "The Drawings of John White" in *Walpole Society*, vol. XIII, 1924-25, pl. XXVI; *The Beginnings of English Topographical and Landscape Drawing*, exhibition catalogue, British Museum, 1949-50, p. 5, no. 14; *Sir Walter Raleigh and Richard Hakluyt*, exhibition catalogue, British Museum, 1952, p. 26, no. 112; D. B. Quinn, ed.: *The Roanoke Voyages, 1584-1590*, p. 433, no. 46A; E. Croft Murray and P. Hulton: *Catalogue of British Drawings*, pp. 45-46, no. 43; P. Hulton and D. B. Quinn: *The American Drawings of John White, 1577-1590*, no. 46A; W. P. Cumming, R. A. Skelton, D. B. Quinn: *The Discovery of North America*, p. 197.

John White

13 An Indian Painted for the Hunt

Watercolours and black lead, touched with white. ca. 1585. 10⅜ x 5⅞ inches (26.3 x 15 cm.). Inscription: *The manner of their attire and / painting themselues when / they goe to their generall / huntings, or at theire / Solemne feasts.* Provenance: As for [9].
London, The British Museum.

A pendant copper and bead ornament is shown at the Indian's left ear, a long six-string pearl or bead necklace is about his neck, a double bracelet of the same kind is on his right wrist, and a leather guard is on his left wrist. A fringed deerskin apron, with a puma's (?) tail reaching almost to the ground, and a quiver partly visible at his left hip, are also shown. The engraving after this drawing in Theodor de Bry's *America*, Pt. I, 1590, Pl. III, is entitled: *A weroan or great Lorde of Virginia.* (A back view of the same figure is shown as Pl. XXIII.) This figure also appears, with considerable modifications, in the title-page to Theodor de Bry's *America*, and again, by William Hole, in John Smith's map of Virginia, first published in 1612 (?).

In his commentary to the engraving in Theodor de Bry's *America*, Thomas Hariot wrote:

> The Princes of Virginia are attyred in suche manner as is expressed in this figure. They weare the haire of their heades long and bynde opp the ende of the same in a knot under their eares. Yet they cut the topp of their heades from the forehead to the nape of the necke in manner of a cockscombe, stirking a faier longe pecher [feather] of some berd att the Begininge of the creste upon their foreheads, and another short one on bothe seides about their eares. They hang at their eares ether thicke pearles, or somewhat els, as the clawe of some great birde, as cometh in to their fansye. Moreover They

The manner of their fishing.

12 John White,
Indians Fishing.
British Museum.

ether pownes, or paynt their fore-head, cheeks, chynne, bodye, armes, and leggs, yet in another sort then the inhabitantz of Florida. They weare a chaine about their necks of pearls or beades of copper, wich they much esteeme, and ther of wear they also braselets ohn their armes. Under their brests about their bellyes appeir certayne spotts, whear they use to lett them selves bloode, when they are sicke. They hange before them the skinne of some beaste verye feinelye dresset in suche sorte, that the tayle hangeth downe behynde. They carye a quiver made of small rushes holding their bowe readie bent in on hand, and an arrowe in the other, radie to defend them-selves. In this manner they goe to warr, or tho their solemne feasts and banquetts. They take muche pleasure in huntinge of deer wher of ther is great store in the contrye, for yt is fruit full, pleasant, and full of Goodly woods. Yt hathe also store of rivers full of divers sorts of fishe. When they go to battel they paynt their bodyes in the most terible manner that their can devise.

For a discussion of John White's drawings of North American Indians and their relation to contemporary attitudes to primitive peoples, see T. D. Kendrick: *British Antiquity*, London, 1950, pp. 123-125 and John H. Rowe: "Ethnography and Ethnology in the Sixteenth Century" in *The Kroeber Anthropological Society Papers*, no. 30 (1964), pp. 1-19.

Literature: *Sir Walter Raleigh and Richard Hakluyt*, exhibition catalogue, British Museum, 1952, p. 27, no. 121; D. B. Quinn, ed.: *The Roanoke Voyages, 1584-1590*, p. 440, no. 51A; E. Croft Murray and P. Hulton: *Catalogue of British Drawings*, pp. 47-48, no. 48; P. Hulton and D. B. Quinn: *The American Drawings of John White, 1577-1590*, no. 52A; W. P. Cumming, R. A. Skelton, D. B. Quinn: *The Discovery of North America*, p. 208.

SAUVAGES AMENEZ EN FRANCE POUR ESTRE INSTRVITS DANS LA RELIGION CATHOLICVE, QUI FURENT BAPTISEZ A PARIS EN L'EGLISE DE S.ᵗ PAUL LE XVII IVILLET 1613.

P. Firens sculp.

Portraict au naturel des barbares amenez. en france du pas de Topinambous. par le S.ᵗ de Razilly pour estre baptisez. et conuertiz. a la foy de Jesus Christ. et presentez a sa Ma.ⁱᵉ en lanne presente 1613.

Joachin Du viert pi.

P. Firens ex

Joachin Du viert pinx

Ce sont icy les vrais portraicts des sauuagie de lisle de Maragnon appellez Topinambous amenez au tres-Chrestien Roy de France et de Nauarre par le S.ᵗ de Razilly en la presente annee. 1613. Ou sont representées les postures quils tiennent en dansant.

Joachim Duviert

Dutch, fl. 1609-1614.
Duviert was a Dutch draughtsman who worked in France and is known only for a series of wash drawings of buildings (Bibliothèque Nationale, Paris) and this print of Brazilians (see below).

Joachim Duviert

14 *Brazilians Brought to France to be Baptised*

Engraving. 1613. Signed: *P.Firens sculp.* and *Joachin Du viert pinx.* 20⅛ x 12¾ inches (51 x 32.7 cm.). Inscription along the top: *Sauvages amenez en France pour estre instruits dans la religion Catholique, qui furent baptisez a Paris en l'eglise de St. Paul le XVII Iullet 1613*, beneath the upper group: *Portraict naturel des barbares amenez en france par le Sr Razilly pour estre baptisez et convertiz a la foy de Jesus Christ et presentez a sa Ma.ie en lanne presente 1613*; and beneath the lower group: *Ce sont ici les vrais portraicts des sauvagie de lisle de Maragnon appellez Topinabous amenez au tres-Chrestien Roy de France et de Navarre par le Sr. de Razilly en la presente annee 1613. Ou sont representées les postures quils tiennent en dansant.*
Paris, Bibliothèque Nationale.

The figures depicted in this print came from the neighbourhood of São Luiz in Maranhao on the north coast of Brazil, where the French established a colony in 1612 but lost it to the Portuguese in 1616. The founders of the colony, François de Razilly and Daniel de La Ravardière, were both Protestants. But the Queen Mother and *Régente*, Marie de Médicis, insisted that they should be accompanied by Catholic missionaries. Two Capuchin monks, Claude d'Abbeville and Yves d'Evreux, were sent out, and both published books which, in addition to describing the history of the mission, provided a very favourable account of the country and its inhabitants. On returning to France in 1613, the former brought with him several Tupinamba, who had been converted to Christianity and whose arrival in Paris caused a sensation. A military guard had to be mounted on the convent where they were lodged to keep out visitors. On 17 July they were baptised with much ceremony in the church of Saint-Paul by the bishop of Auxerre in the presence of Louis XIII and Marie de Médicis. But, like so many South American Indians who had been brought to Europe, they very soon succumbed to illness and died (cf. G. Chinard: *L'Amérique et le rêve exotique*, Paris, 1913, pp. 22-24). In the print exhibited they are shown wearing their traditional feather head-dresses, carrying their fetish rattles, and wearing stones set in the skin of their faces, but otherwise dressed in the fashionable costume of the day. It was engraved and published by Pierre Firens (1597-ca. 1637), the official "Graveur du Roy." Portraits of them were also illustrated in Claude d'Abbeville: *Histoire de la Mission des Pères Capucins en l'isle de Maragnan et terres circumvoisines*, Paris, 1614, p. 367.

Literature: U. Thieme and F. Becker: *Allgemeines Lexikon der bildenden Künstler*, Leipzig, 1914, vol. X, p. 248; *Quatre siècles de la colonisation française,* exhibition catalogue, Bibliothèque Nationale, Paris, 1913, no. 358; E.-T. Hamy: "Les Indiens de Rasilly peints par Du Viert et gravés par Firens et Gaultier" in *Journal de la Société des Américanistes de Paris*, N.S. v (1908), pp. 22-52.

Brent de Bock (?)
Dutch or German, fl. 1615-1616.

15 *Young Man from Virginia*
Pen, ink, and watercolour. 1616.
5 3/16 x 7 5/16 inches (13.1 x 18.5 cm.).
Inscription: *Een Jongheling uyt de Virginis, diese Indiarnse Voghelen en Beesten met den Jongheling syn Ao: 1615:1616 In St. James Parck of diertgaren by Westminster voorde Stadt London tesien geweest* and, in another hand, *Brent de Bock*.
Provenance: Michael van Meer (d. 1653) ... David Laing, 1847, who bequeathed it to the Edinburgh University Library, 1878.
Edinburgh University Library.

This drawing comes from an album of sketches and autographs collected by Michael van Meer, a student from Hamburg, who was in London from 1614 to June 1615. He appears to have been given it by a friend, Georg Philip Marshalk of East Friesland, who signed the page to which it is attached with the date: 23 June 1616. The inscription on the drawing states that "these Indian birds and beasts with the young man were seen in the year 1615-1616 in St. James Park in the zoological garden, in Westminster in the city of London." In fact neither the birds nor the beasts are American (though fat-tailed sheep and goats often figured incongruously in allegories of America in the late seventeenth century). There can be no doubt about the nationality of the youth, however, though no Indian is recorded as being in London in 1615. It is possible that the date in the inscription is incorrect and that he was one of the attendants of Pocahontas who arrived in May 1616. Brent de Bock, who appears to have made the drawing, is otherwise unrecorded.

Literature: J. L. Nevinson: "Sketches of 17th Century London" in *Country Life*, CXLII (1967), p. 1257; Christian F. Feest: "Virginian Indian Miscellany III" in *Archiv für Völkerkunde*, XXVI (1972), pp. 3-5.

II
Unpathed Waters,
Undreamed Shores

The great early sixteenth-century cartographers deserve a place, which they are all too seldom accorded, among Renaissance artists. And if we include among them, as we ought, Jacques Le Moyne and John White, who seem to have been trained as map-makers and to have gone to America partly if not mainly in that capacity, then they largely dominate our view of the New World as it first appeared to Europeans. In addition to impressing the coastal outline of the American continent on the European mind, they depicted its salient characteristics, including its fauna, flora, and inhabitants, and presented some of the earliest, sharpest, and brightest visions of America.[1] They were in close touch with explorers and often better informed than were the naturalists of the day. It is on maps that the first representations of many American animals occur. As early as 1502, for example, the Portuguese maker of the Cantino map nicely distinguished between the large, brightly coloured macaws of South America and the smaller, less showy parrots of Africa.[2] Cartographers knew that the turkey was an American bird, while naturalists went on supposing that it came from Asia. Some of the earliest depictions of the American Indians are also to be found on maps—the first recorded depiction of a cannibal on the "Kunstmann II" planisphere in Munich,[3] Brazilians gathering brazil-wood on the "Miller atlas" [17] (colorplate 2), North American Indians and their wigwams in an atlas of 1542 by Jean Rotz (British Library).[4]

Trained as scientific illustrators, cartographers were able to avoid the visual stereotypes used, consciously or unconsciously, by artists, and they bring the strangeness of America before us more vividly than the written reports of explorers, most of which resound with echoes of mediaeval and Latin literature. Their works enable us to recapture something of the thrill of breaking into "unpathed waters, undreamed shores." Far from creating a new world in the image of the old, they emphasize its alien characteristics. But, of course, they record much that we now know to be mythical. They remind us that to sixteenth-century Europeans, dragons were as credible as iguanas, the kingdoms of Norumbega and Saguenay as real as those of the Aztecs and Incas.

There is nothing on these maps that is intentionally imaginary and very little that is merely decorative. But, thanks to the artistic sensibility of their creators, they often have considerable aesthetic appeal. Cartographers seem to have had an instinctive feeling for colour, which acquires a jewel-like quality from the economy with which it is applied on the crisp white vellum. As draughtsmen they combine fluency with precision. Ships scudding across the ocean in the "Miller atlas" [17] are depicted with a vitality and accuracy achieved by none but the greatest of marine painters. They seem hardly to have been able to draw a flag marking ownership, a scroll for an inscription, or even a compass, without giving it vibrant life. The inscriptions are often very remarkable—beautiful works of art in themselves, which were doubtless appreciated as such by contemporaries. Gerardus Mercator, it may be recalled, was hardly less famous in his lifetime as a calligrapher than as a cartographer. A clear script was both artistically desirable and practically essential to record information which could not be conveyed by means of visual symbols.

The great sixteenth-century development in cartography both was stimulated by and assisted in the exploration of the New World. Explorers were bound to make charts of the lands they had found. No geographical discovery has any value unless it is recorded in such a way that it can be visited again. European rulers needed maps to indicate the territorial claims they had laid or, sometimes, merely hoped to lay. One of the finest maps exhibited here was made for Mary Tudor and shows the extent of her husband Philip II's empire [20, 21]. Another marks the colony which the French intended to establish in Brazil under the governorship of Filippo Strozzi [22]. But increasing interest in geographical discovery soon created a more widespread demand for maps, and this was satisfied at first by woodcuts, like that in Johann Huttich's collection of travel literature [18], and later by copper-plate engravings, with their finer and more precise lines [24]. The need for more accurate ways of delineating the curved surface of the earth on a flat plane—to assist navigators but also to inform the general public—led to the invention of new schemes of cartographical projection—the oval, the cordiform [19], and, eventually, the projection named after Mercator.

This section is supplemented by a facsimile of Martin Waldseemüller's world map, on which America was named for the first time.[5] The only surviving specimen is in the collection of Fürst Franz von Waldburg, Schloss Waldsee, Württemberg, Germany. It was printed from wood blocks on twelve sheets and published in Strassburg in 1507. Waldseemüller's remarkable achievement was to join up the "islands" discovered by Columbus, John Cabot, Miguel Corte Real, Pedro Álvarez Cabral, Vespucci, and Juan Diaz de Solis to form a single landmass, closer to Asia than to Europe but a geographically independent "fourth part of the globe, which since Americus discovered it, may be called *Amerige* or *Land of Americus,* or *America.*" The inscription in the lower left-hand corner of the map described it as:

> A general delineation of the various lands and islands, including some of which the ancients make no mention, discovered lately between 1497 and 1504 in four voyages over the seas, two by Fernande of Castile, and two by Manuel of Portugal, with Americus Vespucius as one of the navigators and officers of the fleet; and especially a delineation of many

places hitherto unknown. All this we have carefully drawn on the map, to furnish true and precise geographical knowledge.

1. Wilma George: *Animals and Maps,* London, 1969.
2. Biblioteca Estense, Modena, cf. A. Cortesão and A. Teixeira da Mota: *Portugaliae Monumenta Cartographica,* Lisbon, 1960, vol. I.
3. Friedrich Kunstmann, Karl von Spruner, and Georg M. Thomas: *Atlas zur Entdeckungsgeschichte Amerikas,* Munich, 1859, pl. II.
4. W. P. Cumming, R. A. Skelton, and D. B. Quinn: *The Discovery of North America,* London, 1971, p. 108.
5. This facsimile, bound in folio size with explanatory text, was published in 1968 by Theatrum Orbis Terrarum Ltd., Amsterdam.

16 *Globe-cup*

Switzerland or Germany. Silver with gilding and enamelling. ca. 1530's-1570. Height 17¾ inches (45 cm.); diameter of globe 6⁵⁄₁₆ inches (16 cm.). Provenance: given in 1662 by Charles de Lorraine to the convent of Tiercelins de Sion; acquired by the city of Nancy during the French Revolution. Nancy, Musée Historique Lorrain.

Early sixteenth-century interest in geography inspired the creation of silver cups made in such a way that the bowl and cover form a terrestrial globe. The example exhibited here is perhaps the earliest known and may have been made as early as the 1530's. Its very finely engraved globe, which separates into hemispheres at the equator, appears to derive from the 1531 World Map of the French mathematician and astronomer Orontius Finaeus (1494-1555). On the Nancy globe, the New World is shown as part of the Asiatic continent, the central section of which corresponds to North America and is labeled "Asia Orientalis" and "Asia Major;" the Gulf of Mexico appears as "Mare Cathayum." Among the numerous regional designations in South America are "Terra Canibale" and "Peru Provincia." Encircling the globe are the tropics, a meridian circle, the equator, and the polar circles. All the land masses are gilded, and the oceans are enamelled in blue.

A statuette of Atlas appropriately serves as a support and the cover is topped with an armillary sphere. A globe cup with a strikingly similar figure of Atlas as a supporter (but with no armillary sphere on top) in the British Museum is inscribed with the date 1569. Other recorded examples of globe cups include one of 1539 by Jakob Stampfer (1505-1579) in the Historisches Museum, Basel, two by Georg Kobenhaupt (fl. 1534-1572) and six by the Zurich goldsmith Abraham Gessner (1552-1613). There is an anonymous specimen dated 1648 in Rosenborg Castle, Copenhagen. A unique example in gold, the "Airthrey" globe cup widely publicised when sold by auction in London in 1936, has been assigned to the sixteenth century but doubts have been cast on its authenticity.

Literature: *Mémoirs de la Société Royale de Nancy 1835*, Nancy, 1836; *Magazine of American History* VIII (1881), pp. 183-187; L. Wiener: *Musée Historique Lorrain: Catalogue des objets d'art et d'antiquité*, Nancy, 1895, p. 174, no. 974; E. L. Stevenson: *Terrestial and Celestial Globes*, New Haven, 1921, vol. I, p. 102; Sir Hercules Read and A. B. Tonnochy: *Catalogue of the Silver Plate Mediaeval and later bequeathed to the British Museum by Sir Augustus Wollaston Franks*, London, 1928, p. 26; E. Zinner in *Encyclopedia of World Art*, New York, 1960, vol. III, col. 8600.

Pedro Reinel

Portuguese, ca. 1500-1540.
He was the leading Portuguese cartographer of his day and worked in close collaboration with his son Jorge. His earliest known map is a North Atlantic chart of ca. 1504 in the Bayerische Staatsbibliothek, Munich, and his last an Atlantic chart of ca. 1540 in the collection of Baron Ricasoli in Florence. A map made by him is known to have been used in preparation for Ferdinand Magellan's voyage. John III of Portugal described him in 1528 as "my servant, master of the charts and navigation compasses in my kingdom and lands" and awarded him a pension for the services he had rendered "to King John [II] my uncle and the King my lord and father."

Lopo Homem

Portuguese, fl. 1517-1565.
He was a member of a noble Portuguese family. In 1517 King Manuel made him "master of our navigation charts" with the privilege "to make and correct all navigation compasses which may belong to our fleets." He was knighted by the governor of Azamor in 1521 and in 1526 became royal cosmographer. The only maps associated with him are those in the "Miller atlas" (see below).

Pedro Reinel and Lopo Homem

17 *Map of South America*
Watercolour on vellum. ca. 1525.
16⅜ x 23¼ inches (41.5 x 59 cm.).
Provenance: Jacques Charavay 1855; Visconde de Santarém before 1865; Bénigne-Emmanuel Clément Miller, who sold it to the Bibliothèque Nationale in 1897.
Paris, Bibliothèque Nationale.
Colorplate 2.

This map forms part of one of the most notable early sixteenth-century Portuguese atlases, usually known as the "Miller atlas." One sheet (a circular world map) is signed by Lopo Homem, who seems, however, to have played only a minor part in drawing the others—including that exhibited here— which are generally thought to be the work mainly of Pedro and/or Jorge Reinel. The atlas has been dated as early as 1516 and as late as 1532. The chart of the North Atlantic reveals that its maker knew of the voyages of João Alvares Fagundes in 1521 and probably of the colony he established on Cape Breton Island (the first in North America since that of the Norsemen), which was abandoned shortly before 1526. They did not, however, know of the voyages of Giovanni da Verrazano and Estévan Gomez in 1524-25. The sheet exhibited shows Portuguese South America, labelled *Teira Brasilis*— land of the brazil trees. In addition to recording the coastline with the many names given to capes and inlets in the course of the first twenty-five years of exploration, it indicates what was known of the country itself. There are macaws and other brightly plumaged birds, monkeys, a large feline (probably a jaguar), and a dragon, which may be derived from a written description of an iguana. There are Indians dressed in feathers and others completely naked, carrying and chopping brazil-wood. The larger figure in the

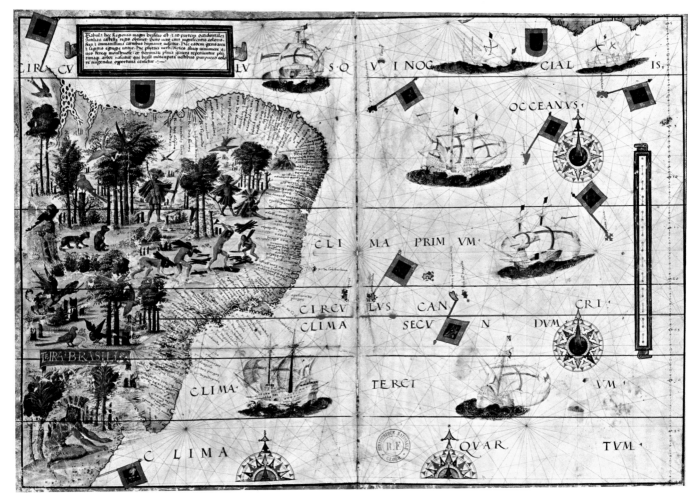

17 Pedro Reinel and Lopo Homem, *Map of South America*. Bibliothèque Nationale.

lower left corner may perhaps represent one of the Patagonian giants encountered by Magellan in 1519. The inscription in the upper left corner may be translated: "This is the chart of the region of great Brazil, and on the Western side it reaches the Antilles of the King of Castile. Its people are somewhat dark in colour. Savage and very cruel, they feed on human flesh. These same people are most skilful in the use of bow and arrows. Here are multicoloured parrots and innumerable other birds and monstrous wild beasts. And many kinds of monkeys are found and there grows in great quantity the tree called brazil which is considered proper for dying clothes in purple."

Literature: Gabriel Marcel in *Comptes Rendus de la Société de Geographie,* Paris, 1897, nos. 16-17; H. Harrisse: *Découverte et évolution cartographique de Terre Neuve,* London-Paris, 1900, p. 84; Jean Denucé: *Les Origines de la cartographie portugaise et les cartes des Reinel,* Ghent, 1908, pp. 42-47; Visconde de Santarém: *Estudios de Cartografia Antiga,* Lisbon, 1919, pt. I, pp. 189-190; *Quatre siècles de colonisation française,* exhibition catalogue, Bibliothèque Nationale, Paris, 1931, no. 22; Armando Cortesão: *Cartografia e cartografos portugeses dos séculos XV e XVI,* Lisbon, 1935, vol. I, pp. 373-375; R. Levillier: *America la bien llamada,* Buenos Aires, 1948, pp. 76-82; J. G. Leithäuser: *Mot nya varldar,* Stockholm, 1954, p. 237; Armando Cortesão and Avelino Teixeiro da Mota: *Portugaliae Monumenta Cartografica,* Lisbon, 1960, vol. I, pp. 55-61; Isa Adonias: *A Cartografia de Região Amazõnica,* Rio de Janeiro, 1963, vol. I, pp. 23-25; Leo Bagrow (rev. R. A. Skelton): *History of Cartography,* London, 1964, p. 166; Götz Pochat: *Der Exotismus während des Mittelalters und der Renaissance,* Stockholm, 1970, pp. 209-211; S. E. Morison: *The European Discovery of America: The Northern Voyages,* New York, 1971, p. 231.

Hans Holbein the Younger

German, 1497/8-1543.
The greatest German artist of the generation after Dürer, Holbein was born in Augsburg and trained under his father, a late Gothic painter. In 1515 he went to Basle, where he worked for book publishers, providing drawings for decorative motifs, as well as painting religious pictures and the first of the portraits which were to bring him international renown. He went to Lucerne and probably Italy in 1517 but returned to Basle and was admitted to citizenship there in 1520. His woodcut illustrations to Luther's translation of the Bible were published in 1522-23. Work for publishers brought him into the world of the humanists, and he painted three portraits of Erasmus in 1523. In 1526 he went by way of Antwerp to London, was back in Basle by the autumn of 1528, but left in 1532 for England, where he spent the rest of his life painting portraits and also providing designs for architectural decorations and metalwork.

Hans Holbein the Younger (after)

18 *World Map from Johann Huttich, ed.: Novus Orbis Regionum, Basle, 1532*
Woodcut. 15½ x 22⅝ inches (39.4 x 57.5 cm.).
Washington, D.C., Library of Congress, Rare Book Division.

This map, often called the Grynaeus map, was first published in Johann Huttich's collection of travel literature, which has a preface by Simon Grynaeus and reprints the Latin versions of the letters of Columbus and Vespucci as well as several accounts of eastward voyages, including extracts from Marco Polo. Cartographically it was already out of date when it first appeared, yet it was reprinted in 1537 and 1555. The New World is derived from Martin Waldseemüller's map of 1507 and from globes of 1515-20 by Johann Schöner. North America is latitudinally limited, labelled *Terra de Cuba,* shown in close proximity to *Zipangri* (Japan), yet separated by a wide stretch of water from Newfoundland, which is called *Terra Cortesia.* The decorations surrounding the map are, however, very remarkable. They are generally attributed to Holbein, because of their similarity to other woodcuts made after his designs at this period. The lower left corner shows the *canibali* of South America. The naked figures above, with extended lower lips, are of a type long associated with the marvels of the East and had often been illustrated (e.g. in the *Nürnberger Chronik* in 1493). Those shown in the upper right corner near spice-bearing trees are probably intended to represent inhabitants of the East Indies, though the feathers they wear seem to be American. The man labelled *Vartomanus* in the lower right corner is Ludovico di Varthema of Bologna, who published an account of his travels in the Orient

(1510), reprinted in Huttich's collection. The sheet as a whole gives a vivid impression of the sense of utter strangeness and alienation with which all parts of the world outside Europe were invested at this period.

Literature: J. D. Passavant: *Le Peintre Graveur*, Leipzig, 1862, Vol. III, pp. 382-383; H. Harrisse: *Biblioteca Americana Vetustissima*, New York-Paris, 1866, no. 171; A. E. Nordenskiold: *Facsimile-Atlas*, Stockholm, 1889, p. 156; H. Harrisse: *The Discovery of North America*, London-Paris, 1892, pp. 586-588; G. Fumagalli, "Bibliografia delle opere concernenti Paolo Toscanelli ed Amerigo Vespucci" in A. M. Bandini: *Vita di Amerigo Vespucci*, Florence, 1898, no. 67; H. Koegler in *Jahrbuch der königlich preussischen Kunstsammlungen*, XVIII (1907), Beiheft pp. 102-103; H. Vignaud: *Americ Vespuce. Sa bibliographie*, Paris, 1917, no. 50; H. A. Schmid: *Hans Holbein der Jünger*, Basel, 1945, vol. I, p. 329, vol. II, p. 43; *The World Encompassed*, exhibition catalogue, The Baltimore Museum of Art, Baltimore, 1952, no. 65; *Mostra Vespucciana*, exhibition catalogue, Palazzo Vecchio, Florence, 1954-55, no. 92; *Die Malerfamilie Holbeins in Basel*, exhibition catalogue, Kunstmuseum, Basle, 1960, no. 428; L. Bagrow (rev. R. A. Skelton): *History of Cartography*, London, 1964, p. 86; G. Pochat: *Der Exotismus*, pp. 162, 212; W. P. Cumming, R. A. Skelton, D. B. Quinn: *The Discovery of North America*, London, 1971, p. 63.

Gerardus Mercator

Flemish, 1512-1594.
Mercator is generally regarded as the greatest cartographer since Ptolemy (fl. 139-161), the Alexandrian geographer and astronomer. He was born at Rupelmonde near Antwerp and studied for the priesthood at the University of Louvain but developed doubts. His career as a map-maker began under the influence of the geographer Gemma Frisius, for whom he helped to make a terrestial globe in 1535-36. In 1537 he published a six-sheet map of Palestine (the only sur-

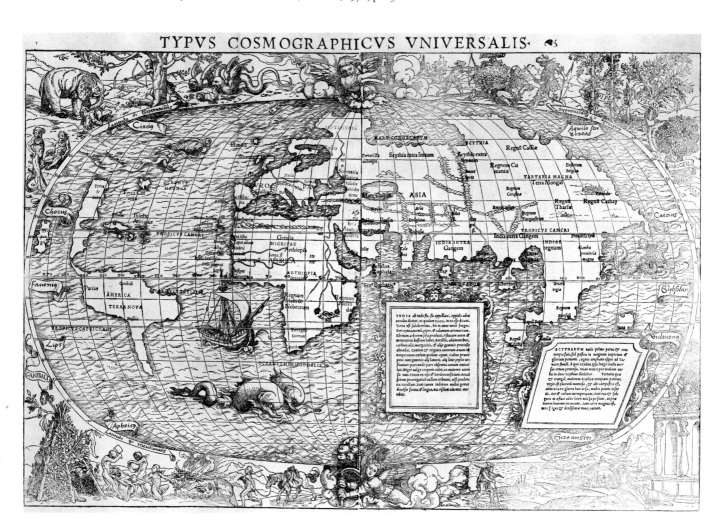

TYPVS COSMOGRAPHICVS VNIVERSALIS.

viving example is in the Biblioteca Civico, Perugia) and in 1538 his first world map (see below). Also a master of calligraphy, he published in 1540 an influential treatise on Italic script. He was charged with heresy in 1544 and imprisoned for some months and, probably to escape further persecution, moved in 1552 to Duisberg, a Protestant city, where he made his famous map of the world, published in 1569 as *Nova et avcta orbis terrae descriptio ad vsvm nauigantium emendati accoadata*. The map is based on the system of cartographical projection named after him, which enables a pilot to lay off a compass course on a chart as a straight line making the same angle with all meridians. Although it did not take on immediately, Mercator's Projection has been used from the early seventeenth century to the present day. He published an edition of Ptolemy (Cologne, 1578-84) and made many other maps, which were collected in a posthumously published *Atlas sive Cosmographiae* (Duisberg, 1595; frequently reprinted)—the first work in which the word "atlas" was used for a collection of maps.

Gerardus Mercator

19 *World Map*

Engraving. 1538. Inscription: In dedication, *Joanni Drosio / suo Gerardus M[ercato]r Rupelmundam dedicabat*. 15 x 22 inches (38 x 55.8 cm.). Provenance: Found by J. C. Brevoort in a 1578 edition of Ptolemy. New York, American Geographical Society, Rare Map Collection.

The only other recorded example of this map (New York Public Library) preserves Mercator's name intact in the dedicatory cartouche. (The "Dros-

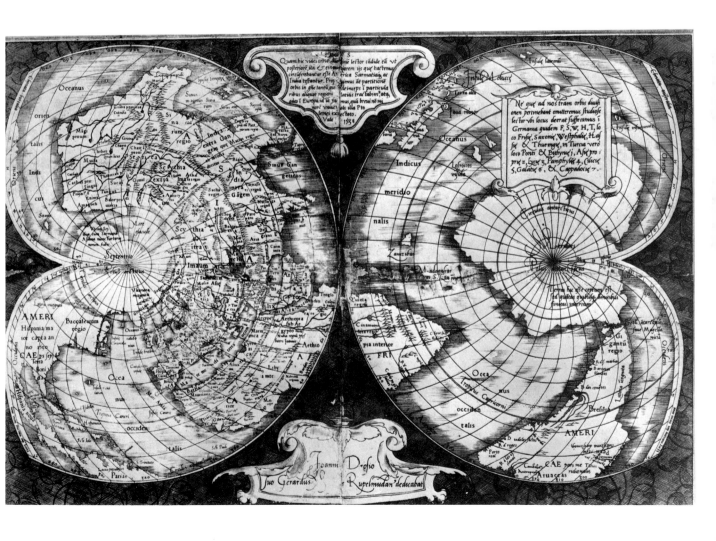

ius" of the dedication is probably Jean Drusius or Droeshout, who entered Louvain University in 1528 and was to be involved in the same trials for heresy as Mercator in 1543-44.) It is based on a map published by the French cosmographer Orontius Finaeus in 1531 and similarly uses the cordiform system of projection, which shows true distance from the North or South Pole to any point. Much of the geographical data is derived from Martin Waldseemüller's world maps of 1507 and 1516. Mercator's is, however, the earliest map on which the name "America" is applied to the northern as well as the southern part of the continent. Other inscriptions on this part of the map record the history of American exploration up to the 1530s—Newfoundland is called *Insulae Corteralis* (for Gaspar and Miguel Corte Real, who reached it in 1500, three years after Cabot), Labrador is named *Baccalearum regio* (land of stockfish), and a wide estuary beneath this inscription is probably that of the Hudson, discovered by Verrazano in 1524. In the southern continent inscriptions record the already notorious presence of cannibals in Venezuela and giants in Patagonia. Peru, which had been invaded by the Pizarro brothers in 1532, is indicated as *regio cultissima ditissimaque* (a highly civilized and rich country). The inscription at the top of the sheet may be translated:

> Greetings to the reader. Let America, with Sarmatia and India bear witness, fair minded reader, that the map of the world which you see here, as it is more recent is also more correct than those which have been published before. We have put before you, however, a division of the earth on broad lines only, which later on we shall treat with more detail in the case of some special lands, and, as a matter of fact, we are already doing this in the case of Eu-

rope. So look for this in a short time, for it will not be smaller than the world map of Ptolemy. Farewell. 1538.

This suggests that the map was published partly as an advertisement for the very much larger maps Mercator was soon to produce. It displays his skill both as a cartographer and as a calligraphist.

Literature: A. E. Nordenskiold: *Facsimile-Atlas,* Stockholm, 1889, trans. Johan Adolf Ekelof and Clements R. Markham, intro. J. B. Post, New York, 1973, p. 90; Emerson D. Fite and Archibald Freeman: *A Book of Old Maps,* Cambridge, Mass., 1926, pp. 54-56; B. van 'T Hoff: *Gerardus Mercator's Map of the World* (1569), Rotterdam-The Hague, 1961, p. 14; A. S. Osely: *Mercator,* London, 1969, p. 65.

Diogo Homem

Portuguese, fl. 1547-1576.
He was the most prolific of the early Portuguese cartographers. Six atlases and eleven charts are signed by him, the earliest of 1557 (British Museum) and the latest of 1576 (Palazzo Borromeo, Isola Bella, Lago Maggiore) both of Europe and the Mediterranean. Little is known about his life, except that he was the son of Lopo Homem [17], was involved in a murder in Lisbon, and was banished to Morocco before 1547, when he is recorded in London. He was probably in London in 1558 and 1567. From 1568 to 1576 he worked in Venice.

Diogo Homem

20 *Map of the World*

Body-colour and gold-leaf on vellum. Signed and dated: *Diegus homem cosmographicus fecit hoc opus anno salutis 1558.* 22¾ x 31¼ inches (56.5 x 80 cm.). Inscription round the border: *Universalis Mundi Figura Atque Navigationum Orbis Terrarum Scitus.* Provenance: Probably Queen Mary I of England and King Philip II of Spain: it is thought to have passed with George IV's library to the British Museum.
London, British Library, Department of Manuscripts.

This comes from an atlas of nine maps, one of which shows the British Isles marked with a shield bearing the arms of Philip II of Spain impaling those of Mary I of England, for whom it would appear to have been made. On the world map the English royal arms are painted above the scale in the lower left corner. The sheet seems to have been intended mainly to show the Spanish and Portuguese overseas possessions as determined by the treaty of Tordesillas. Philip II's arms mark Florida, Peru, Chile, and eastern China,

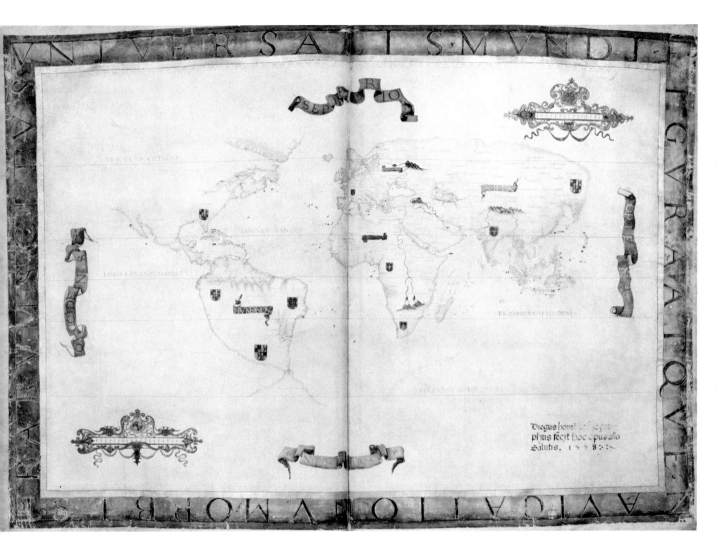

while those of the king of Portugal are on Brazil, Africa, and India. In conformity with Spanish practice, the whole South American continent is labelled *Mundus Novus;* only Venezuela is called *America.* The delineation of America shows that Diogo Homem was aware of Cartier's discovery of the St. Lawrence and Cabrillo's exploration of the Californian peninsula, but not of the recent investigation of the coasts of Peru and Chile.

The tip of Patagonia is separated from an indeterminate antarctic continent only by the Straits of Magellan—as it was to remain on maps until after the discovery of Cape Horn in 1616.

Literature: R. Levillier: *America la bien llamada,* Buenos Aires, 1948, p. 224; A. Cortesão and A. Teixeira da Mota: *Portugaliae Monumenta Cartographica,* Lisbon, 1960, vol. II, pp. 13-15; *Prince Henry the Navigator and Portuguese Maritime Enterprise,* exhibition catalogue, British Museum, London, 1960, no. 292; Isa Adonias: *A Cartografia de região Amazônica,* pp. 114-117; N. Horde, S. Dresner, M. Hillman: *The Conquest of North America,* Garden City, N.Y. 1973, p. 141.

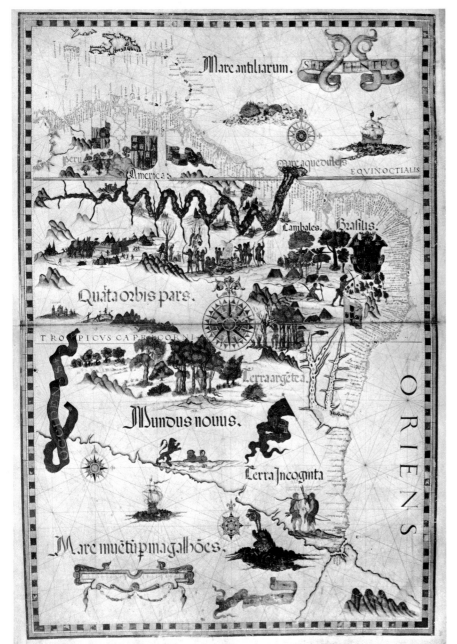

Diogo Homem

21 *Map of South America and Part of the West Indies*

Body-colour and gold-leaf on vellum. 1558. 31¾ x 22½ inches (81 x 57 cm.). Provenance: As for [20]. London, British Library, Department of Manuscripts.

This map of South America comes from the same atlas as [20]. Intended to supply information about the nature of the country and its inhabitants rather than to serve as a chart for a traveller, its configuration is in general defective. But the drawings of figures and trees are remarkable. In Peru, Spaniards with their banners and horses confront the army of "king Atabaliba." To the east of them there is a group of naked savages, one of whom shoots at a parrot, while others enjoy a cannibal feast and human limbs hang from a tree. Below the legend *Quarta orbis pars* the city of *el Cuzco* is marked, and nearby men dig for silver, presumably at Potosí. In Brazil there is a man in a feather head-dress and skirt shooting with bow and arrow, a naked figure sits behind him, a third chops down a brazil-wood tree, and there are several simple huts. Down in Patagonia two giants dressed in skins carry bows and arrows.

Literature: As for [20].

Jacques Vaudeclaye (or Vau de Claye)
French, fl. 1579.
Vaudeclaye was a cartographer working in Dieppe in the last quarter of the sixteenth century.

Jacques Vaudeclaye (or Vau de Claye)

22 *Map of North and North-East Brazil*

Watercolour on vellum. Signed: *Jacques de Vaudeclaye ma faict en Dieppe L'An 1579.* 18½ x 23¼ inches (47 x 59 cm.). Provenance: François Roget de Gaignières, who gave it with the rest of his collection to Louis XIV in 1711.
Paris, Bibliothèque Nationale.

Showing the coast of Brazil from the mouth of the Amazon to the Rio Real,

this map records a voyage of reconnaissance made by French ships with the intention of finding a site for a second French colony in South America after "La France Antartique" had been abandoned in 1560. The coat of arms emblazoned on the flag is that of Filippo Strozzi, who, at the instance of his cousin Catherine de Médicis, was secretly appointed lieutenant general or viceroy of Brazil but died on his way there in 1582, in a battle with the Spaniards off the Azores. The boldly drawn

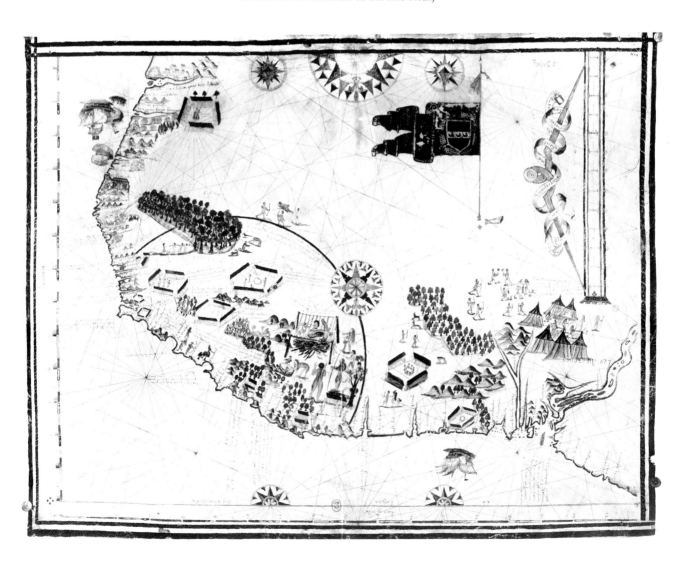

semi-circle marks the area intended for colonization, and the inscription at the top of it declares that the area will "furnish you with ten thousand savages to make war on the Portuguese: and they are bolder than those lower down." Another inscription, just outside the estuary at the right-hand (west) end of the semi-circle, states that "the savages say there is gold in this river." Like many earlier maps, this sheet indicates the wild-life of the region—birds, monkeys, and a forest which yields brazil-wood—as well as the characteristics of the native population, including, on the right, a group of Amazons.

Literature: Gabriel Marcel: *Reproductions de cartes et de globes relatifs à la découverte de l'Amérique du* XVIe *au* XVIIe *siècle*, Paris, 1893, pp. 48-49; *Quatre siècles de colonisation française*, exhibition catalogue, Bibliothèque Nationale, Paris, 1931, no. 354; Isa Adonias: *A Cartografia de região Amazônica*, pp. 459-460.

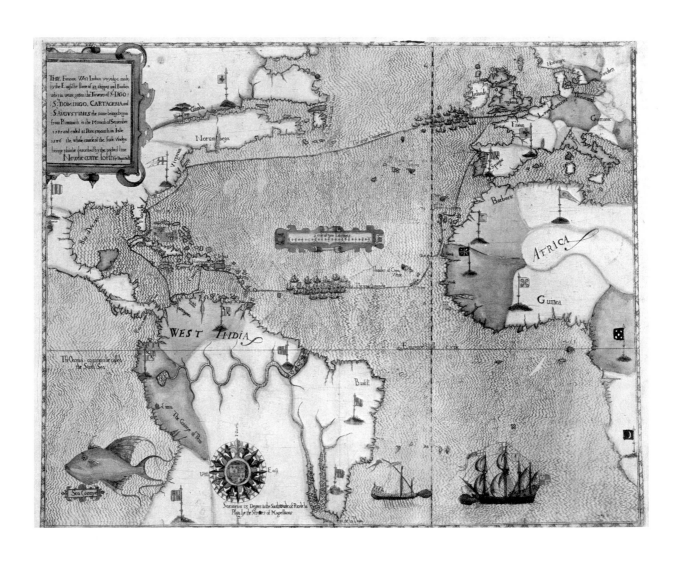

Baptista Boazio

Italian, fl. 1588-1603.

Nothing is known of Boazio before 1588, when he published the map of the "Famouse West Indian voyadge" (see below). At this date he was presumably working in London. It is sometimes said that he had accompanied Drake on his raid of the Spanish West Indies in 1585-86, but this is improbable. He published maps of the Isle of Wight (1591) and the siege of Geertruydenberg in Holland (1595), drew a plan of Cadiz showing the English attack on the city (1596), a chart of the Azores (1597), and a map of Ireland (ca. 1599) copied after Mercator. The subjects of his maps suggest that he may have been in the service of the earl of Essex. He is recorded for the last time in London in 1603.

Baptista Boazio

23 *The Famouse West Indian Voyadge*
Engraving coloured by hand. 1588.
16⁹⁄₁₆ x 21⅞ inches (42 x 55.5 cm.).
Collection of Mr. and Mrs. Paul Mellon.

As the inscription states, this map charts "The Famouse West Indian voyadge made by the Englishe fleete of 23 shippes and Barkes wherin weare gotten the Townes of St. Iago: S: to Domingo, Cartagena and S: Augustines the same beinge began from Plimmouth in the Moneth of September 1585 and ended at Portesmouth in Iulie 1586 the whole course of the saide viodge beinge plainlie described by the pricked line Newlie come forth by Baptista B." It was engraved in the Netherlands and appears to have been published as a single sheet, though it is frequently bound together with four plans of Spanish colonial settlements (unsigned but sometimes attributed to Boazio) in Walter Bigges: *A summarie*

and True Discourse of Sir Francis Drakes West Indian voyage, London, 1588 (cf. Irene A. Wright: *Further English Voyages to Spanish America 1583-1594,* Hakluyt Society Series II, XCIX, London, 1951). Drake, with Martin Frobisher as second in command and some 2,300 sailors and soldiers, captured and ransomed Santo Domingo and Cartagena and sacked St. Augustine in Florida. He then proceeded to the first English colony in America on Roanoake Island in order to provision it. But the governor persuaded Drake to take him and all the 102 surviving colonists, including John White, back to England. The fish in the lower left corner of the map, labelled as a Sea Connye, is a queen trigger fish (*Balistes vetula* Linn.), apparently engraved after a drawing by White now in the British Museum. The place-name *Norumbega* (N.E. of Virginia) marks the area called Orumbega by Giovanni da Verrazano in 1525. An English sailor called David Ingram claimed to have explored this region in 1567-69 and diffused such tall stories about it and its capital city—"a towne half a myle longe" in which houses had pillars of gold, silver, and crystal—that several expeditions were sent there, until Samuel de Champlain in 1613 [24] dispelled its legeand (cf. S. E. Morison: *The European Discovery of America: The Northern Voyages,* New York, 1971, pp. 464-470, 488-491).

Literature: E. Lynam: "Boazio's map of Ireland" in *British Museum Quarterly,* XI (1937), pp. 92-95; *idem: The Map Maker's Art,* London, 1953, p. 75; E. Croft Murray and P. Hulton: *The British Museum: Catalogue of British Drawings,* London, 1960, vol. I, p. 39; W. P. Cumming, R. A. Skelton, and D. B. Quinn: *The Discovery of North America,* p. 186.

Samuel de Champlain

French, ca. 1567-1635.

Samuel de Champlain, the founder of French Canada, was born at Brouage on the west coast of France between La Rochelle and Bordeaux. Little is known of him before 1593-98, when he served in the army of Henry IV. He probably visited the Spanish West Indies in 1599-1600. In March 1603 he joined an expedition to Canada, returning in September and publishing, before the year was out, *Des sauvages, ou, voyage de Samuel Champlain de Brouage, fait en la France nouvelle, l'an 1603*. Next year he went back to Canada as geographer in an expedition led by Pierre du Gua de Monts, who had been granted a monopoly on the fur trade. The results of his explorations during the next three years he recorded on his map of the Bay of Fundy and coast of New England (Library of Congress). After a brief visit to France he was back in Canada in 1608 as lieutenant to de Monts and established a trading post at Quebec. In 1612 Louis XIII appointed him lieutenant to the viceroy of New France, a position he was to hold until 1632, when he was appointed governor of the colony. Not only did he regulate the affairs of the colony and establish friendly relations with the Algonquins and the Hurons but carried out extensive explorations on either side of the St. Lawrence and as far as the Great Lakes—covering some 10,000 miles on foot and by canoe—described in three further books of *Voyages* published in Paris in 1613 (see below), 1620, and 1632.

Samuel de Champlain

24 *Map of New France*
Engraving. 1613. 17¾ x 31³⁄₁₆ inches
(45 x 79 cm.). Inscription: *Carte geographique de la Nouvelle Franse faicte par le Sieur de Champlain Saint Tongois Cappitaine Ordinaire pour le Roy en la Marine.*
Washington, D.C., Library of Congress, Rare Book Division.

This map, engraved after a drawing by Samuel de Champlain to illustrate his voyages of exploration in New France 1608-09, 1610, and 1611, was published in his book *Les Voyages de Sieur de Champlain Xaintongeois, Capitaine ordinaire pour le Roy en la Marine,* Paris, 1613. It marks the village of

Quebec, which Champlain founded in 1608, Lake Champlain, which he discovered in 1609, and Montreal, where he established a settlement in 1611. His information about the lakes shown to the west was, however, derived from the reports of the Indians (not until 1615 did he reach Lakes Ontario and Huron). The four Indians in the lower left corner are Montagnais, who lived by the Saguenay River, and Almouchiquas, who inhabited Acadia (Nova Scotia and New Brunswick). The fruits illustrated below include the summer squash, plums, red currants, chestnuts, grapes, beans, hickory nuts, and acorns. On the map itself the forms of native habitations are indicated, also

several animals (beaver, mink, martin, porcupine, wolf, polar-bear, and moose), and the more notable fish (whale, cod, dog-fish, bull-fish, seal, bass, gar pike, sturgeon, and horseshoe crab).

Literature: W. L. Grant, ed. *Original Narratives of Early American History. Voyages of Samuel de Champlain, 1604-1618,* New York, 1907, p. 224; Emerson D. Fite and Archibald Freeman: *A Book of Old Maps Delineating American History,* New York, 1926, pp. 120-123; L. C. Wroth: "An Unknown Champlain Map of 1610" in *Imago Mundi,* XI (1954), pp. 84-94; Morris Bishop: *Champlain The Life of Fortitude* (1948), revised ed. Toronto, 1963, p. 182; W. P. Cumming, R. A. Skelton, D. B. Quinn: *The Discovery of North America,* pp. 270-274.

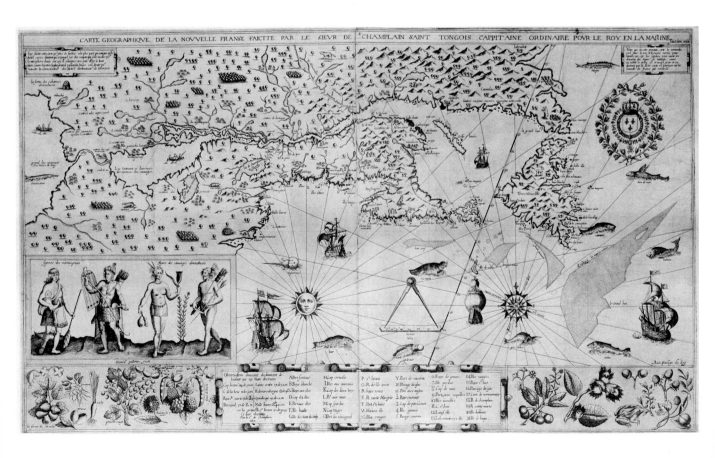

III
Joyfull Newes
Out of the
Newe Founde Worlde

There were no sunflowers, nasturtiums, morning-glories, passion-flowers, dahlias, or petunias, no Jerusalem artichokes, French beans, runner beans, or large, juicy strawberries in the gardens of pre-Columbian Europe.[1] On the dry wasteland of the Mediterranean littoral there were no agaves or prickly pears. All these plants, which now seem so familiar to Europeans, were, like the potato, tomato, and maize, introduced from the New World. Products of American plants, similarly taken for granted by Europeans, include chocolate, vanilla, tapioca, quinine, rubber, and, of course, tobacco. The debt of the Old World to the plant life of the New is far greater than is commonly appreciated. Maize revolutionised the agrarian economy of North Italy, just as potatoes transformed that of Ireland (and, when the crops failed, drove millions of emigrants to the United States). Manihot, or cassava, taken by the Portuguese from Brazil to their other colonies, was eventually to provide a staple food for much of Africa. Nowadays several countries in the Old World thrive on the products of plants introduced from America—Malaysia on rubber from the Brazilian *Hevea* tree, Tanzania on sisal made from the Mexican *Agave sisaliana*, Ghana on cocoa, Egypt on cotton, the best of which is made from an American species of *Gossypium*.

The introduction of American plants into Europe was, however, slow and erratic. A hundred years after Columbus made his landfall, no more than a score were under cultivation, though they included many of the most important.[2] Maize, the annual red pepper or chilli *(Capsicum anuum)*, a kind of squash, the tomato, and so-called "African" marigold *(Tageses patula)* had arrived by 1543. Two species of tobacco, the agave, and the prickly pear are recorded soon afterwards. By the end of the century Europe also had the scarlet-runner and French bean, the sweet potato *(Ipomea battata)* and common or "Irish" potato, the pineapple, the sunflower, a type of *Canna*, nasturtium, spider-wort *(Tradescantia Virginiana)*, and the "Four-o'clock" or Marvel of Peru *(Mirabilis Jalapa)*.

Most of these plants were valued by Europeans either as foods or, more usually, as medicines. The title which John Frampton gave in 1577 to his translation of the first Spanish book on American plants, *Joyfull Newes out of the Newe Founde Worlde* [28], referred to the cures they were supposed to effect. But in addition to describing how the leaves of the tobacco plant might be used to relieve a bewildering variety of ills, he remarks that it had already been grown "more to adornate Gardens with the fairnesse thereof, and too geve a plesaunt sight." He also commented that the sunflower "sheweth marvellous faire in Gardens." The sharp increase in the introduction of American plants in the early seventeenth century seems to have been mainly owing to horticulturalists. Catesby remarked in 1729 that in less than half a century America had "furnished England with a

57

greater variety of trees than had been procured from all other parts of the world for more than a thousand years." Even so, many of the American plants which are now most popular were introduced much later. Not until the 1790s did dahlias, tigridias, Californian poppies, and monkey-puzzle trees make their appearance in European gardens. Exotica for the hot-house arrived in the nineteenth century, including Brazilian orchids and the most spectacular of all water-lilies, *Victoria amazonica*. Thus, the image of America as a land of unequalled floral riches was constantly being renewed and kept fresh.

The gradual discovery of the American flora also coincided with and played a part in the development of scientific botany. In the late fifteenth century the study of plants was confined almost exclusively to physicians and apothecaries, who sought the "simples" from which compound drugs were prepared. Influenced by the revival of classical learning, some of them had already begun to reject mediaeval traditions and were going back to the texts of Theophrastus, Dioscorides, and others who had listed the healing properties of herbs. Throughout the sixteenth century and well into the seventeenth, the identification of plants with those mentioned by the ancients preoccupied the more erudite herbalists. Thus Otto Brunfels, in his epoch-making herbal of 1530, dismissed plants which had no Latin names and were of no use to apothecaries as *herbae nudae*. The flora recently introduced from America found no place in his book. Leonard Fuchs in 1542 discussed and illustrated maize and the pumpkin-gourd, but he was unaware that either was peculiar to the New World, even though the former had been described by several travel writers. He called them "Turkish corn" and "Turkish cucumber."[3]

The descriptions provided by Dioscorides were so vague that American plants could easily be identified with them. As late as 1620 Gaspard Bauhin was still trying to fit the potato into the classical flora, though he knew that it had been found only in the New World. Jacques-Philippe Cornut remarked in 1632 that "in Dioscorides' time neither America nor Canada had been discovered," but cited him nonetheless in an account of Canadian plants.[4] By the mid-seventeenth century, however, naturalists had begun to look more closely at plants than at classical texts, and the authority of the ancients on both botany and medicine had been undermined.

New introductions demanded a higher standard of botanical description and illustration than that achieved by the early herbalists. The faithful depiction of plants preceded their accurate description—in the drawings of da Vinci and Dürer, to mention only the most famous. Maize and the pumpkin are more scientifically illustrated than described in Füch's herbal. Jacopo Ligozzi's watercolours have a sharp-eyed freshness of observation hard to parallel in the work of contemporary writers on plants. Botanists learned from such illustrations and often worked in close collaboration with artists. "It frets a man to see fine objects, and not be able to take draughts of them," wrote the French naturalist J. Pitton de Tournefort in 1717; "for without this help of drawing, 'tis impossible any account thereof should be perfectly intelligible."[5] He had the good fortune to employ the best botanical illustrator of the day, Claude Aubriet, whose drawings indicate plant structure as well as the outward appearance of leaves and flowers [40]. But the illustration of flora reached its unsurpassed height, both of scientific accuracy and exquisite delicacy, in the following decades under the influence of Linnaeus, who was well aware of the importance of introductions from the New World. "We are all devoted to the love of exotic plants, especially those from America," he wrote in 1737.[6]

American fauna also intrigued Europeans. Columbus took back macaws from his first voyage in 1493, and many more were to follow them. A decade later voyagers brought from Newfoundland to the court of Henry VII in London hawks, an eagle, "poppyngais & catts of the mountayne" (probably blue jays or woodpeckers and Canadian lynxes).[7] Turkeys, first noted by Pedro Alonso Nino in 1499, seem to have been taken to Europe soon after, where they were successfully reared and became so fully assimilated that their country of origin was often forgotten (as by Belon, see [25]). Another American bird bred for the table in Europe, the musk- or Muscovy-duck, similarly acquired an Eastern name. Ornamental birds which made their appearance in European aviaries in the sixteenth century included the crested and galleated curassow. Otherwise American birds were known from dead specimens—or from their feathers and beaks—which found their way into cabinets of natural curiosities, together with stuffed armadillos and the shells of turtles. Of American mammals the first to be taken to Europe was probably one of the several types of American monkey. A jaguar was sent to Charles V by the Viceroy Diego Colòn before 1526.[8] Llamas reached Spain soon after the conquest of Peru, and in 1562 the Italian sculptor Gianpaolo Poggini modelled one for a medal. Smaller creatures also crossed the Atlantic. In about 1580 the menagerie of the grand duke of Tuscany seems to have boasted an agouti and a type of West Indian weasel neatly drawn by Ligozzi.

John White drew West Indian birds, fishes, turtles, and crabs, probably when on his way to North America in 1585 [30-34]. But no attempt at a systematic study of the wild-life of any part of the New World was made until Count Maurits of Nassau went to Brazil in 1637. His expedition was a landmark in the natural history of America (see section v). Yet even as late as the 1670s illustrations of American wild-life as fantastic as those in Arnoldus Montanus's account of *De Nieuwe en Onbekende Weereld* [39] could still apparently be accepted without demur. The first illustrated sur-

59

vey of the natural history of any part of North America, including birds, insects, and reptiles as well as plants, was that published by Mark Catesby between 1729 and 1741 [42, 43].

1. The large strawberry resulted from a cross made in France in 1714 between species from Virginia and Chile.
2. S. Killermann: "Zur ersten Einführung amerikanischer Pflanzen im 16. Jahrhundert" in *Naturwissenschaftliche Wochenschrift*, XXIV (1909), pp. 193-200, accounts for only seventeen plants. A few more can be added to his list by reference to F. S. Chittenden, ed.: *The Royal Horticultural Society Dictionary of Gardening*, Oxford, 1951, which also gives dates for later introductions.
3. L. Fuchs: *De historia stirpium*, Basel, 1542; cf. A. Arber, *Herbals Their Origin and Evolution*, Cambridge, 1938, p. 70.
4. J.-P. Cornut: *Canadensium plantarum* (Paris, 1635), ed. J. Stannard, New York and London, 1966, p. 136.
5. W. Blunt: *The Art of Botanical Illustration*, London, 1950, p. 113.
6. M. Kraus: *The Atlantic Civilization*, New York, 1949, p. 165. Linnaeus was indebted for much information to American naturalists, Alexander Garden of South Carolina and Joseph Mutis of Bogotá, also to the Swedish traveller Peter Kalm, who brought seeds of North American plants and grew them.
7. S. E. Morison: *The European Discovery of America: The Northern Voyages*, New York, 1971, pp. 219-220.
8. G. Friederici: *Der Charakter der Entdeckung und Eboberung Amerikas durch die Europäer*, Stuttgart, 1925, vol. I, p. 137.

Pierre Gourdelle

French, fl. 1555-1588.

A draughtsman and painter working in Paris, Gourdelle's earliest recorded works were drawings of birds, from which woodcuts were made to illustrate *L'histoire de la nature des oyseaux* of Pierre Belon, who misnamed him "Pierre Goudet" though praising his "artifice" as a "peintre vraiment ingénieux." Later he seems to have worked mainly as a portraitist. In 1583 he was listed among the "officiers domestiques" of Henri III.

Pierre Gourdelle (after)

26 *Turkeys, illustration in Pierre Belon:* L'histoire de la nature des oyseaux, *Paris, 1555, p. 249*

Woodcut. 1555. Page size 13⅛ x 9⅛ inches (33.3 x 23.2 cm.). Provenance: Richard Heber . . . Philip Hofer, who gave it to The Houghton Library, 1942. Cambridge, Mass., The Harvard College Library (The Houghton Library).

The turkey, which is indigenous to America, was described by several of the earliest explorers of and writers on the New World, including Peter Martyr, who saw one which had apparently been sent to Spain from Mexico by Cortés in 1519. It was also illustrated on maps of the New World. But, reaching Europe before America had been geographically detached from Asia, it acquired, like maize, an Eastern name. In France it was called at first a *poule d'Inde* (hence *dindon*). Like other naturalists of his time, Belon thus described it as an Asiatic species, confusing it with the guinea-fowl mentioned by the first-century BC Latin writer Columella. Pierre Belon (1517-1564) was, nonetheless, a very notable naturalist and the virtual founder of scientific ornithology. He illustrated in his book a macaw and two other South American birds, which he called the "pie de Bresil" and the "merle de Bresil," remarking that he had seen dead specimens brought back by sailors. But the toucan is illustrated only by one of the beaks, which, he says, were to be seen in the collections of men who were interested in "new things."

Literature: P. Delaunay: *L'aventureuse existence de Pierre Belon*, Paris, 1926; E. G. Allen "The History of American Ornithology before Audubon" in *Transactions of the American Philosophical Society*, N.S. XLI, pt. 3 (1951), pp. 386-590; P. Delaunay: *La zoologie au seizième siècle*, Paris, 1963, pp. 33-34.

27 *Tobacco Plant, illustration in Pierre Pena and Mathias de Lobel:* Stirpium Adversaria Nova, *Antwerp, 1574*

Woodcut. 1570. Page size 13 x 9¹⁄₁₆ inches (33 x 23 cm.).
Cleveland Medical Library Association.

Stirpium Adversaria Nova, an important landmark in the history of botanical classification, is the work of Mathias de Lobel, or l'Obel (1538-1616), a physician and one of the greatest naturalists of his day, in collaboration with Pierre Pena, an obscure Provençal botanist. It was first published in 1570 by Christophe Plantin, and the illustrations, like those in several other books issued by Plantin at this period, were probably drawn by Pierre van der Borcht (1545-1608).

Tobacco smoking intrigued explorers of America from Columbus onwards and was illustrated by André Thevet in 1558 [61] and Gerolamo Benzoni, who gave a vivid description of its evil effects in *La Historia del Mondo Nuovo* [62]. The earliest recorded drawing of the plant was made by or for Conrad Gesner, who noted on it that he had grown specimens from seed in 1554 (cf. Heinrich Zoller, ed.: *Conradi Gesneri Historia Plantarum,* Dietikon-Zurich, 1973, vol. I, pl. 14; the drawing is in the Universitätsbibliothek, Erlangen). The miniaturist Georg Höfnagel painted the flower, apparently from a living specimen, in 1570-74 in a margin of the prayer-book he illuminated for Albrecht V of Bavaria (now in the Staatsbibliothek, Munich; cf. S. Killermann: *Die Miniaturen im Gebetebuch Albrechts V von Bayern,* Strassburg, 1911). The woodcut exhibited here is the earliest published illustration of the plant. Pena and Lobel state that it was already cultivated in Portugal, France, Flanders, and England, and also that the habit of smoking had been acquired by many sailors, who "declare that it soothes the brain with a pleasant form of intoxication." Tobacco is "rightly called the *holy herb,* because it satisfies hunger, it heals ulcers and wounds and is good for diseases of the chest and wasting of the lungs," they remark. "In fact there is no new thing that our age has obtained from America that is more efficacious as a remedy."

Nicotiana inserta in fundibulo ex quo hauriunt fumū Indi & naucleri.

Literature: Charles Singer: "The Early History of Tobacco" in the *Quarterly Review* CCXIX (1913), pp. 125-142; Egon Caesar Conte Corti: *Die trockene Trunkheit,* Leipzig, 1930; Agnes Arber: *Herbals Their Origin and Evolution,* Cambridge, 1938, pp. 90-91, 229-230; Wilfred Blunt: *The Art of Botanical Illustration,* London, 1950, pp. 64, 68; Claus Nissen: *Die botanische Buchillustration,* Stuttgart, 1966, no. 1502.

28 *Armadillo, illustration in N. Monardes:* Ioyfull Newes Out of the Newe Founde Worlde, *Englished by John Frampton, London, 1596*

Woodcut. 1577. Page size 7⅞ x 5¹⁵⁄₁₆ inches (20 x 15 cm.).
Cleveland Medical Library Association.

Nicolás Monardes (1493-1588) was a Spanish physician known mainly for his work on the natural products of the New World, first published in two parts (Seville 1569 and 1571) and re-issued in a single volume as *Primera y segunda y tercera partes de la historia medicinal de las cosas que se traen de nuestras Indias Occidentales que siruen en Medicina*, Seville, 1574. This was given much wider circulation in translations into Latin by Charles de l'Ecluse, *De simplicibus medicamentis ex occidentali India delatis*, Antwerp, 1574, Italian by Annibale Briganti, Venice, 1576 (reprinted four times before 1605), and English by John Frampton, first published in 1577 and reprinted in 1580 and 1596. Frampton, an English merchant who had passed many years in Spain, also published the first English translation of Marco Polo (1579).

The *Ioyfull Newes* of the title refers to the medicinal properties ascribed to herbs, stones, and even parts of animals brought back from America. Monardes describes in detail the cures effected by the use of "sarcaparillia" (a name then applied to a bewildering number of different plants from both the Old and New Worlds), sassafras (supposedly a specific against the venereal diseases introduced from America), sunflowers, potatoes, and so on. He recommended the leaves of the tobacco plant applied externally for "paynes of the head . . . any griefe of the body . . . griefes of the Brest . . . griefes of the stomach . . . griefe of the stone . . . griefes of winds . . . the evil of the Mother . . . evill breath . . . wormes . . . toothache . . . chilblaynes . . . venomous wounds" and so on. The armadillo "hath his vertue onely in the Bone of his tayle, which being made small into powder, and taking so much thereof, as the hedde of a great pinne, made in little balles, putting it into the eare, having griefe therein, it taketh it away marvellously, & also if there be any noise or sounding in the head, with any deafness, worketh a great effect in many persons that have used it, & they have been healed therewith."

The armadillo was one of the American animals which most intrigued sixteenth-century visitors to South America and taxed their descriptive powers —it was likened to a rhinoceros and to an armed horse. It seems to have been first depicted on maps, e.g. that of 1529 by Diego Ribero in the Vatican Library. The earliest published illustration is a woodcut in Conrad Gesner: *Historia Anaimalium*, Zurich, 1554, appendix p. 20. Monardes states that the one illustrated in the 1574 edition of his book was drawn from a specimen in the museum of "Gonçalo de Molina," and it is from this that the illustration in Frampton's translation is derived.

Literature: N. Monardes: *Ioyfull Newes out of the Newe Founde Worlde,* intro. Stephen Gaselee, London-New York, 1925.

29 *Tobacco plant, illustration in Rembert Dodoens:* Stirpium Historiae Pemptades Sex, *Antwerp, 1583*

Woodcut. 1583. Page size 14⅝ x 9½ inches (37 x 24 cm.).
Cleveland Medical Library Association.

This volume contains the collected works of the Flemish naturalist Rembert Dodoens (1517-1585), published by Christophe Plantin, who issued several of the most important late sixteenth-century herbals, generally illustrated with woodcuts after paintings and drawings by Pierre van der Borcht (1545-1608). Whether or not the illustration exhibited is after Pierre van der Borcht is not known. Dodens lists the names already given to the tobacco plant—*petun* (whence the related genus later called *petunia*), *Herbam sacram*, *Nicotiana* (after Jean Nicot, the French consul in Portugal, who is said to have introduced the tobacco habit into France), and *Tabaco*. He also refers to André Thevet's account of tobacco smoking in Brazil [61]. But, in a characteristic attempt to assimilate the flora of the New World into that of the Old, he associates it with a common European plant, Hyoscamus, which, like tobacco, belongs to the family of *Solonaceae* and had been described by Dioscorides. The two illustrations represent not, as Dodoens states, two images of the same plant but two distinct species, later to be named by Linnaeus *Nicotiana tabacum* (on the left) and *N. tomentosa* with stalked leaves, the former being much more accurate than earlier published illustrations.

Literature: A. Arber: *Herbals, their Origin and Evolution*, p. 229; Wilfred Blunt: *The Art of Botanical Illustration*, p. 63; Claus Nissen: *Die botanische Buch illustration*, no. 460.

John White
English, fl. 1577-1593.

30 *Flying-Fish*
Watercolours over black lead, heightened with blue body-colours and gold (oxidised). ca. 1585. 10⅞ x 9⅛ inches (27.7 x 23.4 cm.). Inscription: Above the fish, *Bolador.*, and below, *The flyeng fishe*. Provenance: As for [9]. London, The British Museum.

Pez volador is the modern Spanish for a flying-fish. The fish depicted is probably *Exocoetus volitans* Linn. The drawing, or the sketch from which it was made, was presumably made in the West Indies, on the outward voyage in 1585. The flying-fish shown in the engraving of Santiago by an unknown artist in W. Bigges: *A summarie and True Discourse of Sir Francis Drakes West Indian voyage*, 1589, may have been taken from White's drawing or a derivative of it.

Literature: D. B. Quinn, ed.: *The Roanoke Voyages, 1584-1590. Documents to Illustrate the English Voyages to North America*, Hakluyt Society, series II, vol. CIV, 1955, p. 412, no. 27A; E. Croft Murray and P. Hulton: *Catalogue of British Drawings*, The British Museum, London, 1960, pp. 38-39, no. 27; P. Hulton and D. B. Quinn: *The American Drawings of John White, 1577-1590*, London and Chapel Hill, North Carolina, 1964, no. 27A.

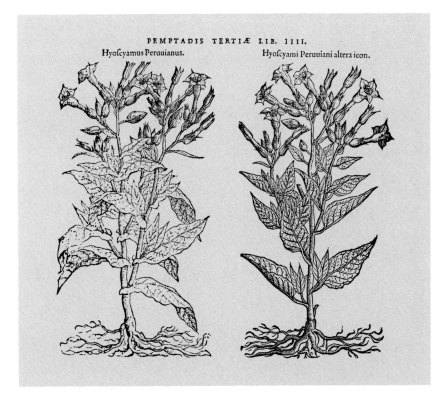

PEMPTADIS TERTIÆ LIB. IIII.
Hyoſcyamus Peruuianus.   Hyoſcyami Peruuiani altera icon.

John White

31 *Flamingo*

Watercolours over black lead, touched with white (oxidised). ca. 1585.
11⅝ x 7¾ inches (29.6 x 19.7 cm.). Inscription: *A Flaminco*. Provenance: As for [9].
London, The British Museum.

This drawing, or the sketch for it, was presumably made in the West Indies on the outward voyage in 1585, since the American or roseate flamingo (*Phoenicopterus ruber* Linn.) is common in the West Indies but is only occasionally found in North Carolina.

Literature: E. G. Allen: "The History of American Ornithology Before Audubon" in *Transactions of the American Philosophical Society*, n.s., XLI, 1951, p. 446; *Sir Walter Raleigh and Richard Hakluyt*, exhibition catalogue, The British Museum, 1952, p. 27, no. 122; D. B. Quinn, ed.: *The Roanoke Voyages 1584-1590*, p. 409, no. 15; E. Croft Murray and P. Hulton: *Catalogue of British Drawings*, p. 36, no. 15; P. Hulton and D. B. Quinn: *The American Drawings of John White, 1577-1590*, no. 15.

Bolador.

The flyeng fishe.

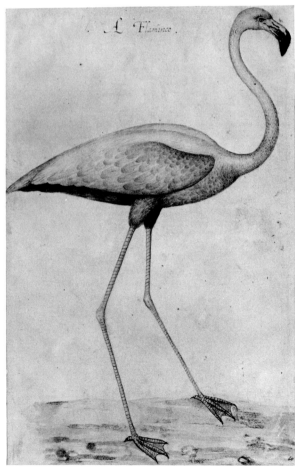

A Flaminco.

Igwano. Some of thes are 3. fote in length. / and lyue on land.

John White

32 *Iguana*

Watercolours over black lead, heightened with white (oxidised) and silver (?). ca. 1585. 5⅝ x 8¼ inches (14.4 x 21 cm.). Inscription: *Igwano. Some of thes are . 3 . fote in length. / and lyue on land.* Provenance: As for [9].
London, The British Museum.

This is the earliest known English drawing of an iguana (*Cyclura* species), and it, or the sketch for it, was presumably made in the West Indies on the outward voyage in 1585, since *igwano* is a word of Spanish West Indian origin. The iguana shown in an anonymous engraving of Cartagena in W. Bigges: *A summarie and True Discourse of Sir Francis Drakes West Indian voyage,* 1589, may have been done from White's drawing.

Literature: L. Binyon: "The Drawings of John White" in *The Walpole Society,* vol. XIII, 1924-25, pl. XXIX a; *Sir Walter Raleigh and Richard Hakluyt,* exhibition catalogue, The British Museum, London, 1952, p. 28, no. 126; D. B. Quinn ed.: *The Roanoke Voyages 1584-1590,* p. 406, no. 8; E. Croft Murray and P. Hulton: *Catalogue of British Drawings,* p. 34, no. 9; P. Hulton and D. B. Quinn: *The American Drawings of John White, 1577-1590,* no. 9A.

A lande Crab.

John White

33 *Land Crab*

Watercolours over black lead, heightened with white (oxidised). ca. 1585. 9⅛ x 10⅞ inches (23.2 x 27.7 cm.). Inscription: *A lande Crab.* Provenance: As for [9].
London, The British Museum.

This drawing of a West Indian land crab (probably *Cardisoma guanhumi*

Latreille), or the sketch for it, was
probably made at Puerto Rico in May
1585, since it also appears in White's
plan of the camp at Mosquetal (Talla-
boa Bay), Puerto Rico, which depicts
events which took place there between
12 and 22 May 1585 (British Museum
1906-5-9-1 [4]).

Literature: D. B. Quinn, ed.: *The Roanoke
Voyages, 1584-1590*, p. 405, no. 4; E. Croft
Murray and P. Hulton: *Catalogue of British
Drawings*, p. 33, no. 5; P. Hulton and
D. B. Quinn: *The American Drawings of
John White, 1577-1590*, no. 5A.

John White

34 *Loggerhead Turtle*
Watercolours over black lead, height-
ened with white. ca. 1585. 7⅜ x 10¼
inches (18.7 x 25.9 cm.). Provenance:
As for [9].
London, The British Museum.

The Atlantic Loggerhead Turtle (*Caretta caretta* Linn.) is the only sea turtle to breed on the Carolina Banks.

Literature: L. Binyon: "The Drawings of
John White" in *Walpole Society*, vol. XIII,
(1924-25), pl. XXIX (b); D. B. Quinn, ed.:
The Roanoke Voyages, 1584-1590, p. 456,
no. 101; E. Croft Murray and P. Hulton:
Catalogue of British Drawings, p. 50,
no. 55; P. Hulton and D. B. Quinn: *The
American Drawings of John White, 1577-
1590*, no. 103A.

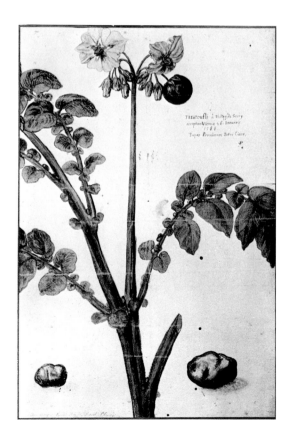

35 Potato plant *(Solanum
  andigenum ?)*
Flanders or Germany.
Watercolour. 1588. 12¼ x 8¼ inches
(31 x 21 cm.). Inscribed: *Taratoufli à
Philippe de Sivry / acceptum Viennae
26 Januarij / 1588. / Papas Peruanum
Petri Ciecae.* Provenance: Given by
Philippe de Sevry to Charles de
L'Ecluse 1589; Plantin family.
Antwerp, Museum Plantin-Moretus.

This is the earliest known European representation of a potato plant. The great Flemish botanist Charles de L'Ecluse, better known as Clusius (1526-1609), recorded in his *Historia* of 1601: "The first mention which I have received of this plant is from Philippe de Sivry, Lord of Walhain and Prefect of the City of Mons, in Hanovia [Hainault], who sent two tubers with fruit to me in Vienna in Austria towards the beginning of the year 1588, and in the following year he sent me a picture of a branch of it with flowers. He wrote that he had received it from a certain friend of the Papal Legate in Belgium under the name of Taratouffli." Clusius went on to cite the first published description of the "common" potato (as opposed to the sweet potato, which is botanically distinct) in Pedro Cieza de Léon: *Parte Primera dela chronica del Peru,* Seville, 1553. He also remarked that "it has now become sufficiently common in many gardens in Germany since it is so fecund." It had, in fact, been first introduced into Spain in the 1570s, and its cultivation soon spread to other parts of Europe in the following decade. But not until the mid-eighteenth century did the potato become the staple food of peasants in Ireland and Scotland.

Literature: Carolus Clusius [Charles de L'Ecluse]: *Rariorum Plantarum Historia,* Antwerp, 1601, p. lxxix; Ernest Roze: *Histoire de la pomme de terre,* Paris, 1898; M[aurits] S[abbe]: *Kunstwerk uit het Museum Plantin-Moretus,* Antwerp, 1925, p. 34; F. W. T. Hunger: *Clusius-Tentoonstellung,* exhibition catalogue; Stedelijk Museum de Lakenhal, Leyden, 1926, no. 159; *idem: Charles de l'Escluse, Carolus Clusius,* The Hague, 1927, p. 175; Max Rooses and Maurits Sabbe: *Catalogus van het Museum Plantin-Moretus,* Antwerp, 1927, p. 56; R. N. Salaman: *The History and Social Influence of the Potato,* Cambridge, 1949, pp. 64-65, 90.

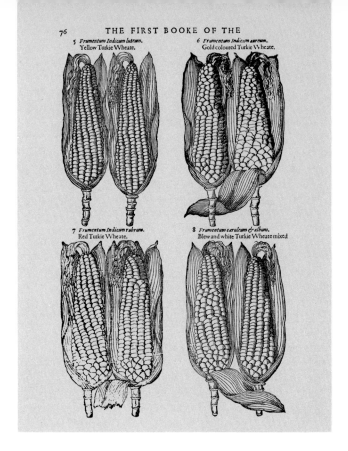

36 *Maize, illustration in John Gerard: The Herbal or Generall Historie of Plantes, London, 1597*

Woodcut. 1597. Page size 12⅝ x 8¹¹⁄₁₆ inches (32 x 22 cm.).
Cleveland Medical Library Association.

Maize was one of the first products of the New World to be brought to Europe. As it was imported at a time when the newly discovered islands were still supposed to lie off the coast of Asia, it acquired (like the turkey, see [25]) an Eastern rather than a Western association, still preserved in its Italian name, *granturco* (Turkish corn). It seems to have been first represented in Hans Burgkmair's woodcut of the "people of Calicut" in *The Triumph of the Emperor Maxi-* milian I [5]. Although it was described in accounts of America, notably that by Oviedo [57], most sixteenth-century botanists and herbalists gave it an Asiatic origin. This mistake was corrected by Pierandrea Mattioli in *Commentarij in sex libros Pedacij Dioscoridis Anazarbei de medica materia,* Venice, 1570, and by Rembert Dodoens, who, in the 1583 edition of his *De Frugum Historia,* wrote that "by no means" did the plant come "from Asia which is subject to the Turkish Emperor (as is commonly believed) or from the Orient, but from the West—from America and neighbouring islands brought first into Spain and then into other states of Europe." Gerard characteristically played safe by giving it a double origin:

These kinds of Graine were first brought into Spaine, and then into other provinces of Europe, out of Asia which is in the Turkes Dominions, as also out of America and the Islands adioyning from the east and west Indies, and Virginia or Norembega, where thet use to sowe or set it, and to make bread of it, where it groweth much higher than in other countries. It is planted in the gardens of these northern regions, where it commeth to ripenes when the sommer falleth out to be faire and hot, as my selfe have seene by proofe in mine owne garden.

The incorrect reference to Asia was, however, omitted from the posthumous 1633 edition of the herbal.

John Gerard (1545-1612) was a notable horticulturalist, who had a fairly large garden of his own in London and was also superintendent of the extensive gardens of Queen Elizabeth's minister Lord Burghley, to whom *The Herbal* is dedicated. This book was one of the most popular herbals of its time and is nowadays perhaps the most famous. It curiously combines fiction and fact, credulity and scientific caution which was sometimes misplaced—Gerard not only accepted but claimed to have seen the barnacle tree, which was supposed to bear geese, while dismissing a drawing of the Mexican *Tigridia* as "meere fiction." Most of his woodcuts, including those of maize, were copied from J. T. Tabernaemontanus: *Neuw Kreuterbuch*, Frankfort-am-Main, 1588. One of his few original illustrations is that of the potato—the first to be published—but his text is responsible for the erroneous belief that this plant was imported into England from Virginia.

Literature: A. Arber: Herbals, *Their Origin and Evolution*, pp. 129-132; John J. Finan: "Maize in the Great Herbals" in *Annals of the Missouri Botanical Garden*, XXXV (1948), pp. 149-191.

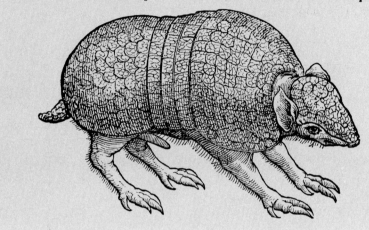

Armadillo, sive Tatou genus alterum.

C A P. XV.

IN epistolâ quam Iacobus Plateau, cujus in hac Exoticorum historiâ crebra sit mentio, Novembri mense anno millesimo sexcentesimo secundo à Christi nativitate ad me scribebat, inter alia significabat, se tria illius animalis, quod Hispani ab armis quibus tectus est, *Armadillo* appellant, Gallis verò voce Brasilianicâ *Tatou* dicitur, in suo Museo diversa habere genera: unum quidem valdè magnum, ejus formæ cujus illud erat, quod in scholio ad Nicolai Monardes caput de Armadillo, Libro de Medicamentis simplicibus ex

37 *Armadillo, illustration in Charles de l'Ecluse:* Exoticorum Libri Decem, *Leiden, 1605*

Holland. Woodcut. 1605. Page size 13⅞ x 8¹¹⁄₁₆ inches (35 x 22 cm.). Cleveland Medical Library Association.

Though remembered mainly as a botanist, Charles de L'Ecluse (or l'Escluse), better known as Clusius (1526-1609), was a true polymath, with an intimate knowledge of zoology, mineralogy, law, philosophy, history, cartography, numismatics, and epigraphy: he could read Greek, Latin, Italian, Spanish, Portuguese, French, Flemish, and German. He was one of the small group of sixteenth-century naturalists who escaped from the thrall of both mediaeval traditions and classical authorities. Thus, unlike Monardes [28], he was more interested

in the armadillo as a natural specimen than for the supposed medicinal properties of its tail. As his text reveals, he was also aware that there were several distinct species of armadillo. *Exoticorum Libri Decem* is his last book, and in it, as the great French palaeontologist Georges Cuvier remarked, "he provided illustrations and perfectly accurate descriptions of several types of animals from different parts of the world." The first six books are entirely original, while the rest are Latin translations of works by Garcia da Orta, Christoval Acosta, and Monardes.

Literature: C. Cuvier: *Histoire des Sciences Naturelles*, Paris, 1841, vol. II, pp. 153-155; F. W. T. Hunger: *Charles de l'Escluse, Carolus Clusius*, The Hague, 1927, pp. 281-293; Claus Nissen: *Die botanische Buchillustration*, no. 369.

Crispin II de Passe (Crispijn vande Pas, Crispinus Passeus)

Dutch, 1589-1670.

The most notable member of a family of engravers working in Germany and the Low Countries, de Passe was born in Cologne, settled in Utrecht in 1612, and began his independent career in 1614, with the publication of *Hortus Floridus* (see below) and portraits of Pope Paul III and Philip III of Spain. From 1617 he worked in Paris, returned to Utrecht in 1630, and in 1639 moved to Amsterdam, where he founded his own publishing house. He was confined in a mad-house in Delft from about 1645 to 1663. His numerous works include portraits, book illustrations, and allegorical prints.

Crispin II de Passe (Crispijn vande Pas, Crispinus Passeus)

38 *Sunflowers (Helianthus annuus), illustration in* Hortus Floridus, *Arnhem, 1617*

Engraving. 1614. Page size 7⅛ x 10¼ inches (18 x 26 cm.).
Cleveland Medical Library Association.

The *Hortus Floridus*, unlike the earlier botanical books exhibited [27, 28, 29, 36, 37], was intended for gardeners and painters rather than for naturalists and physicians. It contains 105 plates and was issued in four parts, each of which is devoted to plants blooming in one of the four seasons. The text of the first edition (1614) is in Latin, but editions with French, Dutch, and English texts were also published, and all the illustrations have multi-lingual inscriptions. The work illustrates—in the words of the English edition (1615)— "the most rarest and excellentest flowers, that the world affordeth: ministringe both pleasure and delight to the spectator, and most espetially to the well affected practisioner." Several

American plants are included, notably *Mirabilis jalapa*, the tobacco plant, a species of *Tagetes* (later to be misnamed the African or French marigold), and the sunflower, all of which had been acclimatised in European gardens by this date. The sunflower, which "sheweth marvellous faire in Gardens" (as Frampton wrote in his translation of Monardes [28]), was the most spectacular of these introductions.

Literature: Th. J. I. Arnold: "Cr. Passaeus Hortus Floridus" in M. Nijnhoff: *Bibliographische Adversaria,* 1875, vol. II, pp. 95-105; D. Franken: *L'Oeuvre gravé des van de Passe,* Amsterdam and Paris, 1881, no. 1346; S. Savage: "The 'Hortus Floridus' of Crispijn vande Pas the Younger" in *Transactions of the Bibliographical Society,* Series 2, 4, (1923), pp. 181-206; Wilfred Blunt: *The Art of Botanical Illustration,* pp. 97-102; C. Nissen: *Die botanische Buchillustration,* no. 1494.

39 *Arnoldus Montanus:* De Nieuwe en Onbekende Weereld, *Amsterdam,* 1671

Printed book with engraved illustrations. Folio page size 12⅝ x 8⁵⁄₁₆ inches (32 x 21 cm.). Provenance: From the library of Edward Duff Balken. Princeton, New Jersey, Princeton University Library.

This is a somewhat indiscriminate summary of information and misinformation derived from histories of the *Conquista* and from travel books. The illustrations engraved by the publisher, Jakob van Meurs [94], sometimes after his own designs, range from the factual to the fanciful, including one of the best early views of New Amsterdam (i.e. New York under Dutch rule) and many wholly imaginary depictions of both the native population and wildlife of North and South America. Translations into German and English were issued by the same publisher and with the same plates in 1673. Montanus wrote a similar account of China and Japan.

Literature: J. Sabin: *A Dictionary of Books Relating to America,* vol. XII, New York, 1880, pp. 303-305.

Claude Aubriet
French. 1665-1742.
One of the greatest of all botanical draughtsmen, Aubriet made the engravings for Tournefort's celebrated *Elemens de Botanique* (1694), which in its later Latin version of 1700 had a far-reaching effect on plant classification. He accompanied Tournefort on his journey to the Levant (1700-1702), succeeded Joubert at the Jardin de Roi, and made drawings for Vaillant's *Botanicon Parisiense* (1727). His name is commemorated in the popular *(Aubrieta* (often mis-spelt *Aubretia).*

Claude Aubriet
40 *Manihot*
Watercolour on vellum. ca. 1710-1735. 16¹³⁄₁₆ x 11¹⁵⁄₁₆ inches (42.5 x 30.3 cm.). Inscription: *Manihot Theveti, Juca & Cassavi.I.B.2.794.* London, British Museum (Natural History).

Cassava, or *Manihot utilissima,* of which this is a drawing, was one of the tropical American plants which most fascinated early explorers, for its root yields both a virulently poisonous juice, and, when this is extracted, the

Manihot Theveti, Juca & Cassavi. I.B.2. 794.

eminently wholesome substance known as Brazilian arrowroot or tapioca. It is similar in appearance to *Manihot dulcis,* from which cassava bread is made, and *Manihot Glazinovii,* the source of Ceará rubber—two plants introduced from America into the tropical regions of the Old World, where they are now extensively cultivated. The drawing, which meticulously illustrates the essential botanical features of the plant, is one of the many which reveal Aubriet's indebtedness to the distinguished botanists for whom he worked.

Mark Catesby
English, 1683-1749.
Catesby was the first European naturalist to travel in Virginia and the Carolinas and to make a systematic study of both the flora and fauna. The son of a fairly well-to-do lawyer, he was born at Castle Hedingham, Essex. In his youth he made the acquaintance of the great botanist John Ray, who lived nearby, and probably through him also of the physician Samuel Dale. He began to study the wild-life of his district, and then, as he later wrote, "my Curiosity was such, that not being content with contemplating the Products of our own Country, I soon imbibed a passionate Desire of viewing as well the Animal and Vegetable Productions in their Native Countries, which were strangers to England." His sister had married a physician, William Cooke, with whom she had emigrated to Williamsburg, and in 1712 Catesby went to stay with them. From there he visited the West Indies in 1714. He returned to England in 1719 with a collection of botanical specimens and also paintings of birds. A group of English naturalists provided him with money to go back to America in 1722. He went to South Carolina, where he collected botanical specimens for Sir Hans Sloane (the founder of the British Museum), Charles Dubois (who cultivated many exotic plants in his garden at Mitcham), and others. In 1725 he visited the Bahamas, returning to England in the following year.

By now he had made a large number of watercolour drawings of American birds, insects, animals, fishes, and plants, which he determined to publish. Unable to afford the high cost of employing a professional engraver, he learned to engrave himself (from Joseph Goupy). William Sherard, founder of the chair of botany at Oxford, helped him to identify the plants he drew. By 1729 he had completed the first part of his *The Natural History of Carolina, Florida and the Bahama Islands* and began to solicit subscriptions for the whole work, which he published in sections of twenty plates with descriptive texts. The first volume was completed in 1731 and the second in 1743. The engravings were all coloured by hand, either by Catesby himself or under his supervision. He was elected a Fellow of the Royal Society in 1733. A three-folio volume collection of his American natural history drawings was bought by George III in 1768 and is now in the Royal Collection at Windsor Castle.

Mark Catesby

41 *Bead Snake*
Gouache. ca. 1722-1726. 10⁷⁄₁₆ x 14¾ inches (26.5 x 37.5 cm.). Inscriptions: In pen and brown ink *Bead S* and on verso *Bead S / Bead Snake Potato;* also on recto *60* and *15.* Provenance: Jekyll Catesby; Thomas Pennant; David Pennant; Henry S. Morgan.
New York, The Pierpont Morgan Library, Gift of Henry S. Morgan, 1961.6:1.

Catesby's engraving after this drawing of the bead snake *(Elaps fulvus)* was published as plate 60 in the second volume of *The Natural History of Carolina, Florida and the Bahama Islands* [43]. The drawing appears to be one of those he made on his second visit to America, 1722-26.

Literature: The Pierpont Morgan Library, *Fifth Annual Report to the Fellows,* New York, 1954, pp. 41-42; *idem: A Review of Acquisitions 1949-1968,* New York, 1969, p. 137.

Mark Catesby

42 *Ivory-Billed Woodpecker and Willow Oak, illustration in* The Natural History of Carolina, Florida and the Bahama Islands, *pl. 16.*

Engraving coloured by hand. 1729. Page size 20 x 14 inches (50.7 x 35.5 cm.). Inscription: *Quercus, Anpotius; Ilex Marilanica folio longo angusto salicis Picus maximus rostro albo.* Provenance: Since publication, this volume and volume two [43] have been in the library of Middleton Place in a collection that dates back to Henry Middleton (1717-1784), who became president of the First Continental Congress in 1774. His son, Arthur Middleton (1742-1787), was a signer of the Declaration of Independence. Charleston, South Carolina, Middleton Place.

This illustration appears in the first section of Catesby's book, which he exhibited at a meeting of the Royal Society in London in 1729. The tree is the *Quercus Phellos,* indigenous to North America. Of the woodpecker *(Campephilus principalis,* now nearly extinct) Catesby wrote: "The Bills of the birds are much valued by the *Canada Indians* who make Coronets of 'em for the great Princes and great warriers, by fixing them round a wreath, with their points outward. The *Northern Indians* having none of these Birds in their cold country, purchase them of the Southern at the price of two, and sometimes three Buck-skins a bill."

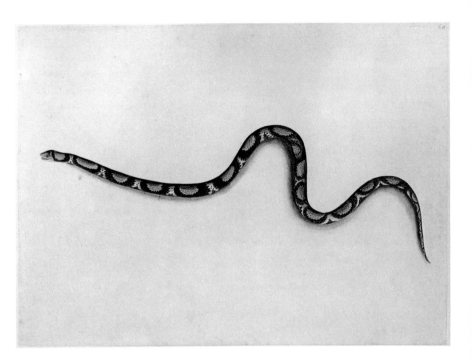

Mark Catesby

43 *Carolina Moth and Custard Apple,
illustration in* The Natural History
of Carolina, Florida and the
Bahama Islands, *vol. II, p. 86*

Engraving coloured by hand. 1731-
1743. Page size 20 x 14 inches (50.7 x
35.5 cm.).
Charleston, South Carolina, Middleton
Place.

This illustration appears in the second
part of Catesby's book, which began to
appear in instalments after the first
part had been completed in 1731: it
was concluded and provided with a
dated frontispiece in 1743. The moth
is the largest of those found in Carolina
(*Phalaena magna*), and the tree is the
custard apple of the southern States,
named by Linnaeus *Annona reticulata*.

Literature: G. F. Frick and R. P. Stearns:
Mark Catesby The Colonial Audubon,
Urbana, 1961.

Georg Dionysius Ehret
German-English, 1708-1770.
Ehret was the greatest botanical
draughtsman of his day and one of the
first exponents of scientific botanical
illustration, having learnt the new
system for description and classification from Linnaeus himself. Born in
Heidelberg, the son of a market-
gardener, his first patron was a wealthy
Nuremberg physician, Dr. Trew, who
commissioned from him an unlimited
number of folio drawings (now in the
University of Erlangen). In 1735 he
went to England, met the great gardener Philip Miller and Sir Hans
Sloane, then went to Holland, where
he met Linnaeus. In 1736 he returned
to England and settled there for the
rest of his life. He illustrated several
notable books, including his own
Plantae et papiliones rariores (1748-73)
and Trew's *Plantae selectae* (1750-73),
but his engravings are less remarkable
than his paintings. In 1757 he was
elected Fellow of the Royal Society for
his services to botany.

Georg Dionysius Ehret

44 *Cotton Plant (Gossypium
barbadense)*

Watercolour on vellum. Signed and
dated: *G.D.Ehret pinxit 1766*. 18⅟₁₆ x
12⅞ inches (47.2 x 32.8 cm.). Inscription: *Gossypium (arboreum foliis
palmatis: lobis lanceolatis, caule fruticoso. Linn.*
London, British Museum (Natural
History).

Cotton plants are indigenous to both
the New and the Old World. The
species illustrated in this drawing is
from a commercial point of view one
of the most important, as it is the
source of "Sea Island Cotton." A native
of the Antilles, Central and South
America, it is probably a plant of the
type noted by Columbus on his first

voice. It was later cultivated in the southern United States, as well as in Egypt and India. Ehret's drawing was probably made from a plant grown in the Chelsea Physic Garden by his brother-in-law, Philip Miller.

Literature: Sir George Watt: *The Wild and Cultivated Cotton Plants of the World*, London, 1907, pp. 256-265.

Georg Dionysius Ehret

45 *Sarracenia flava*

Watercolour on vellum. Signed and dated: *G.D.Ehret pinxit 1766*. 18⁹⁄₁₆ x 12⅞ inches (47.2 x 32.8 cm.). Inscription: *Saracenia flava foliis strietis.Linn.* London, British Museum (Natural History).

The *Sarracenia* are indigenous to North America and are named after Michel Sarrazin, a French naval doctor working in Canada from 1685, who sent specimens of it, as well as of many other plants, to Europe. A member of the genus had, however, been mentioned by Clusius in 1576. They fascinated and perplexed naturalists on account of their tubular leaves, or "pitchers," for which several curious explanations were offered—that they supplied water for frogs in dry weather, or that they drowned insects. Not until the nineteenth century was it discovered that the *Sarracenia* were carnivorous and able to digest insect bodies. *Sarracenia flava*, which flourishes in meadows and bogs in the southeastern United States from Virginia to Alabama and north Florida, had been introduced into cultivation at Chelsea by 1752. Another drawing of it by Ehret, also dated 1766, is in the Fitzwilliam Museum, Cambridge. The inscription on the drawing exhibited refers to Linnaeus.

GOSSYPIUM *arboreum foliis palmatis lobis lanceolatis caule fruticoso.*

SARACENIA *flava foliis strietis.*

Georg Dionysius Ehret

46 *Weymouth Pine (Pinus strobus)*
Watercolour. ca. 1740-1770. Signed: *G.D.E.* (partly cut off). 19¼ x 11¹¹⁄₁₆ inches (48.8 x 29.7 cm.). Inscription: *strobus / Pinus Americana quinis ex uno folliculo fetis longis tenuibus triguetris ad unum angulum per totam longitudinem minutissimis crenis asperatis. Pluk Amalth. 171.* Provenance: Probably from the collection of the 3rd Earl of Bute (1713-1792). London, British Museum (Natural History).

The Weymouth Pine, or White Pine, as it is sometimes called, is indigenous to eastern North America and was introduced to England by 1705 and planted at Longleat, Wiltshire, by Thomas Thynne, first Viscount Weymouth, who was president of the Board of Trade and Foreign Plantations, 1702-07. (There seems to be no foundation for the story that it was introduced a century earlier by the explorer George Weymouth or Waymouth.) Horace Walpole described it in 1755 as "that beautiful tree that we have so much admired . . . for its clean straight stem, the lightness of its hairy green, and for being feathered quite to the ground." When he visited Longleat in 1762, he wrote that "the original Weymouth pine, from the cones of which all the Weymouth pines have come" was "now very shabby" *(The Letters of Horace Walpole,* ed. Mrs. Paget Toynbee, Oxford, 1903-18, vol. III, p. 362, supplement, vol. II, p. 95). The tree yields excellent timber but is subject to "Weymouth Pine Rust," which was named after it but which also attacks other five-needled pines. The inscription on the drawing alludes to Leonard Plukenet: *Amaltheum Botanicum,* London, 1705, in which the plant was first described.

Georg Dionysius Ehret

47 *Cactus melocactus*
Watercolour. ca. 1753-1770. 23¹¹⁄₁₆ x 16³⁄₁₆ inches (60.1 x 41 cm.). Inscription: *Cactus Melocactus.* Provenance: Probably from the collection of the 3rd Earl of Bute (1713-1792). London, British Museum (Natural History).

The many tribes and sub-tribes of cacti are peculiar to America, and a few species (notably *Opuntia Ficus-indica,* the prickly pear) were introduced into Europe very soon after the discovery of the New World. Others arrived much later, and *Cactus melocactus* from Jamaica, represented in this drawing, is not recorded in Europe until 1753, when a specimen was to be found in the Chelsea Physic Garden, London.

Georg Dionysius Ehret

48 *Canary Creeper (Tropaeolum peregrinum)*

Watercolour. ca. 1740-1770. 19$\frac{1}{16}$ x 13$\frac{1}{4}$ inches (48.4 x 33.7 cm.). Inscription: *Tropaeolum peregrinum.* Provenance: Probably from the collection of the 3rd Earl of Bute (1713-1792). London, British Museum (Natural History).

Tropaeolum peregrinum is a native of Peru, which seems to have been introduced into the Canary Islands, whence it acquired its popular name—and a botanical misnomer, *T. canariense*. It was one of the last of its genus to reach Europe. The better known nasturtium *Tropaeolum majus* had arrived much earlier, and a painting of one appears in the prayer-book illuminated for Albrecht V of Bavaria by Georg Höf-nagel in 1570 (Staatsbibliothek, Munich). Linnaeus named this American genus after Roman trophies of arms, from the way in which they were grown, clambering over pyramids of sticks, with their leaves resembling shields and their flowers helmets.

CACTUS *Mikeschue.*

Sydney Parkinson

Scottish, 1745-1771.
Born in Edinburgh, Parkinson came to London in 1767, met Sir Joseph Banks, and was engaged to draw some of the rare plants growing in the Royal Gardens at Kew. In 1768 he joined the team of artists which accompanied Captain Cook's first voyage round the world but died on the homeward journey.

Sydney Parkinson

49 *Passiflora laurifolia*

Watercolour on vellum. Signed and dated: *Sydney Parkinson pinx^t 1767.* 17^{11}⁄$_{16}$ x 12⁷⁄₈ inches (44.9 x 32.7 cm.). Inscription: *Passiflora laurifolia / foliis indivisis ovatis integerrimis, petiolis biglandulosis involucris dentatis. Linn sp.pl. p.1356.* Provenance: Sir Joseph Banks (1743-1820).
London, British Museum (Natural History).

The Passion-flowers, an exclusively American genus, appear to have been named by seventeenth-century missionaries on account of the resemblance of the blooms to the instruments of the Passion. One member of the family was taken to Rome and Bologna in the early seventeenth century, and *Passiflora incarnata* was introduced into England by 1629. *Passiflora laurifolia* is not, however, recorded in Europe until 1690. The inscription on the drawing refers to Linnaeus's classification.

Sydney Parkinson

50 *Alstroemeria pelegrina*

Watercolour on vellum. Signed and dated: *Sydney Parkinson pinxit 1767.* 15⁷⁄₈ x 11⁷⁄₁₆ inches (40.3 x 28.9 cm.). Inscription: *Alstromeria: Pelegrina caule erecto, foliis resupinatis. Linneus sp: plan: 462. No. 1.* and in another hand: *Mr. Lee Hammersmith.* Provenance: Sir Joseph Banks (1743-1820). London, British Museum (Natural History).

Alstroemeria pelegrina was the first species of its genus to be introduced into Europe from Chile and was being grown in London by 1754. It preceded by nearly a century *A.aurantica* and *A.ligtu*, which are nowadays more widely cultivated. The inscription reveals that the specimen from which Parkinson made this drawing was grown in the Hammersmith nursery garden run by James Lee (author of a popular *Introduction to Botany* of 1760), who was responsible for introducing several South American plants to England.

PASSIFLORA *laurifolia.*

Alexandre-Jean Noël

French, 1752-1834.
For biographical note see [175].

Alexandre-Jean Noël

51 *California Lizard*
Pen, ink, and watercolour. 1769.
8½ x 5¹⁄₁₆ inches (21.4 x 17.8 cm.).
Inscription: On the mount, probably
in the artist's hand: *lezard De La
Californie*. Provenance: Acquired by
the Cabinet du Roi, 1778.
Paris, Musée du Louvre, Cabinet des
dessins.

This is one of a group of drawings
made by Noël in 1769, when, still a
student, he accompanied the astronomer Abbé Jean Chappe d'Auteroche
to California [175]. The only other
natural history drawing he made on
this occasion was of a shark (Musée
du Louvre, Cabinet des dessins 31470).

Literature: M. N. Benisovich: "A French
Artist in Mexico in 1769" in *The Art
Quarterly* (1954), p. 142; L. Duclaux:
*Inventaire général des dessins, Musée du
Louvre, Cabinet des Dessins, Ecole
Française*, vol. XII, Paris, 1975, no. 177.

ALSTROMERIA: Pelegrina

John Frederick Miller

English, fl. 1759-1796.
Miller was the son of Johann Sebastian Müller (1715-ca. 1790) of Nuremberg, who settled in London, changed his name to Miller, and made the plates for the *Illustration of the Sexual System of Linnaeus* (1777). John Frederick Miller accompanied Sir Joseph Banks on his expedition to Iceland in 1772.

John Frederick Miller

52 *Dionea muscepula*

Watercolour on vellum. Signed and dated: *John Fred.Miller Pinx^t* 1772. 13 1/16 x 9 1/8 inches (33.1 x 23.4 cm.). Inscription: *Dionea Muscipula*. Provenance: Sir Joseph Banks (1743-1820). London, British Museum (Natural History).

This is one of the earliest drawings of *Dionea muscipula*, better known as Venus's Fly-trap, a native of Carolina first recorded in Europe in 1764. Like the *Sarracenias* (see [45]), it is a carnivorous plant. It attracted the curiosity of naturalists on both sides of the Atlantic, and in 1791 the great Pennsylvania botanist William Bartram discovered how it consumed insects trapped in its leaves. Charles Darwin was later to call it "the most wonderful plant in the world" (cf. J. Ewan: "Annals of the 'Most wonderful plant in the World' " in *Festschrift für Claus Nissen,* Wiesbaden, 1973, pp. 173-184).

DIONEA MUSCIPULA

Frederick Polydore Nodder

English, fl. 1767-1800.

Nodder was employed by Sir Joseph Banks, for whom he made many finished drawings after sketches by Sydney Parkinson, and was also botanic painter to Queen Charlotte. His works include records of plants growing in and around London and also illustrations made from dried specimens. He illustrated Erasmus Darwin's poem "The Botanic Garden," T. Martyn's *Flora Rustica*, and other books.

Frederick Polydore Nodder

53 *Helianthus doronicoides*

Watercolour. 1776. Signed: *P.Nodder.* 20¾ x 14⁷⁄₁₆ inches (52 x 36.5 cm.). Inscription: *Mr. Lee's Garden: 1776* and *Helianthus pubescens.* Provenance: Sir Joseph Banks (1743-1820). London, British Museum (Natural History).

This is a species of an American genus of which the Sunflower (see [38]) and the Jerusalem artichoke *(H.tuberosum)* were introduced into Europe before the end of the sixteenth century. *Helianthus doronicoides* (previously known as *H.pubescens)* is not recorded in Europe until 1759. As the inscription reveals, the drawing was made from a specimen in the Hammersmith nursery garden of James Lee.

54 *A Toucan*

England (?). Oil on millboard. Before 1793. 17¾ x 13¹³⁄₁₆ inches (45 x 35 cm.). Provenance: John Hunter, 1793. London, The Trustees of the Hunterian Collection and the President and Council of the Royal College of Surgeons of England.

The collection formed by Dr. John Hunter (1728-1793), the famous surgeon and anatomist, included a section of paintings of animals and birds, to which the painting exhibited belonged. Paintings by George Stubbs and a painting of a group of American animals (Peccary, two Agoutis, Ichneumon, and red-legged crow) by Jan van Riemsdyk belonged to the same section of the collection.

Literature: William Le Fanu: *A Catalogue of the Portraits and other Paintings, Drawings and Sculpture in the Royal College of Surgeons of England,* Edinburgh and London, 1960, no. 285.

Peter Brown

English, fl. 1755-1799.
Though he did not specialise in flower painting, Brown was appointed Court flower painter to the Prince of Wales, later George IV. He may have been a pupil of Georg Dionysius Ehret and certainly came under his influence.

Peter Brown

55 *Magnolia glauca*
Watercolour on vellum. ca. 1755-1799. Signed: *P.B.* 12⅝ x 9⁷⁄₁₆ inches (32 x 24 cm.). Inscription: *Magnolia glauca.* London, British Museum (Natural History).

The Magnolias belong to a genus found in both the Old and New Worlds. *Magnolia glauca*—also known as *M.Virginiana*—was the first of the American species to cross the Atlantic.

It is recorded in Europe in 1688. It was followed in 1737 by the evergreen *Magnolia grandiflora*, which soon became rather more popular in European gardens.

Franz Andreas Bauer or Francis Bauer

Austrian-English, 1758-1840.
Perhaps the greatest of all botanical draughtsmen, Bauer settled in London in 1788. His brother, Ferdinand Lucas Bauer, was also a botanical draughtsman and had been brought to England a few years previously by John Sibthorp, whose great *Flora Graeca* he illustrated. Francis Bauer became resident artist at the Royal Garden at Kew under the aegis of Sir Joseph Banks, and he remained there for the rest of his life.

Franz Andreas Bauer or Francis Bauer

56 *Tigridia pavonia*
Watercolour on paper. 1801. 21¹⁄₁₆ x 14⁷⁄₁₆ inches (53.5 x 36.6 cm.). Inscription: *Tigridia. 1801.* Provenance: Sir Joseph Banks (1743-1820). London, British Museum (Natural History).

The Tigridias are natives of Mexico. Francisco Hernandez, physician to Philip II, made a drawing of one which provided the basis for an illustration in l'Obel's *Plantarum seu Stirpium Historia* in 1576. But the English herbalist John Gerard dismissed this as "mere fiction," despite his gullibility as regards several fabulous plants. It was not grown in Europe until 1796, and the drawing exhibited here is one of the earliest illustrations of this most spectacular of the smaller American plants.

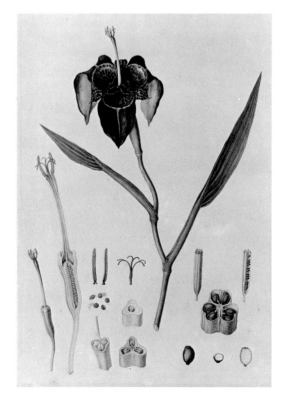

IV
New World
of Words

To what extent European interest in the New World is reflected in the number of books published about it in the sixteenth century is rather problematical. In libraries of the time only a small section seems to have been devoted to travel and geography, and within this limited category works on America formed a minority. It has been ascertained that in France between 1480 and 1609 twice as many books and ten times as many pamphlets were devoted to the Islamic lands as to the American continent.[1] And if we subtract from this the works which either describe the New World as part of Asia (that is to say all publications before the 1520s) or record attempts to reach Asia by way of America, these figures would be still more dramatically reduced.

The inclusion of only three works on the New World in the extensive bibliography of history compiled in 1566 by Jean Bodin, one of the most erudite and wide-ranging thinkers of his day, is, once again, very striking.[2] But statistics are often misleading. The ratio between the number of books published and people who read them can never be established. Several of the more frequently reprinted collections of travel literature, like that published by Giambattista Ramusio in Venice [59] or Richard Hakluyt in England, contain accounts of the New World. But more significant, perhaps, is the fact that interest in America was shown by nearly every major European writer of the century—Politian, Guicciardini, Ariosto, and Tasso in Italy, Ronsard and Montaigne in France, More, Spenser, Marlowe, Bacon, Donne, and Shakespeare in England. They derived their information mainly from books.

The earliest printed accounts of the New World were in the form of letters published either in slender pamphlets of a few pages (if not on single broadsheets) or incorporated into collections to form a volume. In 1516 Pietro Martire d'Anghiera, or Peter Martyr, published the first part of his *Decades of the New World (Decades de Orbe Novo),* of which the remainder appeared posthumously in 1530.[3] He never crossed the Atlantic (though he was created mitred abbot of Santiago in Jamaica), and his work is based on information from explorers (including Columbus) and Conquistadors, which he rendered in good humanist Latin, with echoes from Ovid and Virgil. No one played a larger part in keeping alive the classical Golden Age vision of the New World. A very different picture was provided by Fernández de Oviedo, the first traveller in America to publish an extensive account of it—and one abounding in vivid, gruesome, and often salacious detail [57]. The next substantial additions to the library of Americana were made by F. López de Gómara with his *Primera Parte de la Historia General de las Indias* (1552-53) and P. Cieza de León with his chronicle of the conquest of Peru (1553). All these works presented an "establishment" view of the *Conquista*. But in 1552 Las Casas's *Brevissima*

Relaciòn first appeared and was shortly followed by further denunciations of Spanish atrocities [58].A few years later the French attempt to establish a colony in Brazil produced two notable books, André Thevet's *Singularités de la France Antarctique* [61] and Jean de Léry's *Histoire d'un Voyage fait en Terre de Brésil autrement dite Amérique* (1578), which presents one of the most attractive and sympathetic descriptions of the South American Indian.

North America was neglected, so far as books were concerned, in these early years after the discovery. The "brief recit & succinte narration" of Jacques Cartier's voyage of 1535-36, in the course of which he discovered the St. Lawrence, was not issued until 1545. It was given wide diffusion through an Italian translation included in Ramusio's collection of travel literature, published in Venice [59]. Ramusio was also responsible for printing, in 1550, the first account of John Cabot's voyage of 1497 (the discovery of Newfoundland), hitherto recorded only on maps. In his third volume of 1556, he published for the first time the letters in which Verrazano described his exploration of the American coast from Cape Fear to Newfoundland in 1524. Ramusio was, in fact, initially responsible for diffusing reports on North America and also for revealing that the discovery of the New World had not been achieved exclusively in the service of the kings of Spain and Portugal.

Martin Frobisher's voyages in search of the Northwest Passage were described in books of 1577 and 1578, one of which was republished in German and Latin translations in Nuremberg. But when Richard Hakluyt was in Paris in the early 1580s, he was distressed to hear "in speech and read in books other nations miraculously extolled for their discoveries and noble enterprises by sea, but the English of all others for their sluggish security, and continual neglect of the like attempts in so long and happy a time of peace, either ignominiously reported, or exceedingly condemned." As a corrective, he published the several volumes of voyages later to be called "the prose epic of the English nation." After his death, this great work was continued by Samuel Purchas [70].

Another collection of travel literature which was to have much wider and longer-lasting influence was published between 1590 and 1634 by the de Bry family in Frankfurt [64-67]. Unlike its predecessors, this was richly illustrated (Ramusio's volumes had a few woodcuts and Hakluyt's none), and its numerous engravings were to be copied and imitated for more than a century. Most of the authors selected by the de Brys were, like themselves, Protestants, and all were anti-Spanish. Thus, on page after page, cruel Spaniards confront noble Indians, as in John Donne's simile:

If they stand arm'd with seely honesty,
With wishing prayers, and neat integritie,
Like Indians 'gainst Spanish hosts they be.[4]

But the conflict between the Protestant English and the Indians in the North (recounted and illustrated in the tenth volume) is represented in quite different terms: here the former are the heroes and the latter the villains, with the shining exception of Pocahontas.

1. G. Atkinson: *Les nouveaux horizons de la renaissance française,* Paris, 1935, p. 10.
2. Jean Bodin: *Methodus ad facilem historiarum cognitionem,* Paris, 1566.
3. The ten letters comprising the first of the *Decades* were published in a pirated edition in Seville in 1511.
4. "To Sir Henry Wootton," ca. 1597-98, John Donne: *Complete Poetry and Selected Prose,* ed. John Hayward, London, 1929, p. 158.

57 Gonzalez Fernández de Oviedo y Valdés: *La Historia General de las Indias*

Spain (Salamanca). Printed book with woodcut illustrations. 1547. Folio.
Ann Arbor, William L. Clements Library, University of Michigan.

Fernández de Oviedo (1478-1557) was a Spanish soldier who was sent to the West Indies in 1514 as royal superintendent of the gold smelting works. During the next thirty-five years he made eleven further visits to the Spanish colonies in America, with a variety of official military and civil appointments. Few men of the time can have travelled so widely in the New World. In 1526 he published his *Sumario de la natural y general istoria de las Indias* (Toledo), a brief work with a few woodcut illustrations — including the first representation of a hammock to be seen in Europe. This was but the introduction to his much longer *La Historia general de las Indias,* of which two volumes were published, at Seville in 1535 and Salamanca in 1537, though a third remained in manuscript until 1851. He had a sharp eye for details, and, although his prose is diffuse, he presented a very vivid picture of the strangeness of wild-life in the New World and a highly, sometimes garishly, coloured one of the natives, their way of life and sexual habits — for which he was to be bitterly attacked by Las Casas.

The volume exhibited is a copy of the second edition, titled *Coronica de las Indias. La hystoria general de las Indias agora nueuamente impressa corregida y emendada. Y con la conquista del Peru.* Both editions were illustrated with woodcuts — from new, rather better cut blocks in the second edition — after Oviedo's own drawings, of which some originals survive in the Huntington Library, San Marino,

California. (They would repay further study.) It is open at f. lxi, which shows a stone-headed axe and a dug-out canoe. Although canoes had been mentioned in Columbus's first letter of 1493 and their native name was one of the first Carib words to enter European vocabularies, this is apparently the first (albeit not very accurate) published illustration of one. Oviedo characteristically began his description with a reference to Pliny's account of the boats used in India — an example of how the association of America with Asia survived long after the geographical separation between the two continents was known, and an instance also of the persistent European tendency to fit the New World into the Old.

Literature: H. Harrisse: *Biblioteca Americana Vetustissima,* Leipzig, 1921, pp. 255-259, no. 139; Joseph Sabin: *A Dictionary of Books Relating to America,* New York, 1884, vol. 14, p. 97, no. 57989; Gonzalez Fernández de Oviedo: *Historia General de las Indias,* ed. J. Perez de Tudela Bucse, Madrid, 1959 (standard modern edition).

58 Bartolomé de Las Casas: *Tyrannies et cruautez des Espagnols . . .*

Flanders (Antwerp). Printed book.
1579. Small octavo size.
Ann Arbor, William L. Clements Library, University of Michigan.

Little is known of Bartolomé de Las Casas (1474-1566) until 1502, when he went to Hispaniola and received an *encomienda*—a grant of land with Indians to work it. He was ordained priest in 1610 and two years later took part in the conquest of Cuba, where he was awarded a larger *encomienda.* In 1514 he renounced his lands and devoted the rest of his long life to the cause of the Indians, which he expounded both in the Spanish colonies and in Spain. A few missionaries had preceded him in this work, but none pursued it with greater ardour. After atempting pacific evangelization of the Indians on the Venezuelan coast (with little success), he entered the Dominican order and in 1527 began to write his very extensive *History of the Indies,* which was to remain unpublished until

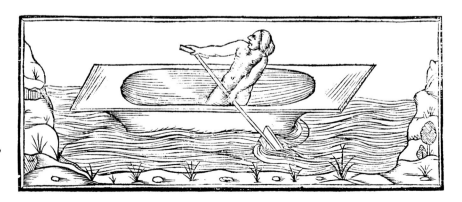

1875. On one of his several return visits to Spain, in 1540-44, he wrote an angry denunciation of Spanish treatment of the Indians, the *Brevissima relación de la destrución de las Indias*, probably intended only for the eyes of Spanish court officials, though it seems to have circulated more widely. He had it printed in Seville in 1552, after he had taken part in the famous but inconclusive public debate ordered by Charles V on the methods and merits of conquest in the New World.

The volume exhibited is a copy of the first edition of this work to be printed outside Spain, where it was warmly received, not only by supporters of the Indians but also by the far more numerous enemies of the Spaniards. No book played a larger part in diffusing the "black legend" of Spanish cruelty. But by presenting the Indians as men with simple virtues superior to those of their oppressors, it also established the myth of the "noble savage." It seems to have been read by Montaigne and to have inspired passages in his essay "Des Cannibales" (1580). It was first translated into English in 1583 and provided material for Robert Greene's *Spanish Masquerade*. John Milton's nephew, John Phillips, made another English translation in 1656, which may perhaps have inspired Sir William Davenant's curious "opera" *The Cruelty of the Spaniards in Peru*. Las Casas was to reappear in late eighteenth-century literature and art as the presiding genius of Jean François Marmontel's novel *Les Incas* [240].

Literature: Lewis Hanke: *Aristotle and the American Indians,* London, 1959; June Friede and Benjamin Keen, ed.: *Bartolomé de Las Casas in History,* Northern Illinois University, 1975.

TYRANNIES

ET CRVAVTEZ

DES

ESPAGNOLS,

PERPETREES

E'S

INDES OCCIDENTALES,

qu'on dit Le Nouueau monde;

Brieuement defcrites en langue Caſtillane par l'Euefque Don Frere BARTELEMY DE LAS CASAS *ou* CASAVS, *Eſpagnol, de l'ordre de S. Dominique; fidelement traduictes par* IAQVES *de* MIGGRODE:

Pour feruir d'exemple & aduertiſſement aux XVII Prouinces du païs bas.

Heureux celuy qui deuient fage En voyant d'autruy le dommage.

A ANVERS,
Chez François de Ravelenghien ioignant le portail Septentrional de l'Eglife noſtre Dame.
M. D. LXXIX.

59 Giovanni Battista Ramusio: *Terzo volume delle navigationi et viaggi nel quale si contengono le navigationi al Mondo Nuouo . . .*

Italy (Venice). Printed book with woodcut illustrations. 1556. Folio, page size 12¹³⁄₁₆ x 8¹³⁄₁₆ inches (32.5 x 22.3 cm.).

Washington, D.C., Library of Congress, Rare Book Division.

Giovanni Battista Ramusio (1485-1557), a Venetian, played a part of major importance in diffusing information derived from original sources about the discovery and exploration of America. The Venetians manifested great interest in geographical discoveries, and one of them, Fracanzio Montalboddo, initiated the practice of publishing compendia of voyages in 1507 with *Paesi nuovamenti retrovati* (including those of Ca da Mosto and Vasco da Gama as well as Columbus, Vespucci, and Cabral). In the first of Ramusio's much bulkier volumes (1550), the letters of Columbus and Vespucci are reprinted alongside many reports of eastward voyages. But his third volume, which is exhibited here, is devoted exclusively to the New World and includes works by Verrazano, Cartier, Peter Martyr, Cortés, Oviedo, and others.

The volume is open at the plan of the Indian citadel of Hochelaga, illustrating the account of Jacques Cartier's voyage of 1535-36, when he discovered the estuary of the St. Lawrence. The plan of the citadel is like that which many Eastern Indians are known to have built for defence and was probably based on a sketch brought back by Cartier, though they did not build fortifications in this manner with smooth vertical planks. The name *Monte Real* refers to the hill which Cartier called Mont Royal and on which the city of Montreal was later to be founded.

Literature: H. Harrisse: *Biblioteca Americana Vetustissima,* Leipzig, 1921, pp. 455-457, no. 304; J. Sabin: *A Dictionary of Books Relating to America,* New York, 1884, vol. 16, pp. 312-313, no. 67740; G. B. Parks: *The Contents and Sources of Ramusio's Navigationi,* New York, 1955.

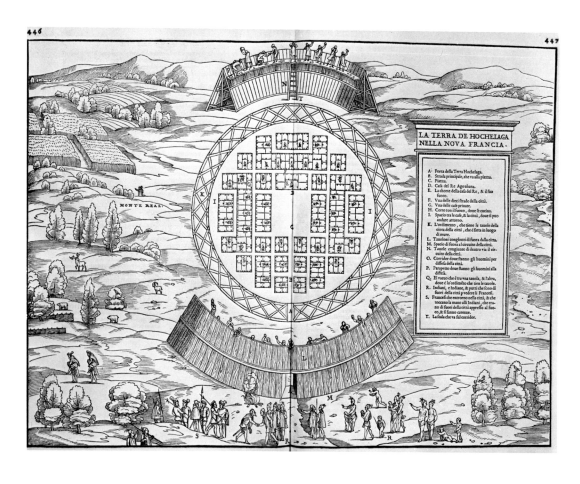

60 Hans Staden: *Warhafftig Historia vnnd beschreibung einer Landtschafft der Wilden / Nacketen / Grimmigen Menschfresser Leuthen / in der newen welt America gelegen*

Germany (Marburg). Printed book with woodcut illustrations. 1557. Page size 7⁵⁄₁₆ x 5¹³⁄₁₆ inches (18.5 x 14.8 cm.).

London, British Library.

This is one of the earliest editions of Hans Staden's *True History and Description of a Country of Wild, Naked, Cruel, Man-eating People in the New World of America*, first published in Marburg in 1557. Staden was a German mercenary from Homberg in Hesse who went in 1547, at the age of about 20, to Portugal, where he joined a ship which took him to Pernambuco and back. He set off on his second Atlantic crossing from Spain in the spring of 1550 and after a very stormy crossing reached the island of Santa Caterina off the coast of Brazil and eventually made his way to Bertioga (near Santos), where there was a Portuguese settlement which he helped to fortify. One day towards the end of 1553, he fell into an ambush and was captured by a party of Tupinamba, who stripped him to their own state of nakedness and took him to their village, making him shout out as he entered it: "Here I come, food for you." For some nine months he remained a prisoner, under constant threat of being killed and eaten. But he was back in Europe by February 1555. Cannibalism is given great prominence in Staden's book, and he described its rites in unprecedented detail. He also provided a very lively account of Tupinamba life in general, at a time when it was still barely touched by European influence.

The woodcuts in the book appear to have been made after Staden's own

drawings. The one exhibited illustrates the story of how the Indians removed a cross which Staden had put up. "Soon afterwards heavy rain began and continued for several days," he wrote.

> They came to my hut and asked me to persuade my God to stop the rain; if it did not stop it would impede the work of planting for which this was the right season. I replied that it was their fault; they had angered my God by taking away the piece of wood near which I was in the habit of conversing with Him. Convinced that this was the cause of the rain the son of my master helped me to erect a new cross. It was about one in the afternoon, to judge from the position of the sun, when we erected it; immediately the weather faired although it had been stormy in the morning. They all marvelled believing that my God would do whatever I wished.

Staden was a Lutheran who attributed his escape from the Tupinamba to divine protection, and this gave his adventure story additional interest to sixteenth-century readers. The book was frequently reprinted and remained very popular, especially in Germany and the Low Countries (some seventy editions are recorded).

Literature: M. Letts, ed.: *Hans Staden, The True History of His Captivity*, London, 1928; R. Maack and K. Fouquet: *Hans Stadens Wahrhaftige Historia*, Marburg, 1964; Amerigo Guadagnin: *La mia prigionia tra i cannibali 1553-1555 di Hans Staden*, Milan, 1970.

61 André Thevet: *Les singularitez de la France Antarctique, autrement nommée Amérique.*

France (Paris). Printed book with woodcut illustrations. 1557. Page size 8¾ x 6⅜ inches (22.2 x 16.2 cm.). Washington, D.C., Library of Congress, Rare Book Division.

André Thevet (1502-1590) was a French Franciscan friar. After travelling for a few years in Italy and the eastern Mediterranean, he returned to France and in 1555 went as almoner on the expedition led by Nicolas Durand de Villegegnon to found a French colony in Brazil. Shortly after his arrival there he fell ill, took to his bed, and after only two months set out on his return to France. His book was thus based largely on hearsay and includes imaginative descriptions of monsters. His impression of the Indians was unfavourable, and he was distressed by their nudity, but declared that they had some misguided religious beliefs and found them less obnoxious than Protestants (for whom the French Brazilian colony was partly founded by Coligny).

The book is open to an illustration which shows Brazilians smoking tobacco and making fire by rubbing two pieces of wood together (a practice which seems to have fascinated early visitors to America and had previously been illustrated by Oviedo). The drawings for this and the several other woodcuts have been ascribed to the Mannerist painter Jean Cousin the Younger (ca. 1525-ca. 1594), who was later to provide the illustrations for Thevet's *Cosmographie Universelle*, Paris, 1575. And they, rather than Thevet's text, may have inspired the poetic description of the Brazilians who "live now in their golden age" in Ronsard's "Complainte contre fortune."

Literature: J. Sabin: *A Dictionary of Books Relating to America*, New York, 1884, vol. 25, p. 112, no. 95339; G. Chinard: *L'Exotisme Amériquain dans la Littérature Française au XVIe Siècle*, Paris, 1913; S. Lussagnet, ed.: *Les Français en Amérique pendant la deuxième moitié du XVIe siècle*, Paris, 1953, vol. I; G. Gliozzi: *La scoperta dei Salvaggi*, Milan, 1971.

62 Gerolamo Benzoni: *La Historia del mondo nuovo*

Italy (Venice). Printed book with woodcut illustrations. 1572. Page size 6⅛ x 3¹³⁄₁₆ inches (15.5 x 9.75 cm.). Cleveland, Cleveland Public Library, History Department.

Gerolamo (or Girolamo) Benzoni was born in Milan in 1519, went to Spain in 1541, and from there went to America, where he travelled extensively in the Spanish colonies, returning to Milan in 1556 delighted—as he wrote—to have seen "so many novelties, so much of the world and so many strange countries" and also astonished "that a human body should have been able to endure so much." His history of the New World was first published in Venice, with a dedication to Pope Pius IV, in 1565, and in a slightly enlarged edition in 1572. Providing an account of the *Conquista* interspersed with per-

sonal observations, it achieved widespread popularity, and more than thirty editions (many of them translations) are recorded before the end of the eighteenth century. Benzoni was particularly anxious to give Columbus full credit for the discovery, and, by recounting several of the anecdotes which were to appeal to the popular imagination—e.g. the "egg of Columbus"—presented him as a vivid human personality. He was, in fact, largely responsible for the creation of the Columbus legend.

Benzoni played a no less important part in diffusing the "black legend" of Spanish cruelty. Although his view of the Indians was far from favourable, he was as vigorous as Las Casas in denouncing the atrocities committed on them. He described how the Indians killed themselves rather than serve the Spaniards. In another passage, however, he gleefully recounted how a group of Indians had wreaked poetic justice on the Conquistadors by pouring molten gold down their throats. The volume exhibited is open at the woodcut of this scene (p. 49), which is also of ethnographical interest, as it shows the penis-sheaths worn by the Indians. Like the other illustrations in the book, it appears to be based on a sketch made by Benzoni.

Literature: J. Sabin: *A Dictionary of Books Relating to America, from its discovery to the present time,* London, 1868-1936, vol. 2, p. 78, no. 4791; A. Codazzi in *Dizionario biografico degli Italiani,* Rome, 1966, vol. VIII, pp. 732-733.

63 *An Eskimo in a Kayak* from [Dionyse Settle]: *De Martini Forbisseri Angli Navigatione in Regiones Occidentis et Septentrionis narratio historica . . .*

England. Woodcut. 1580. Page size 6 x 3⅞ inches (15.3 x 9.8 cm.). Washington, D.C., Library of Congress, Rare Book Division.

This is an illustration in the Latin translation of Dionyse Settle's *A True Report of the Laste Voyage into the West and Northwest Regions,* London, 1577. It shows an Eskimo, brought back by Martin Frobisher from his second voyage to Baffin Island in 1577, giving a demonstration of duck shooting from a kayak in Bristol harbour, England. The artist has, however, provided an imaginative arctic background, incorporating in it another Eskimo carrying his kayak, an Eskimo woman with her child on her back, a dog-sled, and a sealskin tent. Engravings of the same subject, differing slightly in detail, were published in the French translation of Settle's book, *La Navigation du Capitaine Martin Fro-*

DELL'HISTORIE DEL

Come gl'Indiani colauano l'oro in bocca à gli Spagnuoli, & dell'habito che lor portano in diuersi lochi di terra ferma.

QVEGLI, *che pigliauano viui, spetialmente i Capitani, legategli le mani & i piedi, gettatigli in terra, colauano loro dell'oro in bocca, dicendo, mangia, mangia oro Cristiano, et per più stratio, & vituperio, con cortelli di pietra Focaia, chi gli tagliaua vn braccio, chi d'vna spalla, chi d'vna gamba, & arrostitola sopra i carboni, cantando*

PICTVRA VEL DELINEATIO HOMINVM NVPER EX ANGLIA AD-vectorum, una cum eorum armis, tentoriis, & naviculis.

bisher Anglois, és regions de west & nordwest, en l'année M.D. LXXVII [Geneva], 1578, and also in the German and Latin translations (the latter is exhibited here) issued at Nuremberg, 1580. The drawing from which they were made is lost and its authorship unrecorded, but it is generally believed to have been the work of either John White or of the Flemish painter Lukas de Heere (1534-1584), who was in England from 1568 to 1577 and made a drawing of an Eskimo brought back by Frobisher from his first voyage to Baffin Bay (inscribed: *Homme sauvage amené des pais septentrionaux par M.Furbisher L'an 1576*, Universiteitsbibliothek, Ghent).

Literature: Vilhjalmur Stefansson: *The Three Voyages of Martin Frobisher*, London, 1938; K. Birket-Smith: "The Earliest Eskimo Portraits" in *Folk*, I (1959), pp. 1-14; S. E. Morison: *The European Discovery of America. The Northern Voyages* A.D. 500-1600, New York, 1971, pp. 529-531; W. P. Cumming, R. A. Skelton, and D. B. Quinn: *The Discovery of North America*, London, 1971, p. 221.

Vt Matronæ Dasamonquepeuc libe- X. ros gestant.

IN oppido DASAMONQVEPEVC, quatuor aut quinque miliaribus a ROA-NOAC distante, matronæ eadem ratione qua ROANOACENSES amiciuntur & punguntur; corollas tamen capiti non imponunt, nec crura punctiunculis picta habent. Miram habent liberos gestandi rationem, & a nostra plane diuersam: nam nostræ brachiis ante pectus liberos sustinent, illa vero prehensa pueri dextra manu, intergo gerunt, crus illius sinistrum sinistro brachio amplectentes, ratione satis mira & peregrina, vt ex pictura videre licet.

B 2

64 Theodor de Bry, ed.: *Admiranda Narratio fida tamen, de commodis et incolarum ritibus Virginiae ...*

Germany (Frankfurt-am-Main). Printed book with engraved illustrations. 1590. Folio, page size 13 9/16 x 9 1/2 inches (34.5 x 24.2 cm.). Washington, D.C., Library of Congress, Rare Book Division.

This volume is a copy of the Latin translation of Thomas Hariot's *Briefe and True Report of the New Found Land of Virginia*, with engravings after John White. It is the first of the series of illustrated books which were published by Theodor de Bry and his son and which played a major part in the formation of the European vision of America. Theodor de Bry (1528-1598) came of a rich family in Liège, but he was a Protestant and to escape religious persecution went in 1570 to Frankfurt-am-Main, where he set up as a book and art dealer and also began to work as an engraver. He had contacts with England and made engravings after Marcus Gheerhaert's *Procession of the Knights of the Garter* (1576) and also of *The Funeral of Sir Philip Sidney* (1588). On a visit to England in 1587 or 1588, he acquired drawings of American subjects by both John White and Jacques Le Moyne de Morgues, on which he based the illustrations for his first two American volumes, published in 1590 and 1591. In 1592 he published a volume including the accounts of Brazil by Hans

Staden [60] and Jean Léry. Gerolamo Benzoni's history of the New World provided the text for the next three volumes, published in annual instalments, 1594-96. After Theodor de Bry's death the series was continued by his son Johann Theodor (1561-1623), who also published accounts of travel in the Far East.

The volume is open at plate x, showing front and back views of a woman carrying a baby, with Hariot's explanation that the women of Dasemonquepeuc, some four or five miles from Roanoke, have (as it runs in the English language edition) "a strange manner of bearing their children, and quite contrarie to ours. For our woemen carrie their children in their armes before their brests, but they taking their sonne by the right hand, bear him on their backs, holdinge the left thighe in their lefte arme after a strange, and conuesnall fashion, as in the picture is to bee here seene." John White seems to have made at least two sets of finished drawings, worked up from the sketches he had made in America. The engraved view of the woman from the back is similar to his drawing in the British Museum (1906-5-9-1 [15]), though in reverse. De Bry must have worked from a lost drawing which showed the front view as well. He also seems to have made minor alterations in the physiognomy.

Literature: Armand-Gaston Camus: *Mémoirs sur la collection des "Grands et Petits Voyages,"* Paris, 1802; J. Sabin: *A Dictionary of Books Relating to America,* London, 1868-1936, vol. III, pp. 24-30; S. Lorant: *The New World. The First Pictures of America Made by John White and Jacques Le Moyne and engraved by Theodore de Bry,* New York, 1946; D. B. Quinn: *The Roanoke Voyages* (Hakluyt Society II, CIV), London, 1955, p. 419; E. Croft-Murray and P. Hulton: *The British Museum: Catalogue of British Drawings,* London, 1960, p. 42; P. Hulton and D. B. Quinn: *The American Drawings of John White, 1577-1590,* London and Chapel Hill, North Carolina, 1964, no. 37.

65 Theodor de Bry, ed. : *Der ander Theyl, der newlich erfundenen Landtschafft Americae . . . Mit Beschreibung und . . . Contrafactur . . . durch Jacob Le Moyne, sonst Morges gennant . . .*

Germany (Frankfurt-am-Main). Printed book with engraved illustrations. 1591. Folio, page size 13⅝ x 9⁹⁄₁₆

inches (34.5 x 24.2 cm.). Washington, D.C., Library of Congress, Rare Book Division.

This is a copy of the German language edition of Jacques Le Moyne's account of the French colony in Florida, also published in Latin and French as the second part of de Bry's collection of American travel literature. Jacques Le

Moyne de Morgues (d. 1588) was born in Dieppe and was probably trained in the great school of cartography there. In 1564 he joined the expedition led by René de Laudonnière to Florida, where two years earlier Jean Ribaut, acting on the instructions of Gaspard de Coligny, had chosen the site for a French colony, intended partly as a refuge for Huguenots and partly as a beach-head for attacks against the Spanish in America. Le Moyne's instructions were to "map the sea coast, and lay down the positions of towns, the depth and course of rivers, and the harbours; and to represent also the dwellings of the natives, and whatever in the province might seem worthy of observation." The expedition reached Florida in June 1564, but in September 1565 the colony was attacked by a Spanish fleet, and Le Moyne was one of the few who managed to escape and return to France. At about the time of the massacre of St. Bartholomew (1572), he emigrated to England, where he painted and published a book about European plants.

In 1587 or 1588 Theodor de Bry acquired Le Moyne's manuscript account and drawings of Florida. The drawings, probably made from memory after his return from America, are lost, with one exception (New York Public Library, see transparency in Section I). But John White appears to have made copies from some of them [11]. De Bry's engravings after them show ethnographically correct details of costume and ornaments and also some artifacts, though they also include such European objects as hoes (this aspect of the prints will be discussed by William C. Sturtevant in a forthcoming volume on Le Moyne edited by P. Hulton). The figures are, however, endowed with the poise and proportions of classical statues.

The volume is open at plate 15, which shows how the Floridans scalped and dismembered the enemies they killed in battle. The printed description states that, using "slips of reed sharper than any steel blade," they

> cut the skin of the head to the bone, from front to back, all the way round, and pull it off with the hair, more than a foot and a half long, still adhering, done up in a knot on the crown, and with that lower down around the forehead and back cut short into a ring about two fingers wide, like the rim of a hat. Then, if they have time, they dig a hole in the ground, and make a fire, kindling it with some moss, which they carry round with them in their skins and dry these scalps to a state as hard as parchment. They are also accustomed, after battle, to cut off with these reed knives the arms of the dead near the shoulders, and their legs near the hips, breaking the bones, when laid bare, with a club. . . . I used to be astonished at one habit of theirs—for I was one of the party whom Laudonnière sent out under M. d'Ottigny—which was, that they never left the field of battle without shooting an arrow as deep as they could into the arms of each of the corpses of the enemy, after mutilating them as above.

This substantially accurate account makes a striking contrast with the engraving, from which all horror has been eradicated, and also with some of Le Moyne's other descriptions, like that of the prevalence of hermaphrodites in Florida.

Literature: Armand-Gaston Camus: *Mémoirs sur la collection des "Grands et Petits Voyages"*; J. Sabin: *A Dictionary of Books Relating to America,* London, 1868-1936, vol. III, pp. 50-51; S. Lorant: *The New World, The First Pictures of America made by John White and Jacques Le Moyne and engraved by Theodore de Bry,* New York, 1946; W. P. Cumming, R. A. Skelton, and D. B. Quinn: *The Discovery of North America,* p. 189.

66 Theodor de Bry, ed. : *America pars quinta Nobilis & admiratione plena Hieroymi Benzoni . . .*

Germany (Frankfurt-am-Main). Printed book with engraved illustrations coloured by hand. 1595. Folio, page size 13¼ x 9¾ inches (33.6 x 24.7 cm.). Provenance: Said to have come from the monastery of Klosterneuburg, Austria. Providence, Rhode Island, Anne S. K. Brown Military Collection.

This is the fifth volume in de Bry's collection of American travel literature and the second of three devoted to Girolamo Benzoni's *Historia del mondo nuovo* [62]. Unlike the other authors whose books were reprinted by de Bry, Benzoni was a Roman Catholic—but none the less anti-Spanish than any Protestant. He was, however, unusual in protesting the treatment meted out by the Spaniards to black slaves as well as Indians. The volume is open at plate IV, which depicts how Spaniards tortured and killed black slaves who had tried to run away.

Literature: Armand-Gaston Camus: *Mémoirs sur la collection des "Grands et Petits Voyages"*; J. Sabin: *A Dictionary of Books Relating to America,* London, 1868-1936, vol. III, p. 38-39.

67 Theodor de Bry, ed. : *America pars sexta sive Historiae ab Hieronymi Benzoni . . .*

Germany (Frankfurt-am-Main). Printed book with engraved illustrations coloured by hand. 1596. Folio, page size 13¼ x 9¾ inches (33.6 x 24.7 cm.). Provenance: As for [66].
Providence, Rhode Island, Anne S. K. Brown Military Collection.

This is the sixth volume in de Bry's collection of American travel literature and the third of three devoted to Girolamo Benzoni's *Historia del mondo nuovo* [62]. It describes the conquest of Peru with great hostility to the Spaniards. The volume is open at plate x, which shows the Peruvians bringing Pizarro enough gold to fill a room in a vain attempt to ransom Atahualpa (who is here called Attabaliba). De Bry rejected the naive but ethnographically interesting illustrations which appeared in the two original editions of Benzoni and substituted an entirely new series of engravings which present a highly imaginative vision of the New World as seen by an artist in Frankfurt. In the plate exhibited the Peruvians are shown carrying splendid examples of German Mannerist goldsmiths' work.

Literature: As for [66].

68 Ulyssis Aldrovandi: *Ornithologiae, hoc est de avibus historiae libri XII*

Italy (Bologna).
Printed book with woodcut illustrations. 1599. Page size 13¾ x 9⅛ inches (35 x 23.2 cm.).
New York, The American Museum of Natural History Library.

Ulyssis Aldrovandi (1522-1605), the leading Italian naturalist of his day, is a characteristic representative of sixteenth-century scientific humanism. He had a special interest in the New World and vainly hoped to lead a scientific expedition to Mexico. After studying mathematics, philosophy, and medicine, and publishing an account of the antique statues in Rome, he turned his attention to natural history, under the influence of the French zoologist Guil-

laume Rondelet (1507-1566) and the Italian botanist Luca Ghini (ca. 1490-1556). From 1554 he taught at the university of his native Bologna and in 1568 helped to found its botanical garden, of which he became director. His ambition was to compile an encyclopaedic study of all the plants, animals, and minerals of the world. As voracious a gatherer of objects as of information, he assembled a large collection of specimens and also numerous drawings of flora and fauna (including several of American subjects by Giacomo Ligozzi), much of which survives at Bologna University. He also possessed a few, but important, examples of Aztec art, notably a well-known mosaic mask now in the Museo Preistorico Etnografico Luigi Pigorini, Rome.

The only parts of his great project to be printed in his life-time were volumes on birds and insects, though further books derived from his manuscripts were published after his death. They are curious compounds of information, culled with greater enthusiasm than discrimination from classical authors, mediaeval bestiaries, recent works on natural history, and personal observation. Not content with describing in *Ornithologiae* the appearance, song, habits, and *habitat* of numerous types of birds (including the Virginian nightingale), he also discussed their mystical significance, the hieroglyphs derived from them, their appearance in emblems, fables, and proverbs, the ways in which they were caught, and the uses to which they were put for food, medicine, and clothing. Thus, he showed how the feathers of birds were worn by American Indians, as on the page at which the copy exhibited is open. Like the other illustrations in *Ornithologiae*, the woodcut is the work of an artist from Nuremberg who italicised his name as Cristoforo Coriolano.

Literature: M. Cermenati: "Ulisse Aldrovandi e l'America" in *Annali di Botanica,* IV (1906), pp. 313-366; E. G. Allen: "American Ornithology before Audubon" in *Transactions of the American Philosophical Society,* N.S. XLI, pt. 3 (1951), pp. 386-590; G. Montalenti in *Dizionario Biografico degli Italiani,* vol. II, Rome, 1960, pp. 118-124; D. Heikamp: "Pre-Columbian and Colonial Mexican Objects Preserved in Old Italian Collections" in *Proceedings of The International Conference on First Images of America: The Impact of the New World on the Old,* Los Angeles, 1976.

69 John Smith: *The Generall Historie of Virginia*

England (London). Printed book with engraved illustrations. 1624. Page size 11½ x 7¾ inches (29.1 x 19.6 cm.). Provenance: Fletcher Fleming Rayrigg; Frederic R. Kirkland, who gave it to The Houghton Library in 1945. Cambridge, Mass., The Harvard College Library (The Houghton Library).

In this book Captain John Smith described the early history of the English colony founded at Jamestown in 1607. John Smith (1580-1631) was born at Willoughby in Lincolnshire, became a soldier, fought in the Low Countries in 1597-99 and in Austria against the Turks in 1601-03 (made a captain in the Imperial Army), visited North Africa, and went back to England in 1604. In December 1606 he joined the expedition, financed by the newly formed Virginia Company, to establish a permanent English settlement on Chesapeake Bay, where they landed on 26 April 1607. Later that year he was captured by Indians and, according to his own account, sentenced to death but rescued by Pocahontas, daughter of the chief Powhatan. In September 1608 he was elected president of the Council at Jamestown for a year and in the early fall of 1609 went back to England. He returned to America briefly in 1614 and made a map of the New England coast. The rest of his life was spent in England writing several works to encourage the colonization of North America.

The book is open at an engraving which shows a map of "Ould Virginia" and six little scenes illustrating Smith's adventures. In the upper left corner he is captured by Indians and tied to a

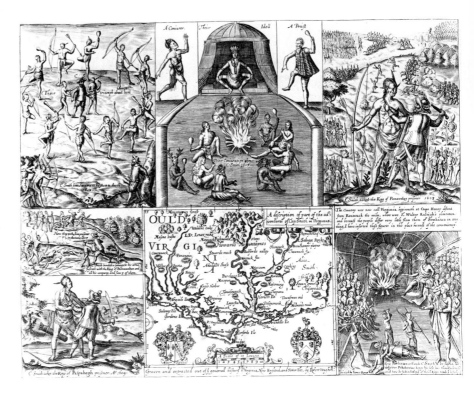

tree to be shot. The central scene shows the Indians' "coniuration about" him. That on the right shows Smith taking the "King of Paspehegh" prisoner. This scene is repeated in the lower left corner, below one in which "Smith bindeth a salvage to his arme, fighteth with the King of Pamaunkee and all his company and slew 3 of them." The scene in the lower right corner is inscribed: "King Powhattan commands C:Smith to be slayne, his daughter Pokahontas beggs his life, his thankfullness and how he subiected 39 of their kings, reade the history."

The engraving was made by Robert Vaughan (fl. 1622-1678), who took the map from the engraving after John White's drawing in de Bry's publication. He derived most of the figures of Indians from the same source, but the attitude towards them has undergone a change. They are, in Smith's words, "an idle, improvident, scattered people, ignorant of the knowledge of gold and silver, or any commodities, and careless of anything but from hand to mouth, except baubles of no worth." His aim was to subdue them, "bring them to be tractable, civil, and industrious, and teach them trades, that the fruit of their labour might make us some recompense."

Literature: J. Sabin: *A Dictionary of Books Relating to America,* London, 1868-1936, vol. xx, pp. 233-239; Philip L. Barbour: *The Three Worlds of Captain John Smith,* Boston, 1964 (with extensive bibliography); W. P. Cumming, R. A. Skelton, and D. B. Quinn: *The Discovery of North America,* p. 281.

70 *Purchas his Pilgrimes. In five bookes. The third, voyages and discoueries of the north parts of the world, by land and sea, in Asia, Evrope; the Polare regions, and in the north-west of America*

England (London). Printed book with woodcut illustrations. 1625. Page size 13 7/16 x 8½ inches (34 x 21.6 cm.). Cleveland, Library of the Western Reserve Historical Society.

This is a copy of the collection of travel literature edited by the Rev. Samuel Purchas (ca. 1575-1626), in continuation of the several volumes of *Voyages* published by Richard Hakluyt in the previous century. It is open to a woodcut reproducing the first page of the *Codex Mendoza*—a pictorial record of Aztec history and customs painted by Mexican artists with inscriptions by Spanish friars for the Viceroy Antonio de Mendoza of New Spain. Mendoza despatched the codex to Spain, but the ship carrying it was captured by a corsair, who presented it to the king of France, from whom it passed in 1553 to the royal cosmographer André Thevet, who sold it to Hakluyt, who bequeathed it to Purchas. The codex is now in the Bodleian Library, Oxford. Purchas called it "the choicest of my jewels" and "a Historie, yea a Politicke, Ethike, Ecclesiastike, Oeconomike History, with just distinctions of times, places, acts, and arts."

Images derived from an Italian copy of a Mexican codex had already been illustrated in 1615 in Lorenzo Pignoria's appendix to Vincenzo Cartari's *Le vere e nuove imagini degli dei antichi.* But Purchas was the first to publish a Mexican codex complete (save for a few repetitive leaves). And although a small section of the pre-Conquista *Codex Vindodonensis* was illustrated in Ole Worm's *Museum Wormianum* (Leyden, 1655, p. 383), the woodcuts in Purchas's book, which

were copied in the Dutch and French translations of 1651 and 1696, provided Europeans with their main source of information about Mexican pictographs until the early nineteenth century.

Literature: J. C. Clark, ed.: *Codex Mendoza,* London, 1938; B. Keen: *The Aztec Image in Western Thought,* New Brunswick, N.J., 1971, pp. 206-208.

V
Dutch Views

Connections between the Low Countries and the New World increased when, under Charles V, they became part of the same empire. As we have seen, Jan Mostaert's *West Indian Scene* [6] suggests that sympathy for the Indians against their Spanish overlords was not lacking in the Low Countries. Soon after the Dutch Protestants rose in revolt against Spain, in the 1560s, they began to build up a large armed merchant fleet. The fleet was used first of all for trade with the Far East but later with America also, especially with Brazil, which came under Spanish rule in the 1580s and began to acquire economic importance for its sugar plantations, originally established by the Portuguese. In 1621, after the end of a period of truce between the United Provinces and Spain, an attack on Hispano-Portuguese America was mounted by the Dutch West India Company, founded in that year.[1]

In the winter of 1623-24 the Dutch sent an expedition to Brazil and succeeded in taking Bahia. The following year it was re-taken by the Spaniards—a much celebrated event in Spain, e.g. Lope de Vega's *El Brasil restituido* and the monumental painting by J. B. Maino[2]—but in 1628 the Dutch captured the entire Spanish treasure fleet (the only occasion on which this feat was achieved) and soon occupied a great part of the coast of Brazil, centred on Pernambuco. In 1637 Count Johann Maurits of Nassau-Siegen (later to be created a prince of the Holy Roman Empire) was appointed the first governor general of this colony.

Count Maurits (1604-1679) was a man of exceptional gifts, an able soldier, an excellent colonial administrator, and a discerning patron of scientists and artists. In addition to clearing the Portuguese out of the area, reviving the sugar industry, and doing his best to smooth the relationship between different races, nationalities, and faiths in the colony, he created zoological and botanical gardens, laid out a new town, Mauritsstad (the centre of modern Recife), and supervised the first efficient scientific survey to be made of any part of the American continent—all within a space of seven years.[3]

He gathered round him some forty-six scholars, scientists, artists, and craftsmen from the Netherlands. The scientists included Willem Pies, better known as Piso, and the more learned Georg Marcgrave, an astronomer who was also a naturalist and made numerous paintings of plants, birds, mammals, fishes, shells, and insects.[4] Of the six professional artists he employed, the most notable were Frans Post, responsible for recording the landscape [76, 79, 80], and Albert Eckhout, the fruits, vegetables, and the people—whom he depicted in the first ethnographically valid portraits to be made of any Amerindians [71, 72, 73, and see also colour photographs]. But the Dutch West India Company was not impressed by news of this scientific and artistic activity. And, as the Portuguese had thrown off Span-

99

ish suzerainty in 1640 and signed a treaty with the United Provinces, in the following year there seemed to be less need for a military garrison in Brazil. To economise, Count Maurits was ordered to return home in 1642 and—with evident reluctance—he finally set sail in May 1644, taking with him the paintings he had commissioned, a vast number of natural history specimens, and examples of Brazilian craftsmanship. Back in the Netherlands he entrusted Johannes de Laet with the task of publishing the treatises on the natural history of Brazil written by Piso and Marcgrave (who had died in Angola) as *Historia naturalis Brasiliae,* Leyden, 1648 [78]. He also commissioned Caspar Barlaeus to write a history of his governorship, which was illustrated with engravings after Frans Post.

Both Post and Eckhout continued to paint Brazilian subjects for the rest of their lives—but now, it seems, to satisfy a taste for exoticism rather than to provide accurate scientific records of the type demanded by Count Maurits. Eventually even the paintings they had made in Brazil were to be transformed into decorative evocations of tropical luxuriance by the weavers of the Gobelins. Interest in South America, probably stimulated by the Dutch adventure in Brazil, also inspired a Flemish marine painter, Bonaventura Peeters, to add conventional figures of Indians to the foregrounds of his purely imaginary coastal scenes and create poetic images of a never-never-land beyond the Atlantic [81]. Demand for American exoticism still more strongly spiced was gratified by Arnoldus Montanus's book on the New World, with its fantastic illustrations of Indians and animals, published in Amsterdam in 1671 [39].

After the end of the ten years' truce with Portugal, a revolt of settlers forced the Dutch out of Brazil in 1654. Their only remaining American possession was Dutch Guiana, or Surinam. This area, settled partly by members of the Labadist sect, attracted the Swiss Maris Sibylla Marian, who went there in 1699 and spent eighteen months making paintings of flowers and insects, which she published as *Metamorphosis insectorum Surinamensium* (Paris, 1705)—a curious book which combines entomology with Christian mysticism.[5] A few years later a Dutch artist, Dirk Valkenburg, was sent to paint the plantations on the Surinam River owned by an Amsterdam merchant [83, 84]. But no further records of South America as revealing as those commissioned by Count Maurits were to be made until the early nineteenth century, under the inspiration of Alexander von Humboldt (see section XIII).

1. C. R. Boxer: *The Dutch in Brazil 1624-1654*, Oxford, 1957.

2. In the Prado, Madrid, together with paintings by Eugenio de Caxés celebrating the retaking of San Juan de Puerto Rico (from the Dutch in 1625) and the island of St. Christopher (from the British in 1629). They formed part of the series to which the *Surrender at Breda* by Velasquez belongs. For another, topographically accurate, record of the re-taking of Bahia and an account of the event itself, see Enrique Marco Dorta: *La recuperación de Bahía por Don Fadrique de Toledo (1625). Un cuadro espanol de la época,* Seville, 1959. The Dutch capture of Bahia in 1624 had been recorded in a painting by Andries van Ertvelt (National Maritime Museum, Greenwich).

3. For the fullest account of Count Maurits's scientific work and a very full bibliography, see P. J. P. Whitehead: "Cupleoid Fishes of the Guianas," appendix I in *Bulletin of the British Museum (Natural History),* Zoological Supplement 5 (1973), pp. 187-219. I am grateful to Professor C. R. Boxer for drawing my attention to this article.

4. For the complicated history of Marcgrave's works, most of which were lost in World War II, though some survive in the Academy of Sciences in Leningrad, see Whitehead, op. cit.

5. The original drawings were acquired by Peter the Great of Russia and are now in the Academy of Sciences in Leningrad.

Albert Eckhout (or Eeckhout)

Dutch, ca. 1610-after 1664.
Eckhout was a figure, animal, and still-life painter, said to have been born at Amersfoort. Little is known of him before 1637, when he accompanied Johan Maurits of Nassau-Siegen to Angola and Brazil, where he stayed until 1644. He painted life-size pictures of natives in both Angola and Brazil, as well as still-life groups of Brazilian fruits and vegetables, all of which are in the National Museum, Copenhagen

(see colour transparencies, gallery 5). Immediately after his return to Europe, he painted eighty pictures of exotic birds to decorate the hunting lodge Hoflössnitz, near Radebeul in Saxony. He also executed decorative paintings of Brazilian subjects for Schloss Schwedt on the Oder (destroyed) and Huis ten Bosch near The Hague.

Albert Eckhout (or Eeckhout)

71 *Tapuya Woman*
Black, brown, red, yellow, and blue chalk on grey paper. 1637-1644.
13 3/16 x 8 1/2 inches (33.5 x 21.6 cm.).
Berlin, Staatliche Museen Preussischer Kulturbesitz Kupferstichkabinett.

Literature: Rüdiger Klessmann: "Unbekannte Zeichnungen von Albert Eckhout" in *Oud Holland*, LXXX (1965), p. 50.

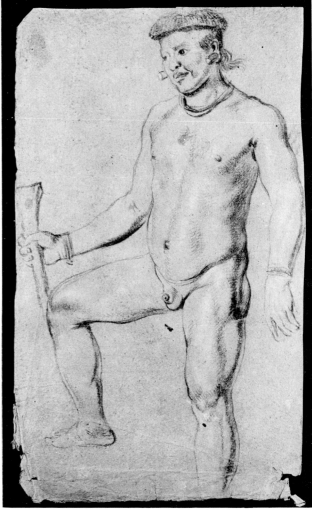

76 Frans Post, *São Franciso River and Fort Maurice*. Musée du Louvre.

Albert Eckhout (or Eeckhout)

72 *Tapuya Indian*
Black, yellow, and white chalk on grey paper. 1637-1644. 16⅛ x 9¾ inches (41 x 24.5 cm.).
Berlin, Staatliche Museen Preussischer Kulturbesitz Kupferstichkabinett.

Literature: As for [71].

Albert Eckhout (or Eeckhout)

73 *Head of a Tapuya Indian*
Black, yellow, white, and red chalk on grey paper. 1637-1644. 14⁹⁄₁₆ x 10⅛ inches (37 x 25.7 cm.).
Berlin, Staatliche Museen Preussischer Kulturbesitz Kupferstichkabinett.

This and [71, 72] form part of a group of four drawings (the other is of a seated female Tapuya with her head on her arm) which are unsigned but were almost certainly executed from life by Eckhout in Brazil. Like his remarkable paintings of Brazilians in the National Museum, Copenhagen, they have something of the naturalist's objectivity when making a scientific record of an animal or bird. Eckhout did not idealise or caricature his subjects, as so many previous artists had done. Yet he contrived to represent accurately their physical peculiarities without robbing them of human dignity.

Literature: As for [71].

Albert Eckhout (or Eeckhout)

74 *Brazilian Fruits*
Oil on canvas. ca. 1637-1644. 36 x 36 inches (91.5 x 91.5 cm.). Provenance: Count Maurits of Nassau-Siegen, from whom it was acquired by King Frederick III of Denmark, 1654.
Copenhagen, The Danish National Museum, Ethnographical Department.

This is one of a set of twelve still-lifes of Brazilian fruits and vegetables painted by Eckhout for Count Maurits of Nassau, probably in Brazil, though possibly after their return to the Netherlands. It incorporates water-melons, cashews, a sugar apple, coconut with inflorescence, a passion-flower (probably the *granadilla Passiflora edulis),* and an outsize pineapple, which was still a great rarity in mid-seventeenth-century Europe, though many travellers to America had written accounts of both its appearance and flavour.

Literature: T. Thomsen: *Albert Eckhout ein niederländischer Maler und sein Gönner Moritz der Brasilianer,* Copenhagen, 1938, pp. 84, 41; C. R. Boxer: *The Dutch in Brazil,* Oxford, 1957, pp. 152-154; E. Larsen: *Frans Post, interprète du Brésil,* Amsterdam, 1962, p. 251; E. Scheffer: "Albert Eckhout e a pintura colonial Brasileira" in *Dedalo,* I (1965), pp. 47-74.

Albert Eckhout (or Eeckhout)

75 *Brazilian Fruits*

Oil on canvas. ca. 1637-1644. 36 x 36 inches (91.5 x 91.5 cm.). Provenance: As for [74].
Copenhagen, The Danish National Museum, Ethnographical Department.

This picture forms part of the same set as [74]. But here Eckhout combined such Old World vegetables as a cabbage and swedes with American pumpkins and vegetable marrows, which were only then becoming familiar in Europe. As if to indicate the fecundity of the Brazilian earth, he invested them all with extraordinary plumpness and juiciness. By skillful composition he also gave them a monumental character silhouetted against the sky. His pictures capture the impression of almost overpowering strangeness made on a European by the natural products of America.

Literature: As for [74].

Frans Jansz. Post

Dutch, ca. 1612-1680.
Post was a landscape painter, the son of a glass painter, Jan Jansz. (d. 1614), and brother of the architect Pieter Jansz. Post (1608-1669). Little is known of him before 1637, when he accompanied Johan Maurits of Nassau-Siegen to Brazil, where he stayed until 1644, painting numerous landscapes. After his return to Holland he provided the drawings (British Museum) for the etched landscapes in the official account of Count Maurit's governorship—Caspar Barlaeus (van Baerle): *Rerum per octenium in Brasilia et alibi gestarum etc. historia,* Amsterdam, 1647. Apparently relying on these and other drawings made on the spot—as well as his memory—Post painted a large number of Brazilian

landscapes in the following decades. One of them, dated 1648, provided a curiously exotic setting with palms, cacti, and an armadillo for a picture of the *Sacrifice of Manoah*, with figures by another hand (Rotterdam, Boymans-Van Beuningen Museum). He was very little influenced by developments in Dutch landscape painting and maintained until his death the style he evolved during his eight years in Brazil.

Frans Jansz. Post

76 *São Francisco River and Fort Maurice*

Oil on canvas. Signed and dated: *F. Post 1638*. 24¹¹⁄₁₆ x 37⅞ inches (62 x 95 cm.). Provenance: Count Johan Maurits of Nassau-Siegen, who gave it to Louis XIV in 1678. Paris, Musée du Louvre. Colorplate 3.

One of the earliest and finest of the views painted by Post in Brazil, this picture vividly conveys the slightly disturbing impression of eerie strangeness made on sensitive European visitors by the alien flora and fauna and seemingly unlimited extent of South America. The tree-like cactus on the left is one of the Opuntias, which were little known in seventeenth-century Europe; the animal is a capybara, the largest of all rodents, which remained unfamiliar to Europeans still longer. (In 1919 Jean Destrem mistook it for a hippopotamus and described the picture as a view in Senegal.) An engraving of the same view without the animal but with Dutch soldiers crossing the river and the inscription: *Castrum Mauritii ad Ripam Fluminis S. Francisci*, was reproduced as plate XVII in C. van Baerle's history of Count Maurits's governorship of Dutch Brazil. Both the painting and the engraving derive from a drawing by Post in the British Museum (A. M. Hind: *Catalogue of Drawings by Dutch and Flemish in the . . . British Museum*, vol. IV, London, 1931, p. 26, no. 8).

Literature: Jean Destrem: "Le Musée de la Marine du Louvre" in *Gazette des Beaux Arts*, LXI (1919), p. 294; Jacques Combes: "Un douanier Rousseau au XVIIᵉ siècle: Frans Post" in *L'Amour de l'art*, XII (1931), p. 488; Joaquim de Sousa-Leão: *Frans Post*, Rio de Janeiro, 1937, pl. V; Robert C. Smith: "The Brazilian Landscapes of Frans Post" in *The Art Quarterly*, I (1938), pp. 247, 262; T. Thomson: *Albert Eckhout*, Copenhagen, 1938, p. 152; J. G. van Gelder: *Beeldende Kunst*, 1940, p. 70; Joaquin de Sousa-Leão: *Frans Post*, Rio de Janeiro, 1948, p. 99, no. 4; *Le paysage hollandais au XVIIᵉ siècle*, exhibition catalogue, Orangerie, Paris, 1950, no. 59; *Maurits de Braziliaan,* exhibition catalogue, Mauritshuis, The Hague, 1953, no. 13; J. de Sousa-Leão: "Du nouveau sur les tableaux du Brésil offerts à Louis XIV" in *Gazette des Beaux Arts*, LVII (1961), pp. 95-104; Erik Larsen: *Frans Post, Interprète du Brésil*, p. 185; Jakob Rosenberg, Seymour Slive, and E. H. ter Kuile: *Dutch Art and Architecture: 1600 to 1800*, Harmondsworth-Baltimore, 1966, rev. ed. 1972, p. 261; *Os Pintores de Mauricio de Nassau*, exhibition catalogue; Museu de Arte Moderna, Rio de Janeiro, 1968, no. 11.

Frans Jansz. Post

77 *The Battle of Porto Calvo*
Pen and brown ink and grey wash. ca.
1637. 7½ x 17⅛ inches (19 x 43.5 cm.).
Amsterdam, Willem Russell Collection.

The Battle of Porto Calvo between the
Portuguese and the Dutch took place
in 1637, the year Post arrived in Brazil.
A large drawing by Post of the battle,
entitled *Praelium prope Portum Cal-
vum* and dated 1645, is in the British
Museum, and the drawing exhibited
appears to be a preliminary study for a
section of it. Dutch pikers and mus-
keteers are seen advancing against the
Portuguese barricades, whilst the opponents take to the hills and Indians
bearing a Dutch flag emerge from the
woods, all identified by the letters and
numbers appearing on the drawing,
underneath.

Literature: *Christie's Review of the Year
1968-1969*, London, 1970, p. 71; J. de
Sousa-Leão: *Frans Post 1612-1680*, Amsterdam, 1973, p. 157.

78 Willem Piso and Georg Marcgrave,
ed. Johannes de Laet: *Historiae
rerum naturalium Brasiliae*
Netherlands (Amsterdam). Printed
book with woodcut illustrations. 1648.
Page size 14⅜ x 9¼ inches (37.2 x 23.5
cm.).
New York, The American Museum of
Natural History Library.

This book is the first systematic account of the natural history of any part
of America to be printed. Its publication was financed by Count Maurits of
Nassau-Siegen, who, during his governorship of the Dutch colony in
Brazil, had employed the authors to
record observations of natural history.
The work is in two parts, devoted respectively to the medicinal properties
of Brazilian plants by Piso and a general account of flora and fauna by
Marcgrave. Willem Pies, who latinized
his name as Piso (1611-1678), was a
physician, and his part in the book is
still influenced by the tradition of the
sixteenth-century herbalists. Georg
Marcgrave (1610-1644) joined the expedition as an astronomer, was learned
in several branches of science, and was
also an able draughtsman. Instead of
returning to Europe with Count Maurits, he went to Angola, where he died
of fever, and although his manuscripts
were taken back to the Netherlands,
they were written in a code which the
editor of the book had difficulty in de-
ciphering. Even so his part of the book
is a landmark in the development of
scientific natural history and remained
a primary source on its subject until
well into the nineteenth century. Piso
later did his best to denigrate Marcgrave, whom he described as a pen-
niless drunkard, while appropriating
most of his work in a later publication
—a theft noted by Linnaeus, who
named after him the *Pisonia*, "a tree
with frightful thorns just as the memory of the man is frightful."

142

GEORGI MARCGRAVI
RERVM NATVRALIVM
HISTORIÆ
LIBER QVARTVS,
Qui agit de Piscibus Brasiliæ.

CAPVT PRIMVM.

Guamaiacu apé species utraque. Guacucuja.

GVAMAIACV APE Brasiliensibus: Piscis triangularis, duplex est, unus cornutus, alter sine cornibus. Cornutus ab ore ad initium caudæ septem digitos est longus, (interdum & longior) à ventre ad dorsi summitatem tres digitos latus seu altus: venter vix duos digitos latitudine complet: cauda unum digitum lata, desinens in pinnam duos digitos longam & toridem latam. Os ipsi parvulum & pisi tantum capax: habens in superiori mandibula duodecim denticulos angustos, acutos, in inferiori quinque. Caput ab ore ad cornua usque in, gibbum assurgit, convexitate sesquidigiti; dorium au-

tem ad eundem modum in gibbum arcuatur: & unicam tantum habet pinnam in postica parte versus caudam, & quidem exilem. Oculos habet satis amplos, diametro trientis, superne in capite in fronte positos prope cornua, ab ore circiter sesquidigiti intervallo: & ante singulos oculos foraminulum unum. Pinnas in universum obtinet quinque, unam in extremo dorso, ut jam dixi, & in quolibet latere unam, longe infra oculos versus posticam corporis partem paulum vergentes, unum digitum longas; & prope utramque rimam, unam plus semidigito longam, branchiarum loco: unam denique pinnam inferius in ventris extremitate prope exortum caudæ, unum pene digitum longam, dimidium latam: quinta facit caudam. Cornua duo directe ante se protensa in fronte gerit prope oculos, magnitudine calcaris galli galinacei; duo itidem æqualis magnitudinis in infimo ventre versus quartam pinnam. Caret squamis, sed tegitur densa cute, in ventre quidem alba, reliquo autem corpore fusca, atque in ventre & lateribus usque ad altitudinem oculorum figuris trigonis, tetragonis, pentagonis, hexagonisque mire distincta & notata. Vbique autem (excepto infimo ventre) eadem cutis variis maculis nigricantibus insignita.

Guamaiacu apé sine cornibus in fronte, paulo minor est antecedente, sed latiore ventre & cauda paulo longiore; & est per totum corpus sexangularibus figuris insignitus, cum innumeris
meris

---

meris tuberculis minimis. Color ventris subflavus, reliquo corpore ex flavo cinereus & subfuscus. Non longe ab Insula Margarita captus à nautis nostris piscis ingens, quem vocant **Jacob Evertsen** in cujus ventriculo Guamaiacu adhuc integer fuit inventus. Piscis autem illius caro cocta à viginti hominibus comesta fuit, qui omnestatim post manducationem male se habuerunt, & vix post multos dies sumtis alexipharmacis convaluerunt: æstima hinc malignam qualitatem guamajacu piscis.

Alium talem accepi, cujus longitudo erat pedalis, altitudo quatuor digitorum, cujus totum corpu: rectum erat testa meris figuris sexangularibus constante, fragili in recenti pisce, & quæ pisce Soli exposito in hexagona corpora dissolvebatur. Os angustum, denticuli oblongi latescentes, inferius quinque, superius undecim. Oculi ampli, rotundi, magnitudine grossi misnici, pupilla crystallina, cætera coloris umbræ cum argenteo mixti. Cauda duos & semis digitos longa, teres extra testam prodiens, molli cute vestita, habens pinnam duos digitos longam & toridem latam, quasi quadratam, sed in lateribus lunatam. Pinnæ ut in aliis hujus speciei. Totus erat coloris albicantis cum argenteo mixti. Quodlibet latus versus posteriora desinebat in pinnam.

Caret fere carne ac cavus est, solam spinam secundum longitudinem habens, cui per membranas intestina adhærent. In ventriculo multum inveni arenæ.

ANNOTATIO. Agit de hoc pisce Aldrovandus lib. de piscibus IV. cap. ult. & dat duas illius Icones. Observavi autem (nam multi ejusmodi pisces siccati, utriusque speciei, ad nos è Brasilia & America afferuntur) figuras quibus cutis insignitur plurimum inter se differre, & in quibusdam se habere instar tessulati pavimenti.

GVACVCVIA Brasiliensibus: Monoceros piscis: Vespertilio Aquaticus posset appellari. Corporis figura anterius est instar vomeris: corpus octo digitos longum, quinque latum in

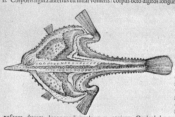

medio, ubi latissimum: medietas antem corporis posterior rotunda est & versus caudæ pinnam fastigiatur in conum: medietas autem anterior vomeris seu lati cordis figuram obtinet. Piscis autem non crassus, sed latus; caput vix prominet seorsum à corpore, estque illi inter oculos supra os cornu im-

positum, durum, duos pene digitos longum, conicum. Oculos habet nummi misnici magnitudine, pupilla crystallina lenticulari, reliqua pars variegata maculis & lineis flavis albisque. Oris hiatus castaneam potest capere, intus edentulum est. Supra os carnea prominentia est instar tonsillæ humanæ fere. In utroque latere in medio piscis, brachium eminet, quatuor digitos longum, una junctura constans; inferius medietas brachii duos digitos longa, plus uno lata, exterior pinna duos digitos longa est, unum lata in infimo ventre inter brachia duas habet pinnas sesquidigitum longas, quæ quasi pedes sunt. Cauda constat pinna duos digitos longa, sesquidigitum lata, ac fere quadrata. In inferiori corpore, sesquidigiti interstitio à cauda etiam pinnulam habet parvam & talem etiam in dorso, trium digitorum intervallo à cauda. Cute tegitur, non squamis, quæ superius fusca est, multis tuberculis duris, per dorsum insignita versus anticam partem, & utrumque latus. In utroque autem latere undecim nigras habet maculas lentis magnitudine & figura, binas ac binas juxta se positas. Prope insertionem utriusque branchii etiam multas ejusmodi maculas nigras habet & ibidem in quolibet latere foramen parvum in corpus. In summa, in lateribus, circa oculos, in extremis branchiis, mire variegatur punctulis albis, nigris, lineisque itidem albis & nigris, ut vix exprimi possit à pictore. In toto autem inferiori corpore egregii miniati est coloris, atque ibi cutis æqualis, verum ad tactum paulum hispida.

CAP.

The volume exhibited is open at the title-page to Marcgrave's account of Brazilian fishes. Its illustrations were derived from drawings probably by Marcgrave, which were sold by Count Maurits to the Elector of Brandenburg, eventually passed to the Preussische Staatsbibliothek, Berlin, but were lost in World War II. A somewhat similar group of drawings survives, however, in the Academy of Sciences, Leningrad.

Literature: E. W. Gudger: "George Marcgrave, the first student of American natural history" in *Popular Science Monthly* (1912), pp. 250-274; A. de E. Taunay, ed.: *Jorge Marcgrave. História natural do Brasil*, Sao Paulo, 1942; P. J. P. Whitehead: "Clupeoid Fishes of the Guianas, Appendix I" in *Bulletin of the British Museum (Natural History)*, Zoological Supplement 5 (1973), pp. 187-219 (with extensive bibliography).

Frans Jansz. Post
Dutch, ca. 1612-1680.

79 *Brazilian Landscape*

Oil on panel. Signed and dated: *F. Post 1656.* 16⅜ x 22⅟₁₆ inches (41.5 x 57.4 cm.). Provenance: Julius S. Weitzner, New York, 1949. Hartford, Connecticut, Wadsworth Atheneum.

Painted twelve years after Post returned to the Netherlands, this picture represents a generalised view of the landscape in the region of Pernambuco made from memory, probably refreshed by drawings made on the spot. Like many of his other pictures of the same period, it suggests that Brazil had become for him an exotic paradise, peopled by happy children of nature dancing among exuberant tropical vegetation.

Literature: Erik Larsen: *Frans Post: Interprète du Brésil,* p. 190.

Frans Jansz. Post

80 *Brazilian Landscape*

Oil on canvas. Signed and dated: *F. Post 1665.* 22 x 32¾ inches (55.7 x 93.7 cm.). Provenance: S. F. Aram, New York, 1934. Detroit, Detroit Institute of Arts.

This is one of the several paintings in which Post shows a partly ruined Roman Catholic Church, perhaps as a symbol of Portuguese rule in Brazil briefly overthrown by the Protestant Dutch, though re-established in 1654. As in other Brazilian landscapes painted after his return to Holland, he has also contrived to incorporate as many examples of Brazilian flora and fauna as possible, including several types of palm, fruit trees, climbing plants, and cactus, and in the foreground an iguana, armadillo, large toad, and a cobra swallowing a hare.

Literature: Robert C. Smith: "The Brazilian Landscapes of Frans Post" in *The Art Quarterly*, I (1938), p. 257; E. Larsen: *Frans Post, interprète du Brésil*, p. 197, no. 83; *The Painter and the New World*, exhibition catalogue, Montreal Museum of Fine Arts, Montreal, 1967, no. 9; Joaquim de Sousa-Leão: *Frans Post 1612-1680*, Amsterdam, 1973, no. 30.

Bonaventura Peeters

Flemish, 1614-1652.
A member of a family of marine painters, Peeters was born in Antwerp, where he became a master of the painters' guild in 1634-35. He worked in collaboration with his brother Gillis (1612-1653) and later with his younger brother Jan (1624-1677/80). With Gillis he painted *The Siege of Calloo* for Antwerp Town Hall in 1639. The ships in his pictures are correctly rendered but are often depicted near fantastic rocky coasts, usually Mediterranean in appearance but sometimes intended to represent the West Indies.

Bonaventura Peeters

81 *West Indian Scene*
Oil on panel. Signed and dated: *B P 1648*. 17¹⁵⁄₁₆ x 27⅞ inches (43.9 x 70.7 cm.). Provenance: Julius P. Weitzner, New York, 1940.

Hartford, Connecticut, The Wadsworth Atheneum: The Ella Gallop Sumner and Mary Catlin Sumner Collection.
This is one of several pictures by Bonaventura Peeters with Amerindians in the foreground: the same group is repeated in an otherwise different composition formerly in the possession of The Leger Gallery, London. Other examples with Amerindians are in the collections of Ambassador A. de Mello Franco, Rio de Janeiro, João Fernando de Almeida Prado, São Paolo, and the Philadelphia Museum of Art. As the ships in the work exhibited and in one of the other paintings fly the colours of the United Provinces, it seems probable that they were painted for Dutch patrons whose interest had been directed to South America by the foundation of the Dutch colony in Brazil. The Amerindian figures are, however, wholly fantastic.

Literature: *Five Centuries of Marine Painting*, exhibition catalogue, Detroit Institute of Arts, Detroit, 1942, no. 16; *Art News*, March 15-31, 1942, pp. 15-17; R. H. Wilenski: *Flemish Painters 1430-1830*, New York, 1960, vol. I, p. 260; *The Coast and the Sea*, exhibition catalogue, Art Association of Newport R.I., Newport, 1964, no. 19; *Century of Rubens*, exhibition catalogue, Musées Royaux des Beaux-Arts de Belgique, Brussels, 1965, no. 164; *The Painter and the New World*, exhibition catalogue, the Montreal Museum of Fine Arts, Montreal, 1967, no. 6; Erik Larsen, "Some Seventeenth Century Paintings of Brazil" in *The Connoisseur*, CLXXV (1970), p. 131.

Dirk Valkenburg

Dutch, 1675-1721.
Valkenburg was born in Amsterdam, where he was trained under M. van Musscher and Jan Weenix. After making a tour of Germany and, probably, Italy in 1695, he was employed by King William III of England. In February 1706 he was commissioned to go to Surinam to paint views of plantations owned by an Amsterdam merchant, Jonas Witsen. There he made a series of topographical drawings (Rijksprentenkabinet, Amsterdam) as well as several paintings, probably including a still-life of fruit from Surinam (Musée des Beaux Arts, Quimper) as well as the two views included in this exhibition. He returned to the Netherlands in 1708.

Dirk Valkenburg

83 *A Plantation in Surinam*

Oil on canvas. Signed and dated: *Valkenburg. Surin:* 1707. 20¾ x 18 inches (52.2 x 45.5 cm.).
Amsterdam, Rijksmuseum.

This is a view of one of the three plantations owned by the Amsterdam merchant Jonas Witsen at Surimombo, Palmeneribo, and Waterlant on the Surinam River. With its figures of free Indians, one of whom is seated in a hammock, it makes a contrast with [84], which shows a group of black slaves. The Dutch had first settled on the Guiana coast in 1597 and in 1616 established a colony in what was later to become British Guiana. Surinam was colonised by the Dutch West India Company, founded in 1621, and settled in the late seventeenth century by members of the Labadist sect. Its economic importance increased in the early eighteenth century with the introduction of coffee-growing.

Literature: A. van Schendel: "Eeen stille plantage in Suriname" in *Bulletin van het Rijksmuseum*, XI (1963), pp. 80-86.

Dirk Valkenburg

84 *Black People Making Merry in Surinam*

Oil on canvas. 1706-1708. Signed: *D. VB.* 22⅞ x 18⅜ inches (58 x 46 cm.). Provenance: Danish Royal Collection before 1840.
Copenhagen, Royal Museum of Fine Arts.

It is more than a little ironic that this happy picture should be set in Surinam, a colony made notorious for the maltreatment of slaves by Aphra Behn in her story *Oroonoko* (1678), which was also dramatised, and given still more damaging publicity, in Voltaire's *Candide* (1759) and in Captain Stedman's *Narrative*, illustrated by William Blake [310]. Like [83], it shows one of the plantations owned by Jonas Witsen, who commissioned Valkenburg to go to Surinam. It is probably identical to a painting in the collection of Witsen's grandson in 1790, described as "Plegtigheid onder de Neegers, gestoffeert met een meenigte lieden en kinderen." But it was incorrectly attributed to Dionysos Verburg (fl. 1677-before 1722), until C. P. van Eeghen ascribed it to Valkenburg and A. van Shendel associated it with the fully signed plantation scene [83].

Literature: U. Thieme and F. Becker: *Allgemeines Lexikon der bildenden Künstler*, vol. XXXIV, Leipzig, 1926, p. 230 (as Verburgh); W. Martin: *De Hollandsche Schilderkunst in de 17de Eeuw*, Amsterdam, 1936 (as Verburgh); C. P. van Eeghen in *Oud Holland*, LXI (1946), p. 65; A. van Schendel in *Bulletin van het Rijksmuseum*, XI (1963), pp. 80-83; *Le Siècle de Rembrandt*, exhibition catalogue, Petit Palais, Paris, 1970-71, p. 218.

VI
The Fourth
Continent

The three continents of the old cosmosgraphy were seldom represented in works of art. But in the second half of the sixteenth century there seems to have been a growing demand for allegorical representations of the four parts of the world,[1] reflecting partly the expanding horizons of the Renaissance but also the growing self-awareness of Europeans as they confronted the rest of the world. The discovery of America was, indeed, largely responsible for the popular idea of continents, each with their individual characteristics which distinguished them from the European norm, and thus for the notion of Europe as a cultural and geographical entity.

Numerous works of art and literature, including some of the very greatest—Michelangelo's Medici tombs, Spenser's *Faerie Queen*—express the sixteenth-century obsession with allegory. This taste was also reflected in numerous transient festival decorations, and it is in these that the four continents seem first to have been personified. The Antwerp *Ommegang*—an annual pageant—of 1564 included a *tableau vivant* of Europe, Asia, Africa, and America as four empresses.[2] It proved so popular that it was repeated two years later. No visual record of it survives, but it may well have established a local tradition for the representation of the continents, on which Martin de Vos could have drawn when he incorporated such figures in the decorations of an arch run up for the ceremonial entry of the Archduke Ernst of Austria into Antwerp in 1594 [88]. Engravings diffused de Vos's delightful vision of America as a nude girl riding an outsize armadillo. But by this time several other allegories of America had been created—on the title page of Abraham Ortelius's *Theatrum Orbis Terrarum* (Antwerp, 1570), in paintings by Giovanni de' Vecchi at Caprarola and Paolo Farinati in a villa near Verona [90], in etchings by Etienne Delaune [85], and in a drawing by Stradanus [86]. And many more were to follow.

In creating their allegories of America, artists attempted to compress into a single image as many as possible of the distinguishing features of the land and its inhabitants. She is thus, almost invariably, represented naked with feather ornaments and some indication of the riches of the continent in gold and silver. A parrot and some four-footed beast—armadillo, alligator, opossum, or llama—accompany her. But America was also famous for its cannibals, gruesomely fascinating to Europeans, partly because anthropophagi, though familiar from classical literature and from Sir John Mandeville's account of the Far East, had never previously been located. The cannibals of America were frequently described and had been depicted in several early sixteenth-century prints and on many maps.[3] As early as 1516 Sir Thomas More in the opening pages of *Utopia* remarked of his conversation with Vespucci's companion, "we made no enquiries after Monsters, than which nothing is more common; for everywhere one may hear of ravenous Dogs and Wolves, and cruel Man-eaters." No such notorious as-

112

pect of American life could, however, be omitted from allegories. Stradanus and Paolo Farinati took over the cartographers' images. The creators of more compact personifications contented themselves with a severed arm or head as a less explicit and distasteful symbol.

The various allegorical formulas developed by artists in the course of the sixteenth century were categorised by Philippe Galle in his *Prospographia* (which is undated but may have been begun in 1579) and Cesare Ripa in his more widely influential *Iconologia,* of which the first illustrated edition was published in Rome in 1603. In the latter work, used by practically every Baroque artist in search of an allegorical symbol, America is shown with a feather head-dress, holding in her hands a bow and arrow, trampling with one foot on a human head, and accompanied by a diminutive alligator. Some of the earlier attributes were to survive for some time —as in Stefano della Bella's *America* in a chariot drawn by armadillos [93]. But Ripa's image remained the standard one until the early nineteenth century, when the personification of America began a long process of mutation and transformation—into Columbia, Uncle Sam, Brother Jonathan, and, eventually, Liberty herself.

1. E. Kollmann, K.-A. Wirth et al. in *Reallexikon zur deutschen Kunstgeschichte,* vol. v, Stuttgart, 1967, cols. 1107-1202 s.v. *Erdteile;* H. Honour: *The New Golden Land,* New York, 1975.
2. Sheila Williams: "Les Ommegangs d'Anvers" in J. Jacquot, ed.: *Les fêtes de la Renaissance,* Paris, 1960, vol. II, p. 352.
3. There was also a more sinister reason for the prevalence of cannibals on maps. Since the Spanish laws prohibiting the enslavement of the Indians excluded man-eaters from their protection, it was to the advantage of an adventurer to attribute cannibalism to any tribe he might subdue.

Etienne Delaune

French, 1518/19-1595.
Delaune was one of the most notable French engravers working in the style of the School of Fontainebleau, also a goldsmith and medallist. He worked in Paris, where he was employed in the mint but, as a Huguenot, fled from persecution in 1573 to Strassburg, where he seems to have spent the rest of his life, apart from a visit to Augsburg in 1576. Some 450 prints by him are recorded, the earliest dated 1557. They are often small, sometimes diminutive, and include numerous allegories—of the arts, elements, seasons, planets, and the four continents.

Etienne Delaune

85 *Americca*

Engraving. Signed and dated: *1575.*
S. F. 2⁹⁄₁₆ x 3³⁄₁₆ inches (6.5 x 8.2 cm.).
Provenance: James Hazen Hyde.
New York, The New-York Historical Society.

This forms part of the first recorded set of allegorical prints of the four continents. It may, however, derive from a slightly earlier project for mural decorations, possibly at Fontainebleau. America is shown nude with bow and arrows, a Brazilian club, and an animal probably intended to represent a llama.

Literature: Robert-Dumesnil: *Le peintre-graveur français*, 1854, vol. VI, no. 200; *Katalog der Ornamentstichsammlung der Staatliche Kunstbibliothek Berlin*, Berlin and Leipzig, 1939, p. 555; E. Köllmann, K. A. Wirth, et al. in *Reallexikon zur Deutschen Kunstgeschichte*, vol. V, Stuttgart, 1967, col. 1164.

Jan van der Street, called Stradanus

Flemish, ca. 1523-1605.
Stradanus was born in Bruges, the son of a noble but impoverished family, and trained in Antwerp, where he became a master of the painters' guild in 1545. After working for a short time in

Lyon he went to Italy, first to Venice and then to Florence, where he worked from 1555 to 1571, coming into close contact with Giorgio Vasari. He provided numerous cartoons for the Medici tapestry factory. He also executed several paintings for the Palazzo Vecchio, Florence (notably the *Glass Factory* in Francesco I de Medici's Studiolo) and also designed various festival decorations.

Jan van der Street, called Stradanus

86 *Vespucci Discovering America*

Pen and brown ink heightened with white. 1589. Signed: *Joannes Stradanus.* 7½ x 10⅝ inches (19 x 26.9 cm.). Inscription: *Americus Vespuccius Florentinus 1497.* Provenance: William A. Baillie-Groham, 1919; James Hazen Hyde, who gave it to The Metropolitan Museum, 1959.
New York, The Metropolitan Museum of Art, Gift of the Estate of James Hazen Hyde, 1959.

This is a preparatory design for one of a series of engravings by Philipp Galle and others published under the title *Nova Reperta* (New Discoveries). Other less highly finished drawings for the same series survive (with many marginal notes) in the Biblioteca Laurenziana, Florence (Cod. Pal. 75). Vespucci is shown holding a mariner's astrolabe in one hand and, in the other, a banner marked with the stars of the Southern Cross—tributes to his astronomical knowledge, of which he made much in his *Mundus Novus* [2]. The group of cannibals in the background is similar to many which had appeared on maps. America herself bears a close resemblance to the figure on the title page of Abraham Ortelius: *Theatrum orbis terrarum,* Antwerp, 1570. The hammock and the Brazilian wooden club may well have been drawn from imported specimens, of which there were several in Europe at this date. Several animals in the drawing are labelled with inscriptions: *Tamandoa* beneath the ant-eater, *Cerigon* over the bear-like creature above it, *Anta* beneath the horse-like tapir in the background, and *Pigritia* above the sloth; the pineapple plant is labelled *Ana-naze.* On the *verso,* manuscript notes in Dutch by Stradanus refer to Petrus Moffe: *Historiarum Indicarum,* book II (Florence, 1588) and also give brief descriptions of the animals depicted.

The ant-eater, Stradanus writes, "is as large as a sheep; it has broad feet with which it scratches ants together; it has a large slit instead of a mouth, a long tongue to lick up ants, and a round stern." The *cerigon* (presumably an opossum) is said to have "two bags at its stomach in which it carries its young who hold on by sucking." Of the *pigritia,* or sloth, Stradanus wrote: "it is as large as a fox, climbs trees, has fingers on its feet: because of its big belly it walks in fifteen days not further than one can throw a stone."

Literature: William A. Baillie-Grohman: *Sport in Art. An Iconography of Sport,* London, 1919, pp. 138-145; *Quatre Siècles de Colonisation Française,* exhibition catalogue, Bibliothèque Nationale, Paris, 1931, no. 417; *Masterpieces of Drawing,* exhibition catalogue, Philadelphia Museum of Art, Philadelphia, 1950-1951, no. 44; Gunther Thiem: "Studien zu Jan van der Straet, genannt Stradanus" in *Mitteilungen der Kunsthistorischen Institutes in Florenz,* VIII (1958), pp. 91-92.

87 *Plaquette: America*

Germany. Lead with traces of gilt. ca. 1580-1590. Diameter 7 inches (17.7 cm.). Provenance: Alfred Walcher Ritter von Molthein, Vienna, 1918.

New York, The Metropolitan Museum of Art, 1960, Rogers Fund.
The attributes surrounding the feather-cinctured America include emblems of wealth (vessels of precious metals and what appear to be gold nuggets in a sack), monkeys, and a parrot. The animal on the left is difficult to identify, though it bears a certain similarity to one on Waldseemüller's world map of 1516 probably intended to represent an opossum. On the right an armadillo has been transformed into a rhinoceros, which it was often said to resemble and which figures in several allegories of America of this period.

Literature: Edmund W. Braun: *Die deutschen Renaissanceplaketten der Sammlung Alfred Walcher Ritter von Molthein,* Vienna, 1918, no. 174; Clare Le Corbeiller: "Miss America and her Sisters" in *Metropolitan Museum of Art Bulletin,* XIX (1961), p. 214.

Marten de Vos

Flemish, 1532-1603.
De Vos was the leading painter of his time in Antwerp. He was probably trained by his father, Peter, but also came under the influence of Frans Floris, then travelled to Rome, Florence, and Venice, where he is said to have worked in Tintoretto's studio. He was back in Antwerp by 1558, when he became a member of the painters' guild. He painted numerous religious pictures, often to fill the place of the altarpieces destroyed by Protestant iconoclasts, also several fine portraits. But he is perhaps most widely known through the many engravings for which he provided the drawings.

Marten de Vos

88 *America*

Pen and wash. 11¼ x 6½ inches (28.5 x 16.5 cm.). Inscription: *America*. Provenance: Collection de la Faille.

Antwerp, Stedelijk Prentenkabinet (Municipal Print Room).
The drawing is one of a series of designs for allegories of the continents made by de Vos for the decoration of the triumphal arch of the Genevans erected on the occasion of the state entry into the city of Antwerp by the archduke Ernst, governor of the Austrian Netherlands, in 1594. The idea of symbolising America as a naked woman holding a bow and seated on an outsize armadillo seems to have been original. The print after the drawing, engraved by Adrien Collaert (ca. 1560-1618), was widely diffused, and

de Vos's figure of America was copied from it onto stove-tiles (Burg Trausnitz near Landshut, destroyed) and the facade of a house in Wernigerode, East Germany.

Literature: Antoinette Doutrepont: "Marten de Vos et l'entrée triomphale de l'Archduc Ernest d'Autriche" in *Bulletin de l'Institut historique belge de Rome,* XVIII (1937), p. 155; A. J. J. Delen: *Catalogue des dessins anciens du Cabinet des Estampes de la Ville d'Anvers,* Brussels, 1938, no. 77; B. Knipping: *De Iconografie van de Contra-Reformatie in de Nederlanden,* Hilversum, 1940, p. 161; Erich Köllmann and others s.v. "Erdteile" in *Reallexikon zur deutschen Kunstgeschichte,* vol. V, Stuttgart, 1967, col. 1181 ff.; *Antwerpens gouden eeuw,* exhibition catalogue, Antwerp, 1956, no. 176; *De eeuw van Bruegel,* exhibition catalogue, Brussels, 1963, pp. 213-214; *Antwerp's Golden Age,* exhibition catalogue, New York Cultural Center and elsewhere, 1973-75, no. 17.

89 *America*

Flanders. Pen and black ink with ink wash. ca. 1600. Diameter 4 ⅞ inches (12.5 cm.). Provenance: Josef Carl von Klinkosch, Vienna 1889 (Lugt 577); G. C. Boerner, Düsseldorf 1960. Ann Arbor, The University of Michigan Museum of Art.

In addition to the attributes usually given to America at this period— feather head-dress and skirt, pearls, parrot, severed human head, and an anachronistic rhinoceros—this drawing includes a dolphin and large feline, presumably intended to represent a jaguar or puma. The instrument which the figure holds in her right hand seems to be an elongated version of the club used for the ritual killing of prisoners of war by the Tupinamba, described and illustrated in Hans Staden's *Wahrhaftiger Historia* [60]. The drawing appears to have been made as a design for a plaquette. It is inscribed on the *verso* with the name of Marten de Vos, but the attribution to this artist cannot be maintained.

Literature: *Architectural and Ornament Drawings of the 16th to the early 19th centuries in the Collection of the University of Michigan Museum of Art*, Ann Arbor, 1965, no. 5.

Paolo Farinati

Italian (Verona), 1524-1606. Farinati was born and trained in Verona and began his career working in a style akin to that of his greater compatriot Paolo Veronese, who was four years younger. As the latter moved to Venice in 1550, Farinati soon emerged as the leader of the local school. An immensely prolific artist, he painted a very large number of altarpieces for churches and frescoes for both churches and private houses in and around Verona. Although he suffers from comparison with Paolo Veronese, he was no mere imitator, either of him or of the Emilian and Lombard painters, by whom he was also influenced. He was a fine draughtsman, and his drawings have been collected since the seventeenth century. But his paintings, most of which remain in Italy, have only recently begun to receive the attention they merit.

90 *Allegory of America*

Pen, brown ink, and wash, heightened with white. 1595. 10 ⁷⁄₁₆ x 16 ¹³⁄₁₆ inches (26.8 x 42.8 cm.). Inscription: On the verso, *P. Farinato.* Provenance: Probably William Gibson (1644-1702). London, Executors of the late C. R. Rudolf.

This is one of the earliest known visual images of the evangelization of America. The human arm and shoulder roasting on a spit recall the cannibal scenes on many earlier maps, but the figure of the Indian holding a crucifix, which he rests on the back of a turtle, is unprecedented. The drawing is a preliminary design for one of four fresco lunettes of the continents painted by Farinati in 1595 in the Villa delle Torre (now Stegagno) at Mezzane near Verona (cf. Lionello Puppi: *Paolo Farinati: Giornale 1573-1606,* Florence, 1968, p. 134). In the fresco Farinati placed the spit further away from the convert and painted by it a group of unregenerate Indians.

Literature: T. Mullaly in *Master Drawings,* VI (1968), p. 288.

Philipp Galle

Flemish, 1537-1612.
Galle was born in Haarlem but went as a youth to Antwerp, where, after working under Hieronymus Cock, he established in 1570 an engraving studio, which soon became the most famous and prolific in the city. He published numerous single prints as well as engraved illustrations and frontispieces for books, notably those published by the house of Plantin and Moretus.

Philipp Galle

91 America

Engraving. ca. 1579-1600. 7½ x 4⁵⁄₁₆ inches (19 x 11 cm.). Inscription: *America* and *Estrix dira hominum scatet auro America: pollet / Arcu: psittacum alit: plumea serta gerit.*
Provenance: James Hazen Hyde.
New York, The New-York Historical Society.

The print is no. 43 of the series issued by Philipp Galle under the title *Prosopographia* (graphic personifications). The inscription describes America as a female glutton who devours men, is rich in gold, is mighty and powerful with the bow, rears parrots, and wears garlands of feathers. These characteristics are combined in the image of a naked woman wearing feathers on her head and bow and arrows, carrying an elongated Brazilian club in one hand and a head in the other, stepping over a severed arm, followed by a parrot.

Literature: R. van Marle: *L'Iconographie de l'art profane au Moyen Age et dans la Renaissance,* The Hague, 1932, vol. II, p. 310; A. Doutrepont in *Bulletin de l'Institut historique belge de Rome,* XVIII (1937), pp. 149, 152; B. Knipping: *Iconographie van der Contra-Reformatie in der Niederlanden,* Hilversum, 1940, pp. 162, 165; K.-A. Wirth et al. in *Reallexikon zur Deutschen Kunstgeschichte,* Stuttgart, 1967, vol. V, cols. 1164, 1178.

Marcus Gheeraerts (or Geeraards)

Flemish, ca. 1519-before 1604.
A painter of religious pictures in his native Bruges, Gheeraerts is now better known for his etchings (e.g. 108 illustrations to Eduard de Dene's edition of Aesop's fables, 1567) and the many engravings after his designs. In 1568 he accompanied his son (Marcus Gheeraerts the Younger) to England. He returned to the Low Countries and is said to have worked in Antwerp from 1577 to 1586 but appears to have died in England.

Marcus Gheeraerts

92 America

Engraving. ca. 1590-1600. Signed: *Marc.Gerar.inven.* and *Phls Galle excud.* 8⅛ x 5⅝ inches (20.6 x 14.3 cm.). Provenance: James Hazen Hyde, New York, 1959.
New York, The Metropolitan Museum of Art, Gift of the Estate of James Hazen Hyde, 1959.

This is one of a set of four allegories of the continents engraved by Philipp Galle [91] in Antwerp. The two Eskimos are strikingly similar to those drawn by John White [10] and perhaps derive from White's drawings, though Gheeraerts may himself have seen the Eskimos brought to England in 1576. The Southern Indians at the top and in the centre are of types already conventionalised. The parrots seem to be South American, but the presence of the goat and the other animal is difficult to explain.

Literature: F. W. Hollstein: *Dutch and Flemish Engravings and Woodcuts,* Amsterdam, 1949-56, vol. VII, p. 102; Edward Hodnet: *Marcus Gheeraerts the Elder,* Utrecht, 1971, p. 71.

Stefano della Bella

Italian, 1610-1664.

One of the leading print-makers of his time, della Bella was born in Florence and trained first as a goldsmith. He published his first print in 1627. His early drawings and etchings are in the manner of Jacques Callot. Although patronised by the Medici, he left Florence for Rome in 1633. He returned to Florence from time to time until 1639, when he settled in Paris, where he worked for several publishers and also received royal commissions. He went back to Florence in 1650.

Stefano della Bella

93 Eleven playing cards entitled *Amerique, Castille d'or, Popaian, Brezil, Chile, Quiuira, Peru, Mexique, Floride, Virginie, Nouvelle France*

Etchings. 1644. Each 3 7/16 x 2 1/8 inches (8.8 x 5.4 cm.). Provenance: James Hazen Hyde, New York, 1959. New York, The Metropolitan Museum of Art, Gift of the Estate of James Hazen Hyde, 1959.

These cards form part of a set entitled *Jeu de Géographie*, devised, on Cardinal Mazarin's instructions, by Jean Desmarets de Saint-Sorlin to teach the young Louis XIV the elements of geography. Similar sets of cards were devoted to history and ancient mythology. Each of the American cards is decorated with a delicately fanciful figure of an Indian and a few lines of text explaining, for instance, that Florida is "fertile and of great extent" inhabited by "brave and cruel people," and that Nouvelle France "includes Canada and extends along the St. Lawrence. A country covered with woods and badly cultivated. To the North lie Newfoundland, Labrador and Estotiland." On another card he personified the American continent as a regal figure seated in an armadillo-drawn chariot—an image which proved popular and was imitated by several craftsmen, e.g. on a copper-gilt clock signed by J. P. Pfleger of Augsburg (Museo Civico dell'età cristiana e moderna, Brescia) and a silver dish by Adolf Gaap, also of Augsburg [113].

Literature: Phyllis Dearborn Massar: "Presenting Stefano della Bella" in *Metropolitan Museum of Art Bulletin*, XXVII (1968), pp. 159-176; Alexander Baudi de Vesme (revised and introduced by Phyllis Dearborn Massar): *Stefano della Bella*, catalogue raisonné, New York, 1971, nos. 582, 583, 584, 585, 586, 587, 590, 591, 592, 594.

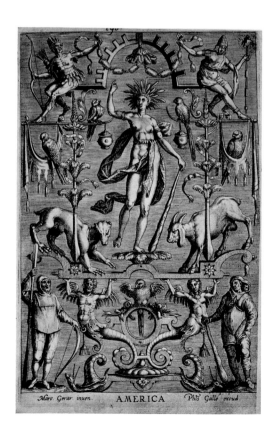

Marc Gerar. inuen. AMERICA Phls Galle excud.

Amerique
Quatriesme partie du monde, découuerte depuis 150 ans, autrement dicte, les Indes Occidentales, ou le nouueau monde. située vers l'Occident, et diuisée en deux grandes peninsules, l'vne appellée Amerique Mexicane, l'autre Peruane. elle s'estend sur toutes les zones.

America wel is het vreemfte van de Deelen. Dit fach den Batavier, hy quam omt hoeckien kyicken. **AMERICA** Dees Landen geven uyt Goudt, Silver, Papegayen. D'inwoonders van dit Landt elck ander los ontfielen.
Hier fyn de Volcken woeft, en leven fonder wett. En letten op fyn kans, hy vandt de foeticheyt. En veelderhande Vee, Toeback, Brafilien Hout. En flachten als het Vee, op ongehoorde wys.
Maer den Caftiliaen quam in dit landt te teelen. Hy gingh allenxkens met een Stadt of Schanfke ftrycke. Campetji Stockvis-Hout, en Ebben, all verfcheyen. Als Dull en onbefindt, malkanderen vernielen.
En heeft de Havens meeft met fchanffen vaft befett. Daer hy nu als de Moll vaft in fyn voordeel leyt. *Viffcher Excudebat.* De Suycker abondant, oock Huy den Vis en Sout. En braden dan het Vlees tot haer gewone Spys. 4

Cornelis Visscher

Dutch, ca. 1619-1662.
Visscher was a portrait draughtsman
and engraver who became a member
of the Haarlem guild of artists in 1653.
Most of his engravings are reproduc-
tive prints after paintings by Titian,
Guido Reni, Rubens, van Dyck,
Ostade, and others.

Cornelis Visscher

93A *America*

Engraving. ca. 1650-1660. Signed:
Visscher excudebat. 19¹⁵⁄₁₆ x 26 inches
(50.7 x 66 cm.).
Inscription:
America is by far the strangest
continent;
Here people live as lawless savages.
But the Spanish came to cultivate this
land,
And occupy the harbours with their
forts.

This the Dutchman saw. He came,
looking around the corner,
Watching for his chance, and he found
the sweetness.
One by one he ensnares a city or fort,
Which like a barge he pulls in to his
profit.
These lands give forth gold, silver,
parrots,
All kinds of cattle, tobacco, Brazilian
wood,
Campetji-stockfish wood, and ebony
all appear;

Sugar abounds, and also Hüyden fish
and salt.
The inhabitants of this land take each
others' lives
And slaughter each other like cattle in
an unheard of manner.
Like mindless and innocent animals,
they destroy each other,
Then roast the flesh as their usual fare.

Provenance: James Hazen Hyde, 1926.
New York, The New-York Historical
Society.

This print is derived from Marten de
Vos [88] by way of an engraving of ca.
1595-1600 by Adrien II Collaert, which
it repeats with only minor alterations.
As in many earlier allegories of America the fauna includes several Old
World animals, notably the fat-tailed
sheep and goat (described at the time
as *Capra indica*) which were associated
with Asia.

Literature: J. H. Hyde: "The Four Parts of
the World as represented in old-time
pageants and ballets" in *Apollo*, IV (1926),
p. 232.

Jacob van Meurs
Dutch, 1619-1680.
Van Meurs was an engraver and publisher who worked in Haarlem and
probably Leeuwarden before settling
in Amsterdam. He engraved a number
of portraits and also illustrations for
books.

Jacob van Meurs

94 *America, frontispiece to Arnoldus
Montanus:* De Nieuwe en
Onbekende Weereld, *Amsterdam,
1671*
Engraving. 1671. 12¼ x 7¹³⁄₁₆ inches
(31 x 19.8 cm.).
Washington, D.C., Library of Con-
gress, Prints and Photographs Division.

This print, dominated by the figure of
America prodigally scattering gold,
includes various types of Indians, a
llama, beaver, and fat-tailed sheep
(often incongruously incorporated in
such allegories); in the background
there are European figures and their
stone-built fort. It served as the frontispiece to the richly and sometimes fantastically illustrated account of the
New World by Arnoldus Montanus
[39].

Literature: W. P. Cumming, S. Hillier, D.
B. Quinn, and G. Williams: *The Exploration of North America 1630-1776*, London, 1973, p. 59.

AMERICA

T' AMSTERDAM
By Jacob van Meurs, *Plaetsnyder en Boeckverkooper op de Kerserrs graft inde Stadt Meurs.1671.*

Nicolaes (or Claes) Berchem

Dutch, 1620-1683.
Born in Haarlem, Berchem studied
under his father, the still-life painter
Pieter Claesz., and travelled to Italy,
probably between 1650 and 1653. His
best known works are very delicate
and imaginative Italianate landscapes
and pastoral scenes, which were greatly
admired in eighteenth-century France.
He was an accomplished etcher and
also executed a few designs for
engravers.

Nicolaes (or Claes) Berchem

95 *America*
Black chalk, ink, and grey wash. ca.
1640-1650. Signed: *Berchem*. 17⅞ x
11⅞ inches (14.3 x 30.1 cm.). Provenance: James Hazen Hyde, 1959.
New York, The Metropolitan Museum
of Art, Gift of the Estate of James
Hazen Hyde.

This seems to be an early drawing by
Berchem, probably intended for a book
illustration. The distinctly Protestant
figure of Religion in the sky, casting
down a helmeted and moustachioed
figure of Iberian appearance while an
Indian holds his hands in an attitude
of prayer, suggests that it may allude
to the conflict between the Dutch and
Portuguese in Brazil. Another drawing
of an allegory of America is in the
English Royal collection at Windsor
Castle, probably intended to decorate
an engraved map (cf. E. Schaar:
"Zeichnungen Berchem zu Land-
karten" in *Oud Holland,* LXXI (1956),
239-243).

VII
American Dancers

When Sir Humfry Gilbert sailed for North America in 1583, he took with him "for solace of our people, and allurement of the Savages . . . Musicke in good variety not omitting the least toyes, as Morris dancers, Hobby horsse, and manylike conceits to delight the Savage people, whom we intended to winne by all faire meanes possible."[1] Thus Elizabethan music and folk dances were performed on the barren coast of Newfoundland and "fishermen of all nations" (Spanish, Portuguese, French, and English), sheltering in the harbour of St. John's, joined in. Unfortunately there is no visual record of this occasion. Nor are the reactions of the "Savage people" known. But even if they also mingled with the stamping, jingling morrismen, the bizarre scene must have been quite unlike those presented by the European producers of masques and ballets, which were soon to include American dancers delicately dressed in brightly coloured feathers.[2]

One of the first references to America in English literature appears in a kind of masque—*An Interlude of the Four Elements*, written by John Rastell soon after 1517, when he had himself crossed the Atlantic.

> Westwards he founde new landes,
> That we never heard tell of before this
> By wrytynge nor other meanys,
> Yet many nowe have ben there,

one of the characters declaims, and then goes on to lament:

> O what a thynge had be than,
> Yf that they that be Englyshemen
> Myght have ben the furst of all
> That there should have take possessyon,
> And made furst buyldynge and habytacion,
> A memory perpetuall![3]

Another plea to support English colonization was made just under a century later, in a masque performed before James I in 1613, with words by George Chapman and sets and costumes by Inigo Jones, including "Virginian Princes" dressed in cloth of silver embroidered with suns and dancers "all showfully garnished with several-hewed feathers."[4] Colonization was also the theme of a ballet danced before Louis XIV at Fontainebleau in 1685, only three years after Louisiana had been named and acquired for him by René Robert de La Salle. In songs and dances "savages of the French provinces in America" expressed their pleasure at coming under his rule.

As these examples show, court masques and ballets were intended to combine aesthetic pleasure with instruction. They were indeed closely linked with the allegorically complex processions and schemes of festival decoration created for such events as royal marriages, funerals, or state visits to cities. "Americans" and personifications of America made not infrequent appearances on such occasions. For Charles V's entry into Milan in 1541, Giulio Romano designed a triumphal arch with a sculptured group of a figure on horseback riding over a Turk, a "barbarian," and an American Indian.[5] Lest the message should be overlooked, the author of the booklet commemorating the entry remarked: "Our age will be more rich and perfect with the new world discovered and vanquished." When Henri II made his entry into Rouen in 1550, he was provided with the spectacle of a Brazilian jungle village, complete with fifty real live Brazilians —a show put on by the citizens, several of whom were engaged in the dye-wood trade and probably hoped to persuade the king to establish a French colony in South America [8]. On other occasions and also in court ballets, "Americans" sometimes appeared as representatives of their continent, joining Africans and Asians in offering their homage to an all-powerful European monarch.

It would, however, be a mistake to suppose that American dancers in ballets invariably had a political significance. Some were no more than decoratively exotic figures. The Indian feather skirt was a very practical dress for a dancer, leaving the limbs free for agile movement. And it seems to have been popular with costume designers, some of whom used it for Moors and Ethiopians as well as Indians, thus perpetuating the old confusion between East and West.

1. Edward Haye's account of Gilbert's voyage printed by Hakluyt, quoted by S. E. Morison: *The European Discovery of America: The Northern Voyages,* New York, 1971, p. 573.
2. James Hazen Hyde: "The Four Parts of the World as Represented in Old Time Pageants and Ballets" in *Apollo,* IV (1926), pp. 232-238, V (1927), pp. 20-26.
3. *Percy Society,* XXII (1848), pp. 28-29.
4. D. J. Gordon: "Le masque de George Chapman" in J. Jacquot, ed.: *Les fêtes de la Renaissance,* Paris, 1960, vol. 1, pp. 309-313; S. Orgel and R. Strong: *Inigo Jones—The Theatre of the Stuart Court,* London, 1973, pp. 253-263.
5. A. Chastel: "Les entrées de Charles Quint en Italie" in J. Jacquot, ed.: *Fêtes et cérémonies au temps de Charles Quint,* Paris, 1960, pp. 197-206; R. Strong: *Splendour at Court,* London, 1973, p. 97.

Giulio Parigi

Italian, d. 1635.

Parigi was the son of a Florentine architect, Alfonso I Parigi, and, through his
mother, a grand-son of the sculptor
Bartolommeo Ammanati. After being
trained under Bernardo Buontalenti as
an architect and designer of court
festivals, he was employed in both
capacities by the grand dukes Francesco I and Cosimo II dei Medici. He
also ran a drawing school for young
Florentine noblemen. His son Alfonso
II was similarly employed by the
grand-ducal court.

Giulio Parigi (after)

96 *The Ship of Amerigo Vespucci*
Etching. 1608. 8¼ x 11⁵⁄₁₆ inches (20.9
x 28.6 cm.). Inscription: *Nave di
Amerigo Vespucci Intermedio Quarto.
Remigio Canta Gallina.F. Come: rapp.
nelle nozze del Ser:mo Principe di
Toscana lan 1608. Giulio parigi.I.*
Paris, Bibliothèque Nationale, Cabinet
des Estampes.

This print records the scenery for an
intermezzo entitled *La Nave di
Amerigo Vespucci,* one of a number of
spectacular entertainments put on in
Florence to celebrate the marriage of
the grand duke's son (soon to succeed
as Cosimo II) to the Hapsburg arch-
duchess Maria Maddalena (daughter
of the emperor Rudolph II). Three incidents which succeeded one another in
the *intermezzo* are combined in the
print and labelled *A, B,* and *C.* The
scene represented a rocky gulf with
naked natives on the shore and parrots
fluttering in the sky; a ship decorated
with the Florentine lion and lilies *(A)*
carried Vespucci across the stage; a
reef *(B)* then rose out of the waters
carrying personifications of *La Tran-
quillità* (Calm), in a blue robe, with
nests of seagulls in her hair, stormy
winds fettered to hollows in the rock,

and "gentle winds" playing round it;
finally Immortality appeared in the sky
together with Apollo, the muses, and
poets, including Homer, Pindar,
Horace, Virgil, Dante, and Petrarch
(C). Such elaborately contrived *intermezzi,* which attracted far more attention than the plays they interrupted—
in this instance *The Judgment of
Paris*—were intended to be morally or
politically improving as well as entertaining and dramatically spectacular.
La Nave di Amerigo Vespucci glorified
Italian and especially Florentine genius.

The print is one of a set of seven
etched by Remigio Cantagallina (fl.
1602-1635), who assisted Giulio Parigi
in the design of the various entertainments in 1608. The *intermezzo* was
fully described by Camillo Rinuccini
in *Descrizione delle feste fatte nelle
reali nozze de 'Serenissimi Principi di
Toscana D. Cosimo de' Medici e Maria
Maddalena Archiduchessa d'Austria,*
Florence, 1608. In 1635 Inigo Jones
copied the landscape of the print for a
scene in the masque *The Temple of
Love,* performed in London.

Literature: J. A. B. von Bartsch: *Le Peintre
Graveur,* Vienna, 1821, vol. XX, p. 61, no.
16; V. Mariani: *Storia della scenografia
Italiana,* Florence, 1930, p. 56; E. Poveledo
in *Enciclopedia dello spettacolo,* vol. VII,
Rome, 1960, p. 1676; A. M. Nagler:
Theatre Festivals of the Medici, New
Haven and London, 1964, pp. 109-110;
C. Molinari: *Le nozze degli Dei. Un saggio
sul grande spettacolo italiano nel seicento,*
Rome, 1968, pp. 64-65; G. Gaeta Bertelà
and A. Petrioli Tofani: *Feste e apparati
Medicei da Cosimo I a Cosimo II,* exhibi-
tion catalogue, Gabinetto disegni e stampe
degli Uffizi, Florence, 1969, no. 62; R.
Strong, *Splendour at Court,* London, 1973,
pp. 206-211.

NAVE DI AMERIGO VESPVCCI INTERMEDIO QVARTO

Giulio Parigi

97 *Design for a Ballet Costume*
Pen, ink, and watercolour. ca. 1600-
1610. 10¹¹⁄₁₆ x 6¾ inches (27 x 17 cm.).
Florence, Biblioteca Marucelliana.

This design for a feathered American
Indian costume was probably made for
one of the many entertainments devised
for the Medici Court in Florence by
Giulio Parigi, though presumably not
for the *intermezzo* entitled *La Nave di
Amerigo Vespucci* [96], in which the
Indians are described as being
"naked." It is a drawing of the type
which influenced designers of masques
and ballets in northern Europe, especially Inigo Jones [99]. It was recently
identified by Dr. Detlef Heikamp.

Daniel Rabel

French, ca. 1578-1637.
Rabel was the son of a draughtsman
and engraver, Jean Rabel, by whom he
was trained. In about 1611 he was sent
to Madrid by Marie de Médicis to
paint the portrait of Anne of Austria,
who was betrothed to Louis XIII. As
"ingénieur du Roy" he was responsible
for the elaborate stage mechanism of
court ballets, for which he designed costumes. He was also a very fine botanical painter (examples in Bibliothèque
Nationale and Muséum National
d'Histoire Naturelle, Paris) and a notable book illustrator (e.g. H.d'Urfé's
L'Astrée).

Daniel Rabel

98 *American Musicians*
Pen and ink with watercolour. 1626.
9¼ x 15⅛ inches (24.7 x 38.4 cm.).
Inscription: *Musique de l'Amérique.*
Paris, Bibliothèque Nationale, Cabinet
des Estampes.

These are costume designs for the *Ballet royal du grand bal de la Douairière
de Billebahaut,* given by Louis XIII in
the Salle Bourbon of the Louvre in
early February 1626 and repeated in
the Hôtel de Ville, Paris, some days
afterwards, on 23 February. On both
occasions the king danced in it. The
whole entertainment lasted three

hours. Its story was no more than a device for involving dancers in a wide variety of exotic costumes: the dowager of Billebahaut throws a ball for people from all parts of the world, so that they may hear the wise words of her fiancé Fanfan de Sotteville. The first arrival is "King Atabalipa," accompanied by numerous "Americans," including musicians dressed as parrot-catchers. The following scenes were devoted to the entries of the "Grand Seigneur" with his Asiatic train of attendants, the people of the North represented by Greenlanders, the "Grand Cacique" of Africa mounted on an elephant with a troupe of Africans, the "Grand Cam" and his followers, and finally the people of Europe. The drawing exhibited comes from the set in the Bibliothèque Nationale; there is an almost identical set in the Cabinet des Dessins of the Louvre, and there are fifteen others in the Houghton Library, Harvard University. The association of all these designs with the ballet of the Douairière de Billebahaut was made by M. M. MacGowan.

Literature: M. Paquot: *Les étrangers dans les divertissements de la cour, de Beaujoyeulx à Molière (1581-1673)*, Brussels, s.d. p. 80; *Quatre siècles de la colonisation française,* exhibition catalogue, Bibliothèque Nationale, Paris, 1931, no. 359; James Hazen Hyde: "The Four Parts of the World as Represented in Old-Time Pageants and Ballets" in *Apollo,* v (1927), pp. 20-26; Margaret M. MacGowan: *L'art du ballet de cour en France 1581-1643,* Paris, 1963, pp. 149-153, 292.

Inigo Jones

English, 1573-1652.
Famous as the architect of the Banqueting House in Whitehall, which brought English Renaissance architecture to sudden maturity, Jones first became prominent as a designer of masques for the Stuart court. He was the same age as Ben Jonson, who wrote several of the masques, and only nine years younger than Shakespeare. His masque designs owe much to those of Buontalenti and Parigi, some of whose designs for *intermezzi* at the Tuscan grand-ducal court in Florence were used by Jones. America and Americans appear in three of the masques designed by Jones—*The Memorable Masque* by George Chapman (1613), *Tempe Restored* by Aurelian Townshend (1632), and *The Temple of Love* by Sir William Davenant (1635), for which he adapted one of Parigi's designs.

Inigo Jones

99 *An Indian*
Pen and brown ink washed with grey. 1632. 6⅞ x 4⁷⁄₁₆ inches (16.9 x 11.2 cm.). Inscription: Top left—*Indians* / 7; top right—*a scincote of / olive flesh-coller / feathers on a / bend a collor / of tin[s]ell of gould / in s[c]allopes about / the neck.* Provenance: John Webb; William Talman (?); Richard Boyle, 3rd Earl of Burlington and by descent to present owners.
Devonshire Collection, Chatsworth. Lent by the Trustees of the Chatsworth Settlement.

This is a design for one of the antimasquers in *Tempe Restored* by Aurelian Townshend, a Queen's masque performed at court on 14 February 1632. It was based on Balthasar de Beaujoyeulx's *Balet Comique de la Reine,* danced at the French court in 1581. It tells the story of the vanquish-

ing of the evils of the passions by the heroic example of the king (Charles I), the embodiment of rational order and intellect. The Indians play only a subsidiary, decorative role in the antimasque, unlike those in the earlier *Memorable Masque,* who alluded to the Virginia Company, which had been recently formed. The Indians' costumes for *Tempe Restored* are based on those in Matthias Greuter's engraving of *Il Giuco del Ponte,* a mock battle fought by Pisan noblemen on the Ponte Santa Trinita in Florence on 28 October 1608.

Literature: P. Simpson and C. G. Bell: "Designs by Inigo Jones for Masques and Plays at Court," *Walpole Society,* XII (1923-24), no. 143; S. Orgel and R. Strong: *Inigo Jones—The Theatre of the Stuart Court,* London, 1973, no. 224.

Henry Gissey

French, 1621-1673.

Gissey was famous for his costume designs for the magnificent ballets, fêtes, and *carrousels* in the early years of the reign of Louis XIV. In 1660 the king appointed him draughtsman "de la Chambre et du Cabinet." He designed festival decorations for rooms at Versailles and also had a hand in the arrangement of firework displays. But he was known mainly for his ballet designs, and a poet of the period, Michel de Marolles, declared: "Jessé fut admirable / A former des dessins pour les jeux de ballet / Ses crayons achevés ne portaient rien de laid." ("Gissey was remarkable / in making designs for ballet festivals / his exquisite pencil drawings had nothing ugly about them.") Jean I Berain, the great ornamentalist of the late Louis XIV period, was trained in his studio.

Henry Gissey (Studio of)

100   Choreographic design: *Sauvages*
Pencil drawing. ca. 1660. 7 x 10½ inches (17.8 x 26.6 cm.).
London, Victoria & Albert Museum.

Figures such as these—described as savages, Americans or Indians, and dressed in skin-tight tights, feather skirts, and head-dresses—made not infrequent appearances in seventeenth-century French court ballets, even when their subjects were derived from classical mythology. In 1645, for instance, they had danced in *La Finta Pazza,* which was set in Homeric Greece! The drawing exhibited belongs to a group which, like many of Gissey's works, reveals the influence of Stefano della Bella.

Literature: Brian Reade: *Ballet Designs and Illustrations 1581-1940,* London, 1967, no. 32 (as French anonymous).

François Chauveau

French, 1613-1676.

Chauveau was born in Paris, studied painting under Laurent de la Hyre, and began his independent career as a miniaturist. But he soon turned his attention to print making and became one of the best and most productive copper-plate engravers in France. His work comprises at least 950 and possibly as many as 3,000 engravings, both original and reproductive, including portraits, religious and mythological subjects, title-pages, and other decorative devices for books. He was nominated a member of the Académie royale in 1663.

François Chauveau

103 *American Footmen and Muleteers*
Engraving, coloured and gilded by hand. 1670. 12 x 10¼ inches (30.4 x 26 cm.). Inscription: *Estafiers, Cheval de main et Palfreniers Ameriquains.* Paris, Bibliothèque Nationale, Cabinet des Estampes.

This print and [104, 105] record the exotic costumes worn in one of the most magnificent spectacles staged by Louis XIV—the *carrousel* or tournament held on 3, 4, and 5 June 1662 to celebrate the birth of the Dauphin. Nearly all the male members of the royal court seem to have taken part in it. Accompanied by numerous attendants and all dressed in fantastic costumes devised by Henry Gissey [100], they rode through the streets of Paris before taking part in the tournament held in the courtyard of the Louvre, which has been called ever since the Place du Carrousel. Louis XIV himself appeared as a Roman king, with attendants in fanciful antique attire. His younger brother, Monsieur, figured as a Persian king. The prince de Condé, the duc d'Enghien, and the duc de Guise were dressed as kings of Turkey, India, and America. The event was commemorated in a lavishly produced volume with text by Charles Perrault and engravings by François Chauveau and Israel Silvestre (1621-1691), made under the direction of Henry Gissey: *Courses de testes et de bagues faites par le Roy et par les princes et seigneurs de la Cour en l'année MDCLXII* (Paris, 1670). The engraving exhibited, which shows the American attendants of the duc de Guise, comes, like [104, 105], from one of the only two recorded hand-coloured copies of this work (the other is in the Bibliothèque Municipale de Versailles).

Literature: As for [105].

François Chauveau

104 *American Drummer and Trumpeter*
Engraving, coloured and gilded by hand. 1670. Signed: *F. C. deli et Sculp.* 12 x 10¼ inches (30.4 x 26 cm.). Inscription: *Timballier et Trompette Ameriquains.* Paris, Bibliothèque Nationale, Cabinet des Estampes.

The "American" drummers and trumpeters who attended the duc de Guise

Cinquiesme Quadrille

59

LE DVC DE GVYSE, ROY AMERIQVAIN.

L A cuirasse étoit de peau de Dragons, dont les deux testes se rencontrant sur les épau-
les, vomissoient les manches, dont celle de dessus étoit de brocart vert, rebrodé de
même que l'habit, & celle de dessous de toile d'argent qui descendoit jusque sur le poignet,
étoit liée d'un bracelet de grosses Emeraudes, & les queües de Dragons faisoient des lam-
brequins; le tout chargé d'une broderie de perles & de rubis, ainsi que les brodequins.

Sur la coeffure qui étoit un morion d'or, rampoit vn Dragon de même métal, qui sou-
tenoit deux cercles de brillans d'or, chargez de plumes vertes & blanches, surmontées de
trois bouquets de plumes en Aigrette, d'où sortoient trois masses de Heron, qui donnoient
quatre pieds de hauteur à cét habillement de teste, duquel une queüe de plumes encor descendoit sur le dos du Chevalier.

Son Cimeterre étoit d'or garny de pierreries, le fourreau à la Chinoise enrichy de même, il portoit une masse d'armès à aîles dorées, & découpées à jour, dont le bâton étoit
entouré d'un Serpent au naturel. Iii

at the *carrousel* in 1662 wore branches of coral on their heads. They had green satin jackets embroidered with silver shells, and their horses were capari-soned with tiger skins, bands of green velvet and cloth of gold, and many tassels.

Literature: As for [105].

François Chauveau

105 *The Duc de Guise as the American King*

Engraving, coloured and gilded by hand. 1670. 12 x 10¼ inches (30.4 x 26 cm.). Inscription: *Le Duc de Guyse, Roy Ameriquain.*
Paris, Bibliothèque Nationale, Cabinet des Estampes.

In this fantastic costume Henri II de Lorraine, duc de Guise, appeared in the *carrousel* of 1662. According to the written description, his cuirass was made of dragon skin, his sleeves of green brocade and cloth of silver em-broidered with pearls and rubies. His head-dress was composed of feathers rising from a gold helmet.

Literature: *Quarte siècles de la colonisa-tion française,* exhibition catalogue, Bib-liothèque Nationale, Paris, 1931, no. 157; R. A. Weigart: *Bibliothèque nationale, Cabinet des estampes. Inventaire du fonds français. Graveurs du XVIIe siècle,* Paris, 1939, vol. II, pp. 499-502; *Louis XIV Faste et Décors,* exhibition catalogue, Musée des Arts Décoratifs, Paris, 1960, no. 592.

VIII
Baroque America

By the mid-seventeenth century Europeans could look across the Atlantic to a New World which they had discovered and largely conquered. Every major power with the exception of Austria had colonies there—Spain and Portugal in the centre and south, England in New England, France in La Nouvelle France, the Netherlands in Nieuw Nederland. This nomenclature is significant, revealing more than merely pride of possession. The continent which had seemed at first to be just an inconvenient obstacle in a westerly route to Asia had now acquired its own importance and was completely assimilated into the European world view. The allegorical figure of America became as familiar an item in the European artist's repertory of motifs as the gods of classical mythology or personifications of virtues and vices.

The feather crowned and skirted Indian was to make her appearance in nearly all the great Baroque palaces and in many houses and even churches as well—painted on walls and ceilings, woven in tapestries, modelled in stucco, carved in stone, cast in bronze, embossed in silver, or engraved on glass—often forming part of an allegory of the four parts of the world. But magnificent and sumptuous though these Baroque schemes of decoration often are, decorative splendour was not their only or, indeed, their main purpose. They were expressions and symbols of European self-confidence: and the more grandiose were often devised according to complex intellectual programmes.

As we have already seen, personifications of the continents made their first appearance in festival decorations, and they continued to figure in them until late in the eighteenth century. Such allegorical allusions to the New World were, of course, particularly appropriate in festivals honoring members of the House of Hapsburg. Thus, when the Cardinal Infante Ferdinand, as governor of the Spanish Netherlands, made his ceremonial entry into Antwerp in 1635, Rubens gave a double significance to the archway erected outside the mint by giving it the form of the mountain of Potosí—a symbol both of Spain's wealth and her dominion over the New World [106, 107]. On these occasions America was more often represented simply as one of the four continents, which, as a group, alluded to the ruler's world-wide power or fame. Allegories of the continents might have the same significance, just as they had the same inconographical attributes, when they were painted on palace ceilings or carved to adorn a royal garden, as at Versailles.[1] Alternatively they might signify commerce with the distant regions of the world, as on the carved pediment of Amsterdam's town hall or in the very popular set of tapestries woven after designs by Ludwig van Schoor [123].

When they appeared in church, these personifications acquired a different meaning, signifying the universality of the Christian religion.[2] On the ceiling of the great Jesuit church of Sant Ignazio in Rome, Andrea Pozzo identified this general idea with the work of the Jesuit missions, showing the divine light passing from Christ to Saint Ignatius, through whom it is refracted to the four corners of the world [124]. In one corner the light strikes America, who casts down paganism with her arrow. Little altered, this figure soon reappeared in an entirely secular allegory by the Neapolitan Francesco Solimena [128]. Elsewhere, however, Solimena depicted the discovery of America as a triumph of Christianity [129].

In "The Church Militant" George Herbert wrote shortly before 1630:

Religion stands tiptoe in our land
Readie to passe to the American strand.

From the beginning the conquest of America had been undertaken in the name—if rarely in the spirit—of the Christian religion. In the seventeenth century, missionary activity was extended to North America, and the Jesuits in Canada attracted considerable attention, especially in France, through their widely diffused *Relations,* or annual reports, which contained gruesome descriptions of their martyrdoms [108]. However, it was the triumphs rather than the tribulations of the Church that were celebrated in Baroque art—the four continents welcoming the Gospel or revering the Holy Name—and, perhaps significantly, the Jesuit martyrs in Canada were not canonised until 1930. The first American saint was St. Rose of Lima, whose good works were devoted to the poor Indians of Peru.[3]

On a different level, Baroque allegories catered to the seventeenth-century taste for the exotic by gathering together the flora, fauna, and peoples of distant lands. In this way they are connected with the *Wunderkammer,* in which natural and artificial curiosities from all regions of the globe were assembled. One piece exhibited here—a rhinoceros horn carved into a cup—was in fact created for just such a collection [110]. And Jan van Kessel's extraordinary paintings provided a pictorial equivalent in miniature [109]. At the other end of the scale, the great series of Gobelins tapestries, *Les Indes,* seems to have been conceived as a grandiose and permanent record of the collection of Americana made by Count Maurits of Nassau and given to Louis XIV [114]. But the fact that these were woven shortly after France acquired Louisiana suggests that they may have also had, like so much of the decoration at Versailles, a political significance.

1. A variation on the usual pattern was made by Francis Bird in his monument to Queen Anne (1711-1712), where America was accompanied by Britannia, Hibernia, and Gallia. The monument was erected outside St. Paul's Cathedral, London, but replaced in 1885 by another without America. The figure of America from the original monument is in St. Paul's churchyard.

2. For several Flemish pulpits with figures of America, see B. Knipping: *Iconographie van der Contra Reformatie in den Nederlanden*, Hilversum, 1940, pp. 159-166.

3. There are paintings of the life of St. Rose by Lazzaro Baldi in Santa Maria sopra Minerva, Rome. But she was usually represented in portrait-type images simply as a mystic, without any reference to America. The archbishop of Lima who befriended her, Toribio Mogrobejo, and the Franciscan missionary Francis Solano, who worked in Peru for twenty years, were both canonised in 1726. A painting of St. Toribia baptising Indians by Sebastiano Conca is in the Vatican Museum.

Peter Paul Rubens

Flemish, 1577-1640.
Scholar, collector, antiquarian, and diplomat as well as painter, Rubens was one of the outstanding artists of the seventeenth century and in some ways a Northern Baroque counterpart to Giovanni Bernini in the south. Trained in Antwerp, he became a master of the Antwerp Guild of St. Luke in 1598. In 1600 he went to Italy, where he remained for eight years in the service of Vincenzo Gonzaga, duke of Mantua. In 1608 he returned to Antwerp and settled there for the rest of his life—his major commissions there include the decoration of the Jesuit Church, begun in 1620—but he also travelled widely both as a painter and as a diplomat. His great series of decorations for Marie de Médicis in the Luxembourg Palace in Paris (1621-25, now in the Louvre) were followed by the Banqueting House ceiling in Whitehall, London (1631-35) for Charles I, who knighted him in 1629, and finally the huge scheme of decoration commissioned by Philip IV of Spain for the Torre de la Parada near Madrid, on which he was working when he died.

Peter Paul Rubens

106 *The Front Face of the Arch of the Mint*

Etching. 1641-1642. Signed: *P.P.Rub. Inventa* and *C.Geu. epig. Illust. / T.a. Thul fe.* 18½ x 11½ inches (47 x 29.2 cm.). Inscription: *Arcus Monetalis, pars Anterior.*

107 *The Rear Face of the Arch of the Mint*

Etching. 1641-1642. Signed: *P.P.Rub. Invent* and *C.Geuar.epigrap. illustrab. T. a. Thulden fe.* 18⁷⁄₁₆ x 12¼ inches (46.8 x 31.2 cm.). Inscription: *Arcus Monetalis, pars Posterior.*
New York, The Metropolitan Museum of Art, The Elisha Whittlesey Fund, The Elisha Whittlesey Collection, 1951.

In November 1634 the city of Antwerp invited the Prince Cardinal Ferdinand of Austria, the new governor of the Spanish Netherlands, to make a solemn entry, and Rubens agreed to design the elaborate street decorations for it. Don Fernando of Austria (1609-1641) was the younger brother of Philip IV of Spain. He had been made a cardinal in 1619 and archbishop of Toledo in 1620. In 1631 it was announced that he would go to the Netherlands to assist the Archduke Albert's widow, the Infante Isabella, in the government and administration of the Netherlands. However, he did not reach Brussels until September 1634, almost a year after the death of the Infante Isabella.

Among the very elaborate, temporary decorations designed by Rubens for the Prince Cardinal's entry was an arch some 17 metres high and almost 11.5 metres wide, spanning the entrance to Sint-Michielsstraat (or Klosterstraat), erected by the men and officers of the Mint. No specifications, contracts, or other documents survive concerning it, and nothing is known about its construction, but two oil sketches for it by Rubens survive (Antwerp, Koninklijk Museum voor Schone Kunsten, nos. 316 and 317), as well as the etchings here exhibited of the front and rear faces of the arch as constructed. (Two studies of a river god in the Museum of Fine Arts, Boston, have been associated with one of the figures on the front side of the arch.)

The iconographic programme for the arch, as for all the decorations for the Prince Cardinal's entry, was devised by Rubens, together with his close friend Jan Caspar Geraerts or Gevartius (1593-1666), the scholar and humanist and *Griffier,* or clerk, of the city of Antwerp. They decided to celebrate the wealth of gold and silver acquired by Spain through the conquest of Peru, and Rubens assimilated the regular form of a triumphal arch into that of a rocky hill representing Potosí, "the silver mountain of Peru," at that time the richest silver mine in the world. His conception was probably inspired, as H. G. Evers has suggested, by the engraved title-page of Theodor de Bry's *America pars sexta,* Frankfurt, 1596 [67], which shows a similar mountain with miners at work.

On the front face of the arch, river gods occupy niches on either side of the portal. Rising from this lower stage are two columns ("the pillars of Hercules"), and from this level the arch becomes Potosí. The figures all refer to the expansion of the Spanish Empire and to the treasures of New Spain. At the summit is a cut-out of Jason and the Golden Fleece. Jason is about to remove the fleece from the tree, in the branches of which are brightly coloured parrots and the legend PRETIUM NON VILE LABORUM (the reward of his labour is not worthless). Gevartius called the Conquistadors the "new Jasons and Argonauts." The importance of Spanish navigation in the conquest of the New World is represented by *Felicitas* (an allusion to a happy voyage), with a ship in one hand. The rabbit (*cuniculus*) below *Felicitas* both symbolises the mines of Peru and *Hispania,* of whom it was an attribute. (In the sketch Rubens depicted *Hispania* here also, but later transferred her to the rear face of the arch.) Of the remaining figures, those on the left—the side of the sun, bathed in

sunshine—represent the region of gold, while those on the right—the side of the moon, bathed in moonlight—represent the region of silver. *Moneta,* the goddess of coinage and money, is enthroned in a niche immediately above the portal, wearing a diadem and holding in one hand a horn of plenty and in the other a caduceus, a purse, and a balance. These personifications derive from Roman imperial coinage, and the symbolism is continued by festoons of coins suspended on either side of the arch, those on the left of gold, those on the right of silver. Above *Moneta* is a medallion bearing a profile of King Philip IV, with an inscription referring to him as *locupletatur orbis terrarum.* The two freestanding composite columns on high plinths are emblems (pillars of Hercules) of Charles V, in whose name Mexico and Peru were conquered, and also symbolise the vast extent and vast wealth of Spain. Guarded by ferocious lions, the left-hand column supports the golden disk of the sun and the right-hand the silver crescent of the moon. The banderoles entwined about them bear legends that amplify Charles V's motto, *plus ultra (ultra anni solisque vias*—beyond the paths of the year and the sun). The coats of arms beneath the column are of Philip IV and the Cardinal Infante Ferdinand. The river gods on either side represent two of the streams that flow through lands rich in gold and silver—on the left Peruvius (which, according to José de Acosta, gave its name to the land of Peru) and, opposite, the Rio de la Plata, the river of silver.

The rear or south face of the arch similarly represents Potosí, with two herms guarding the portal. The figure subjects allude to the exportation of precious metals from the New World to the Old. At the top there is a cut-out of Hercules in the Garden of Hesperides. While Hercules clubs the dragon

to death, *Hispania* plucks the golden apples from the tree. (The pose of Hercules virtually repeats that of Hercules crushing Discord in the Banqueting House ceiling in London.) Elsewhere on this face of the arch, Rubens abandoned allegory in favour of more realistic depictions of the mines of Potosí. On the left, two workmen strike at the rock with picks in search of silver, veins of which were said to lie just below the surface. On the right, two men, one with a candle, emerge from the mouth of a mine with loads of ore on their backs. (Similar scenes are depicted on the engraved title-page of the sixth volume of Theodor de Bry's *America,* Frankfurt, 1596.) In the niche over the portal is Vulcan, forging a golden thunderbolt, with the legend *Aurum potentis ictu Fulmina* (gold is more powerful than the lightning). Above Vulcan's smithy is a large medallion with three figures personifying the three metals of Roman coinage, *Aurum, Argentum,* and *Aes,* as they are represented on imperial coins. The smaller coins hung on ribbons to the right and left are specimens of moneys struck at the Royal Mint. The niches at the base, which on the other facade are occupied by river gods, here contain implements for the coining of money. Above the niches are two river gods, from whose urns "the streams of gold-producing Peru" spill over the stones below. One river god—Condorillo—holds a cornucopia as a symbol of abundance; the other—Marañon, a branch of the Amazon—holds a rudder.

The etchings are by Theodor van Thulden (1606-1669), who was a pupil of Rubens and worked as an assistant on the decorations for the entry of the Cardinal Infante Ferdinand. He became a painter as well as an engraver and print maker. The etchings first appeared in Jan Casper Geraerts: *Pompa Introitus . . .,* Antwerp, 1641-42.

Literature: *Triumphael Incomst vander Doorluchtichsten Prince Cardinal Ferdinandus Infant van Hisp. binnen Antwerpen den 17 April 1635*, Antwerp, 1635, fols. E2 verso and E3 verso; *Corte Wtlegginghen van alle de Triumph-wercken ghemaeckt ende ghestelt ter eeren . . .*, Antwerp, 1635, fol. E2 verso, fol. E3 recto; Jan Casper Geraerts, *Pompa Introitus*, Antwerp, 1641-42, pp. 151-154, 155-158; C. G. Voorhem Schneevoeght, *Catalogue des estampes gravées d'aprés P. P. Rubens*, Haarlem, 1873, p. 226, nos. 27, 35; M. Rooses, *L'Oeuvre de P. P. Rubens, histoire et description de ses tableaux et dessins*, Antwerp, 1886-92, vol. III, pp. 320-322, no. 786, 787; I. von Roeder Baumbach, *Versieringen bij' Blijde Inkomsten gebruikt in de Zuidelijke Nederlanden gedurende de 16e en 17e Eeuw*, Antwerp-Utrecht, 1943, pp. 70, 167; H. G. Evers, *Peter Paul Rubens*, Munich, 1942, pp. 380-383; H. G. Evers, *Rubens und sein Werk*, Brussels, 1943, p. 183; L. van Puyvelde, *De Blijde Intrede van Ferdinand van Oostenrijk te Antwerpen in 1635 en Rubens' Tussenkomst*, Standen en Landen XVI, 1958, pp. 31, 32; J. R. Martin: *The Decorations for the Pompa Introitus Ferdinandi (Corpus Rubenianum Ludwig Burchard, Part XVI)*, Brussels, 1972, pp. 189-200; E. McGrath: "Rubens' Arch of the Mint" in *Journal of the Warburg and Courtauld Institutes*, vol. XXXVII (1974), pp. 191-217.

Grégoire Huret

French, 1606-1670.

A draughtsman and engraver, born and trained in Lyon, Huret worked in Paris from 1635 and was appointed "dessinateur et graveur ordinaire de la maison du Roi" in 1669. His numerous prints, usually engraved after his own designs, comprise portraits, mythological subjects, and allegories, including a set of the continents. But he is best known for his prints of religious subjects.

Grégoire Huret

108 *Jesuits Martyred by the Iroquois*
Engraving. 1664. 13 x 17½ inches (33 x 44.3 cm.).
Paris, Bibliothèque Nationale.

This print was published as an illustration to François de Creux: *Historiae Canadensis* (Paris, 1664, opposite p. 480), which provided an account of missionary activity in Canada, 1625-58, based on the Jesuit *Relations*, which were issued by the same publishing house. It depicts the death of ten men, each of whom is marked with a number: (1) Anne de Noüe de Champagne, frozen to death while on his way to administer the sacrament to French soldiers, 1646; (2) Isaac Jogues, killed by a hatchet blow on the head at Ossernenon, 1646; (3 and 4) his two companions, murdered at the same time; (5) Antoine Daniel, killed at the St. Joseph Mission, 1648; (6) Jean de Brébeuf, killed by the Iroquois, 1649; (7) Gabriel Lalemant, killed by the Iroquois, 1649; (8) Charles Garnier, killed by the Iroquois, 1649; (9) Noël Chabanel, killed by an apostate, 1649; (10) Joseph Onahare, a young Algonquin tortured to death for refusing to abandon Christianity, 1650. Six of these men were canonised in 1930. A large painting derived from the print is in the Hôtel-Dieu, Quebec (see J. Russell-Harper: *Painting in Canada*, Toronto, 1966, pl. 2). A group of paintings by Goya has been associated with the martyrdoms of Jean de Brébeuf and Gabriel Lalemant [290, 291].

Literature: R. Strong: *A Pageant of Canada*, exhibition catalogue, National Gallery of Canada, Ottawa, 1967, no. 46.

Jan van Kessel the Elder
Flemish, 1626-1679.
Van Kessel was born in Antwerp, the son of a portrait painter, Hieronymus van Kessel, and, through his mother, grandson of Jan Breughel the Elder. After being trained under the genre painter Simon de Vos and possibly his uncle Jan Breughel the Younger, he became a master of the Antwerp painters' guild in 1644-45. He was mainly a meticulously accurate painter of flowers, insects, and animals. But his work is usually decorative in intention and often relieved by touches of fantasy, e.g. his use of snakes and caterpillars wriggling to form the letters of his name. He often depicted exotic flora and fauna, sometimes combining them with fabulous beasts.

Jan van Kessel the Elder

109 *America*

Oil on copper. Signed and dated: *Jan van Kessel fecit 1666.* 19⅛ x 26⅝ inches (48.5 x 67.5 cm.). Provenance: Probably in the Düsseldorf Gallery ca. 1716; from 1780 in the Mannheim Gallery, with which it was transferred to the collection of the Elector of Bavaria in Munich, 1799.
Munich, Bayerische Staatsgemälde-sammlungen.
(Exhibited in Washington only.)

This painting is inscribed on its original frame *Parajba en Brasil,* but seems to have been conceived as an evocation of a seventeenth-century *Wunderkammer,* or collection of natural and artificial curiosities. It forms part of a series of paintings in which each of the four continents is represented by a panel of this size surrounded by sixteen small landscapes crowded with birds, beasts, and reptiles associated with the region. The American landscapes thus include such birds as the macaw, turkey, and toucan, monstrous bats, snakes, monkeys, and alligators. But they are joined by many Old World beasts—elephants, giraffes, zebras, and, for good measure, a unicorn charging across the pampas near Buenos Aires. In the central panel, exhibited here, a personification of America is seated on the floor beside a group of gold weights as emblems of mineral riches. On the wall there are paintings of Tapuya Indians, including a female cannibal with a human foot sticking out of her basket, derived from paintings by Albert Eckhout (see colour transparencies, gallery 5). Most of the wild-life is American and derived from recent books on natural history, notably that by Piso and Marcgrave [78] and perhaps also J. E. Nierembergius: *Historia Naturae,* Antwerp, 1635—armadillo, agouti, ant-eater, iguana, curassow, toucan, several types of fish, and some outsize butterflies and beetles. But some elements in the painting come from the "other" Indies—the figures dancing through the door, the statues of Brahmins, the painted scenes of suttee, and the Japanese armour in the corner are all Far Eastern, partly or largely derived from J. H. van Linschoten: *Itinerario Voyage ofte Schipvaert naar Oost ofte Portugaels Indien 1579-1592,* Amsterdam, 1596. Thus, while each item is represented with the fidelity demanded of naturalists of the time, the effect is one of fantasy and generalised exoticism.

The inventory of the possessions of an Antwerp silversmith, Jan Gillis, drawn up in 1681 mentions a set of *Continents* painted by van Kessel in collaboration with Erasmus Quellinus (1607-1678). It cannot be established whether this is identical with the set now in Munich. Several other small landscapes by van Kessel very similar to those in the Munich group are in the Prado, Madrid, and he is known to have painted at least one other set of the central panels as well. But it seems probable that Quellinus, who is known to have collaborated with van Kessel on other occasions, was responsible for the human figures in the panel exhibited.

Literature: F. J. van Branden: *Geschiedenis der Antwerpsche Schilderschool,* Antwerp, 1883, p. 1100; K. Zoege von Manteuffel in *Monatshefte für Kunstwissenschaft,* XIV (1921), p. 42; E. Greindl: *Les peintres flamands de nature morte au XVIIème siècle,* Paris-Brussels, 1956, p. 128; E. Köllmann, K.-A. Wirth et al. in *Reallexikon zur deutschen Kunstgeschichte,* vol. V, Stuttgart, 1967, cols. 1141, 1163; Ulla Krempel: *Jan van Kessel d.A. 1626-1679—die vier Erdteile,* exhibition catalogue, Alte Pinakothek, Munich, 1973.

110 *Covered Cup*

Germany (Augsburg). Carved rhinoceros horn with a silver gilt mount. ca. 1660-1668. Marked on the mount with the Augsburg city hall-mark and *HL* in monogram for the unidentified goldsmith. Height 22 7/8 inches (58 cm.). Provenance: Acquired for the Kunstkammer of the Elector of Saxony, 1668.
Dresden, Grünes Gewölbe.

In a collection of the type called a *Kunstkammer* or *Wunderkammer,* such an object as a carved rhinoceros horn had a double significance: as a curiosity of nature and as an example of ingenious artistry. The piece exhibited here—from one of the largest and most impressive of all *Kunstkammer,* that of the Electors of Saxony in Dresden—was given still stronger appeal by the exotic subject-matter with which it was decorated. The horn is carved in the form of two embracing American Indians with feather skirts and head-dresses serving as the stem of the cup, which is ornamented with richly dressed personifications of the four continents. The anonymous Augsburg goldsmith responsible for the mount embossed the base with a rhinoceros (derived from Dürer's famous woodcut) and an elephant battling with a crocodile and dragon. But he crowned the work with a European figure of Eros, perhaps intending to suggest that love rules mankind in all four parts of the world, thus transforming the object into a Baroque *concetto* of a type popular with poets and artists.

Literature: M. Rosenberg: *Der Goldschmiede Merkzeichen,* Frankfurt-am-Main, 1922, vol. I, p. 138; J. L. Sponsel: *Das Grüne Gewölbe zu Dresden,* Leipzig, 1932, vol. IV, p. 154; Sylvia Rathke-Köhl: *Geschichte des Augsburger Goldschmiedegewerbes,* Augsburg, 1964, pp. 101, 165; E. Köllmann, K.-A. Wirth et al. in *Reallexikon zur deutschen Kunstgeschichte,* vol. V, col. 1183.

Rintie Jans

Dutch, fl. 1646-1673.

Jans was admitted to the guild of silversmiths in Leeuwarden (Friesland) in 1646, served as its assayer in 1655 and 1663, and was elected alderman in 1665. His richly wrought silver with much figurative decoration and a modicum of auricular motifs is among the best made in the Netherlands in the mid-seventeenth century.

Rintie Jans

111 *Dish*

Silver, embossed. ca. 1670. Stamped with the master's mark of Rintie Jans (a beaker). Diameter 16⅚ inches (41.3 cm.). Provenance: The Popta Foundation.
Leeuwarden, Fries Museum.

The dish is embossed with allegories of the four continents, in which the main figures are derived from prints after Jan Sadeler the Elder, which seem to have been particularly popular with metal-workers. Rintie Jans, however, transformed Sadeler's female personifi-

cations into men and made various minor additions—in the case of America he added the parrots and monkeys. A similar dish by Rintie Jans dated 1670 is in the collection of B. A. Ph. Baron van Harinxma thoe Slooten.

Literature: *Oude Kunst,* 1920-21, p. 97; *De Vrije Fries,* XXVIII (1928), p. 296; *Oude Kunst,* 1929-30, pp. 184-191; E. Voet, Jr.: *Merken van Friesche goud- en zilversmeden,* The Hague, 1932, p. 149; *De Vrije Fries,* XXXIX (1948), p. 9; J. W. Fredericks: *Dutch Silver,* The Hague, 1952, vol. I, pp. 278-279; Erich Köllmann, Karl August Wirth et al. in *Reallexikon zur deutschen Kunstgeschichte,* vol. V, col. 1180; *Catalogus Fries Zilver van het Fries Museum,* Leeuwarden, 1968, p. 64.

112 *Tankard*

Nuremberg, Germany. Silver, partly gilt. 1650-1700. Stamped with an N within a circle (Nuremberg city mark, 1650-1700) and an unidentified maker's mark of a windmill within a shaped reserve (Rosenberg, vol. III, no. 4258). Height 11 inches (27.9 cm.). Provenance: James Hazen Hyde, New York, 1959.
New York, The Metropolitan Museum of Art, Gift of the Estate of James Hazen Hyde, 1959.

The image of America on this tankard seems to have been derived from the popular de Vos allegory [88], with the armadillo replaced by an alligator, as became usual in the seventeenth century.

Adolf Gaap

German, d. 1695.
Gaap belonged to a large family of
Augsburg goldsmiths, and his mark is
recorded on several rich pieces of secular plate.

Adolf Gaap

113 *Dish*

Silver and silver-gilt. Signed *Gaap 1689*
with the pineapple mark for Augsburg
and *A G*. Oval, 28⅜ x 24¹³⁄₁₆ inches
(71.9 x 63 cm.). Provenance: James
Hazen Hyde.
New York, Cooper-Hewitt Museum of
Design, Smithsonian Institution, Gift
of the Trustees of the Estate of James
Hazen Hyde.

The four reliefs of the continents on
the border of this dish are derived from
Stefano della Bella's playing cards of
1646 [93]. Asia, turbaned, is in a chariot drawn by two elephants; Europe,
crowned, is drawn by horses; Africa,
with feather head-dress and parasol, is
drawn by lions; and America, in
feather head-dress and tunic, is drawn
by armadillos. The centre relief of
Alexander and Darius, inscribed *Alexander beweiint den Todt des Königs
Darius*, is after an etching of 1656 by
Hans Ulrich Frank.

Literature: *The Four Continents from the
Collection of James Hazen Hyde*, exhibi-
tion catalogue, Cooper Union Museum,
New York, 1961, no. 91.

Gobelins Tapestry Factory, after Albert Eckhout, Frans Post, and others

114 *Les Indes: The Elephant and the Light Bay Horse*

France (Paris). Tapestry of dyed wool and dyed silk. 1690. 185 x 191 inches (470 x 485 cm.). Provenance: Garde Meuble de la Couronne.
Paris, Mobilier National.

This is one of a set of eight panels woven at the Gobelins factory and entitled *Les Indes.* They are all derived from paintings commissioned from Albert Eckhout and Frans Post by Count Maurits of Nassau-Siegen, who presented them to Louis XIV in 1678, together with a collection of stuffed birds and various Brazilian artifacts. Count Maurits remarked of the paintings that they represented "tout le Bresil," its inhabitants, animals, birds, fishes, fruits, and plants, all life-size, and that they might form the basis for a series of tapestries to decorate a large room or gallery "which would be a very rare thing to be found nowhere else in the world." The whole gift was put on show in the Louvre in the late summer of 1679, was inspected by the king and other members of the royal family, and is said to have caused quite a stir. But it was not until 1687 that M. de la Chapelle, controller of the *Bâtiments du Roi* at the Gobelins, proposed to make use of the paintings for tapestries.

"Les Sieurs Houasse, Bonnemer et Baptiste"—i.e. René-Antoine Houasse (1644-1710), François Bonnemer (1638-1689), and Jean-Baptiste Monnoyer (1636-1699)—were ordered to "raccomoder les tableaux." This phrase has been interpreted to mean that the paintings by Eckhout and Post were merely restored and used as cartoons for the tapestries. But, as M. Benisovich points out, it is more probable that artists of such repute would have been employed to make models for cartoons based on the works of Eckhout and Post but presented in greater conformity with artistic taste of the Louis XIV period. The tapestries themselves also suggest this. For not only do they show a command of baroque composition absent from known paintings by Eckhout and Post, but they combine the flora and fauna of Brazil with those of Africa. Count Maurits, on his way to Brazil in 1636, stopped for a short while in Angola, where his artists made drawings and paintings of the country and its inhabitants (e.g. full-length portraits of Africans by Eckhout in the National Museum, Copenhagen). Some of these were presumably included in the gift to Louis XIV, and the artists employed by the Gobelins presumably used them indiscriminately, combining them with those of Brazilian scenes and subjects to create an evocation of tropical exoticism of unparalleled splendour. Eight sets of the tapestries were woven (in two different sizes) between 1687 and 1730. In 1692-93 slight alterations were made to the cartoons by A.-F. Desportes, who was to be commissioned in 1735 to provide a new and larger series retaining many of the original features and known as *Les Nouvelles Indes* [133].

The panel exhibited incorporates an elephant from Africa and a peacock from Asia. The horse is of a type imported into America by European settlers. But most of the other fauna is South American, such as the ant-eater, tapir, toucan, and the snake coiled round a branch of the cashew tree. The landscape background recalls a picture by Frans Post in the Louvre, while the black woman on the left and the heap of exotic fruits are reminiscent of paintings by Eckhout [74, 75].

Literature: M. Fénaille: *Etat général des tapisseries de manufacture de Gobelins,* Paris, 1903, vol. II, p. 375; H. Göbel: *Die Wandteppiche und ihre Manufacturen in Frankreich, Italien, Spanien und Portugal,* Leipzig, 1928, vol. II, i, pp. 145-147; M. Benisovich: "The History of the Tentures des Indes" in *The Burlington Magazine,* LXXXIII (1943), pp. 216-225; M. Jarry: "Dessins et études provenant de l'atelier de Desportes concernant la tenture des Indes" in *Bulletin de la Société de l'histoire de l'art français,* 1957, pp. 39-45; *idem:* "Les 'Indes' série triomphale de l'exotisme" in *Connaissance des Arts,* May, 1962, pp. 62-69; J. de Sousa Leão: "Du nouveau sur les tableaux du Brésil offerts à Louis XIV" in *Gazette des Beaux Arts,* LVII (1961), pp. 95-104; *Les Gobelins,* exhibition catalogue, Mobilier National, Paris, 1966, no. 12.

Alexandre-François Desportes

French, 1661-1743.

The leading French animal painter of the generation before Jean-Baptiste Oudry, Alexandre-François Desportes was born at Champigneulles (Meurthe-et-Moselle) and went at the age of twelve to Paris, where he studied under a Flemish animal painter and probably saw works by Jan Weenix. In 1692-93 he was employed at the Gobelins to repair the cartoons from which the tapestries *Les Indes* [114] were woven. He went to Warsaw early in 1695, returning to Paris in 1696. In 1699 he became a member of the Académie and was granted a royal pension and accommodation in the Louvre. During the following years he was extensively employed by the Crown and from 1717 provided cartoons for the Savonnerie carpet factory and the Gobelins tapestry factory [133]. He was very prolific, specialising in animal subjects (still lifes and hunting scenes) of great virtuosity, and also painting portraits.

Alexandre-François Desportes

115 *Tapir*

Oil on paper. ca. 1692. 6½ x 9¼ inches (16.5 x 23.5 cm.).

116 *Llama*

Oil on paper. 11¼ x 13 inches (28.5 x 33 cm.).

117 *Yucca plant*

Pencil, charcoal and white on colored paper. 19⅞ x 11⅝ inches (50.5 x 29.5 cm.).

Provenance: Inherited from the painter by his son Nicolas Desportes, who sold them to the Direction des Bâtiments du Roi, 1784.
Sèvres, Manufacture Nationale de Sèvres.

The tapir and the llama were among the South American animals which most fascinated Europeans from the sixteenth century onwards. In the eighteenth century their dissimilarity from animals of the Old World was stressed by Buffon, who cited them as

examples of the inferiority of American nature. Believing the tapir to be the largest of American mammals, he scornfully referred to it as "this elephant of the New World" which is the size "of a six month calf or a very small mule." The llama he compared unfavourably with the camel.

American plants were, on the other hand, admired in Europe mainly on account of their diversity from those of the Old World. The Yuccas are an exclusively American genus, of which one species *(Yucca gloriosa)* was introduced into Europe in the mid-sixteenth century. The plant in Desportes's painting seems to be *Yucca recurvifolia,* which is not known to have been grown in Europe until the late eighteenth century.

The sketches exhibited were almost certainly not made from living specimens of the animals but either from the tapestry cartoons of *Les Indes* [114] or the paintings by Eckhout and Post on which they were based. It seems probable that Desportes painted them when he was employed to repair the

cartoons in 1692, though they may alternatively date from the late 1730s, when he provided the cartoons for *Les Nouvelles Indes* [133].

Literature: L. Hourticq: "L'atelier de François Desportes" in *Gazette des Beaux Arts,* 5ᵉ période, II (1920), pp. 117-136; M. Jarry: "Dessins et études provenant de l'atelier de Desportes concernant la tenture des Indes" in *Bulletin de la Société de l'histoire de l'art français,* 1957, pp. 39-45; *idem:* "Les Indes. Série triomphale de l'exotisme" in *Connaissance des Arts,* 1959, pp. 62-69.

Johannes Sayller

German, 1597-1668.
Sayller was a clock- and watchmaker working from ca. 1617 in Ulm, for whose city council he made his masterpiece, a rolling ball clock completed in 1626 (now lost). In 1646 he became a master of the guild, and in 1650 the city presented three of his time-pieces to the Swedish general Douglas. A pocket watch by him is in the Kunsthistorisches Museum in Vienna and another is in the Schatzkammer of the Residenz in Munich.

118 *Table Clock*

Brass, silver, and steel. ca. 1650-1660. Movement signed: *Johann Sayller Ulm.* 4½ inches (11.4 cm.) high, 5½ inches (14 cm.) square. Provenance: James Hazen Hyde, New York. New York, The Brooklyn Museum, Bequest of James Hazen Hyde.

The sides of the clock are decorated with allegories of the continents, that of America including a hammock, monkey, parrot, and alligator as well as a man, woman, and child. The man holds in his hand a decorated club of the type illustrated by Hans Staden [60].

The case of this clock, with the exception of the inserted plaques, appears identical to that of another Sayller table clock formerly in the Strause

Collection. The scroll-and-masque feet and cherub's head spandrels of the exhibited clock repeat those features found on the Strause clock, and the feet also appear, with minor modifications, on a *Türmchenuhr* (table clock in the form of a tower) by Sayller in the Württemburgisches Landesmuseum in Stuttgart.

The movement of the Brooklyn clock, ornamented with delicate piercing and engraving, incorporates a calendar and alarm and also shows the phases and age of the moon.

Literature: U. Thieme and F. Becker, *Allgemeines Lexikon der Bildenden Künstler,* vol. XXIX, p. 517; *Catalogue— The Henry P. Strause Collection of Clocks,* Richmond, Virginia, 1937, pp. 12-13; G. H. Baillie, *Watchmakers and Clockmakers of the World,* third edition; Alfred Leiter and Dr. Alma Helfrich-Dörner, *Die Uhr— Zeitmesser und Schmuck in fünf Jahrhunderten,* Korwestheim, 1967, pp. 124-125.

119 *Coconut Cup*

England or the Netherlands. Carved coconut in silver mount. ca. 1675-1700. Height 7½ inches (19 cm.). Mr. and Mrs. Warren H. Corning Collection.

The coconut is carved with three scenes of life in tropical America—two stark naked Indians, one carrying a club, in a jungly landscape; a man and woman carrying fish on a sea-shore; and an Indian shooting from behind a palm-tree at a fully dressed European.

The costume of the European is mid-seventeenth century, but the carving seems to have been executed slightly later. The silver mount is un-marked, but the cover is engraved on the outside with a coat of arms and crest, and on the inside with the inscription: *George Lewis Tiverton Feby 1st 1760.* Coconuts are known to have been mounted in silver to serve as cups as early as the thirteenth century, and very frequently from the fifteenth to the late seventeenth century.

120 *Stove Tile of America*

Switzerland or Austria. Green glazed earthenware. Late seventeenth century. 11½ x 9⁷⁄₁₆ inches (29.2 x 23.9 cm.). Provenance: James Hazen Hyde.

New York, Cooper-Hewitt Museum of Design, Smithsonian Institution, Gift of the Trustees of the Estate of James Hazen Hyde.

Literature: *The Four Continents from the Collection of James Hazen Hyde,* exhibition catalogue, The Cooper Union Museum, no. 72.

121 *Tile with Circular Medallion of America*

Spain, Talavera de la Reyna Pottery. Tin-glazed earthenware with underglaze painting in blue. Eighteenth century. 10⁹⁄₁₆ x 10⁷⁄₁₆ inches (26.7 x 26.5 cm.). Provenance: James Hazen Hyde. New York, Cooper-Hewitt Museum of Design, Smithsonian Institution, Gift of the Trustees of the Estate of James Hazen Hyde.

Literature: *The Four Continents from the Collection of James Hazen Hyde,* exhibition catalogue, The Cooper Union Museum, no. 78.

This allegory of America is derived from an engraving by Theodor de Bry after Jacques Le Moyne de Morgues and published as plate 37 in his *Brevis Narratio Eorum Quae in Florida Americae Provincia Gallis Acciderunt,* Frankfurt, 1591. The tile forms part of a set decorated with allegories of the four continents in the Cooper-Hewitt Museum of Design.

122 *Standing Cup with Figures of the Four Continents*

Silesia. Glass, cut and engraved. Early eighteenth century. Height 8¼ inches (20.9 cm.). Provenance: James Hazen Hyde.
New York, Cooper-Hewitt Museum of Design, Smithsonian Institution, Gift of the Trustees of the Estate of James Hazen Hyde.

Asia is shown with arrow and bow, attended by a lion; Europe is seated on a bull and holds a cornucopia and a banner with the coats of arms of the House of Hapsburg and the eight Electors; Africa is seated on a crocodile and wears a large flat hat; America wears a feather skirt and head-dress, carries an arrow and coral, and is attended by an elephant.

Literature: *The Four Continents from the Collection of James Hazen Hyde,* exhibition catalogue, The Cooper Union Museum, no. 83.

Ludwig van Schoor

Flemish, ca. 1675-after 1726.
Ludwig van Schoor is known only as the painter of cartoons for the tapestry weavers in Antwerp and Brussels: his cartoons included mythological subjects, a series depicting the life of Alexander, and sets of months and continents.

Albert Auwercx Tapestry Factory, Brussels, after Ludwig van Schoor

123 *America*

Tapestry of dyed wool, dyed silk, and metallic yarns. ca. 1700. Signed: *L. van Schoor inv. et pinx.* 151½ x 231 inches (384.8 x 586.7 cm.). Provenance: James Hazen Hyde.
Washington, D.C., National Gallery of Art, Gift of James Hazen Hyde, 1959.

The tapestry was woven in the factory of Albert Auwercx, a member of a family of weavers active in Brussels, and formed part of a set of four continents. Of the very many tapestries of the continents woven in Europe, this set, designed by Ludwig van Schoor, was among the most popular. The memorandum book of the Antwerp merchant Nicolaes Naulaerts, who owned the original cartoons, reveals that he sold fifty-eight sets between 1699 and 1709. Other examples of the America panel are at Holkham Hall, Norfolk, and at Mamhead, Devonshire. Tapestries from the same cartoons were later woven in the factory of Josse de Vos. The designs were imitated, with variations, in the factories of Alexander Baerts in Amsterdam and at Soho in England (information from the Marillier tapestry archive, Victoria and Albert Museum, London).

Comparison of the panel exhibited with earlier allegorical representations of America reveals some significant modifications—references to cannibal-

ism, previously rather prominent, are
omitted altogether, nudity is covered,
and the emphasis is placed on the prodigious riches of the New World (with
ships to carry it to Europe!). American
wild-life is represented by an alligator,
parrot, large tortoise, snake, and shells.
The tapestry exhibited in Cleveland
and Paris is a slightly smaller version
(133 x 197½ inches, 337 x 500 cm.)
loaned by the National Gallery of Art,
Gift of the Honourable Lewis Einstein,
1950.

Literature: James Hazen Hyde: "L'Iconographie des quartre parties du monde dans
les tapisseries" in *Gazette des Beaux Arts*,
S.5e x (1924), pp. 253-272.

Andrea Pozzo

Italian, 1642-1709.

Erroneously known as "Padre Pozzo," Andrea Pozzo was a lay brother, who entered the Jesuit order in 1665. Both architect and painter, he is famous for his illusionistic ceiling paintings, notably those in S. Ignazio, Rome (see below), but also those in the Chiesa della Missione, Mondovi, and the Palais Liechtenstein, Vienna. He worked in Rome from 1681 until 1702, when he settled in Vienna. His book *Perspectivum pictorum et architectorum,* Rome, 1693-1702, was influential and frequently reprinted.

Andrea Pozzo

124 *Allegory of the Missionary Work of the Jesuit Order*

Oil on canvas. 1688. 66⅝₆ x 130¹¹⁄₁₆ inches (168 x 331 cm.). Provenance: Acquired from the Collegio Romano, 1895.

Rome, Galleria Nazionale.

This is the preliminary model for one of the most prominent and probably the most influential of religious allegories of the four continents, painted on the ceiling of the church of S. Ignazio, Rome, and completed in 1694. Nowhere else is Pozzo's extreme virtuosity in illusionistic ceiling painting better displayed than here. For the programme he was inspired by a text from the Gospel according to St. Luke: "I am come to send fire on the earth; and what will I if it be already kindled?" He adapted this reference to St. Ignatius, who had been "most zealous to propogate the Catholic Religion and the light of the Gospel throughout the World." Thus, he wrote, in the centre of the ceiling, he "painted the figure of Jesus, who sends forth a ray of light to the most distant hearts of the four parts of the world." The continents are represented by personifications, including America as a feather-crowned bare-bosomed Indian woman, who directs her arrow at the falling figures of paganism.

When Pozzo was commissioned to paint the ceiling in 1688, he was required to provide, for the approval of "the leading painters" and the general of the Jesuit Order, a large *modello,* sixteen by eight palms, which would demonstrate "that the beauty of the figures and the architecture could be appreciated not from only one place but from all view-points" (i.e. unlike Pozzo's paintings in a corridor at S. Ignazio, which were grotesquely distorted when seen from the wrong end). In painting the vast ceiling, he maintained the general design of the *modello* but altered many details. So far as the allegory of America is concerned, his only changes were to omit the feather crown from the head of one of the falling figures and insert a macaw perching just above the Indian woman.

Personifications of the continents had previously appeared in allegories of the Jesuit missions. They are shown with St. Ignatius in the frontispiece by Jan Miel and Cornelis Bloemart to Daniello Bertoli's history of the Order (1653). Pozzo incorporated them in his fresco of the *Apotheosis of St. Francis Xavier* in the Jesuit Chiesa della Missione at Mondovi in 1679. But the iconographical programme of the S. Ignazio ceiling is far more complex and its authorship remains a mystery. For, although Pozzo claimed to have originated it, the scheme is likely to have been worked out in detail by a theologian.

Literature: L. Pascoli: *Vite de'pittori, scultori, ed architetti moderni,* Rome, 1730, vol. II, p. 258; H. Voss: *Die Malerei des Barock in Rom,* Berlin, 1924, p. 583; F. Hermanin: *Catalogo della R. Galleria d'Arte Antica nel Palazzo Corsini a Roma,* Bologna, 1924, p. 68; E. K. Waterhouse:

Baroque Painting in Rome, London, 1937, p. 87; *Il Seicento Europeo,* exhibition catalogue, Palazzo delle Esposizione, Rome, 1856-57, no. 231; F. Haskell: *Patrons and Painters,* London, 1963, p. 90; P. Wilberg-Vignau: *Andrea Pozzos Deckenfresko in S. Ignazio,* Munich, 1970, pp. 3, 18-20, 35; B. Kerber: *Andrea Pozzo,* Berlin-New York, 1971, pp. 70-74.

Godfried Maes

Flemish, 1649-1700.
A history painter and etcher born in Antwerp, Maes is known mainly for his pictures of religious subjects. His etchings include both original works and prints after other artists. He also provided designs for book illustrations.

Godfried Maes

125 *America*
Pen and black ink with grey wash, ca. 1700. 10½ x 8⅛ inches (26.6 x 20.6 cm.). Inscription: *G.Maes in: et. d: America chauchet* (partly erased) *fiecit 1710.* Provenance: James Hazen Hyde, 1929.
New York, The Metropolitan Museum of Art, Gift of the Estate of James Hazen Hyde, 1959.

This is one of a set of designs for tapestries of the four parts of the world, woven, with variations, by Jan van der Beurcht at Antwerp. The inscription was probably added to the drawing, after Maes died, by an artist called

"Chauchet" (otherwise unrecorded), who was preparing to make a print from it—though no such print is known.

Literature: Z.v M. in U. Thieme and F. Becker: *Künstler Lexikon,* vol. XXIII, Leipzig, 1929, p. 545; *Quatre Siècles de Colonisation Francaise,* exhibition catalogue, Bibliothèque Nationale, Paris, 1931, no. 416.

Jan Weenix

Dutch, 1640-1719.
Weenix was a still-life and animal painter, the son of Jan Baptist Weenix, by whom he was trained. He became a member of the painters' guild in Utrecht in 1664. Pictures of dead game or ornamental birds in Italianate gardens with statues, urns, and fountains were his speciality. His major work is a series of large hunting and animal pictures painted in 1702-12 for the hunting lodge at Bensberg of the Elector Johann Wilhelm of the Palatinate (now in the Alte Pinakothek, Munich).

Jan Weenix

126 *American Menagerie*

Oil on canvas. ca. 1695-1700. 48¹³⁄₁₆ x 66½ inches (124 x 169 cm.). Signed: *Weenix f.* Provenance: Mrs. Sally A. Hart, Louisville, sold Parke Bernet, New York, 25 to 26 November 1949; Mrs. Paula de Koenigsberg, Buenos Aires, 1956.
Ambassador Herbert de Ribbing.

The painting has been entitled an *American Menagerie*, though only the macaw on the right, the toucan, and the two squirrel monkeys on the left come from the New World. It shows how American creatures were assimilated among the exotica so greatly prized by Europeans in the late seventeenth and early eighteenth centuries. In composition and in one or two details (though not the fauna) the picture is similar to one signed and dated by Weenix, 1696 (cf. *Apollo*, XCVII [1973], advertisement section, p. 5).

Literature: Gilberte Margin-Méry: *L'Europe et la Découverte du Monde,* exhibition catalogue, Musée des Beaux Arts, Bordeaux, 1960, no. 41.

Francesco Bertos

Italian, fl. 1693-1733.
Very little is known about Bertos. A Venetian by birth, he is recorded in Rome in 1693, was active in Venice ca. 1710, and in 1733 received a commission for two candlesticks for the Santo in Padua. He developed a unique type of bronze sculpture which appears to have been admired and collected, especially by foreign visitors to Italy.

Francesco Bertos

127 *America*

Bronze. ca. 1695-1733. Height 26⅞ inches (68.3 cm.). Provenance: Spiradon Collection, Paris; Jacques Seligman & Co., from whom it was purchased 1917 by H. Walters. Baltimore, Walters Art Gallery.

The violence of the subject matter is off-set, in this allegory of America, by the athletic elegance of the acrobat-like figures. It forms parts of a set of four groups of the continents, one of which (Europe) is signed *F. Bertos fecit et fusit.* The group is modelled in the same highly individual style found in

bronzes of other subjects signed by Bertos (cf. L. Planiscig: "Francesco Bertos" in *Dedalo*, IX (1928-29), pp. 209-221, 561-575). The central figure and the man pierced by an arrow also bear some resemblance to the allegory of America by Andrea Pozzo on the ceiling of S. Ignazio, Rome. No other group of America by Bertos is recorded, but somewhat similar bronzes of Europe and Asia were in the sale of the Rusca Collection, Florence, 10-21 April, 1883, nos. 113 and 114.

Literature: W. L. Hildburgh: "Some Bronze Groups by Francesco Bertos" in *Apollo*, XXVII (1938), p. 85.

Francesco Solimena

Italian (Naples), 1657-1747.
Solimena was born at Nocera, the son
of a painter, and settled in 1674 in
Naples, where he began his career
under the influence of Luca Giordano,
though he gradually developed a
lighter and more elegant style. After
Giordano left for Spain in 1692, Solimena emerged as the undisputed leader
of the Neapolitan school, a position he
was to hold for half a century. He ran
a private academy (in which several
notable eighteenth-century painters
were trained) and ended his career as
a rich man, enrolled in the nobility
with the title of Baron. His output was
considerable and included numerous
religious paintings, mythological and
allegorical pictures, and a few portraits. Although he rarely left Naples,
his works were in demand throughout
Europe. In about 1708 he was commissioned by the Republic of Genoa
to execute a series of paintings for their
senate chamber, one of which represented *The Landing of Christopher
Columbus in the Indies* [129]. The only
other occasion on which he is known
to have alluded to America in his work
is in a series of allegories (see below).

Francesco Solimena

128 *America*

Oil on canvas. ca. 1730-1738. 36 x 28⅜
inches (92 x 72 cm.).
London, private collection.

This is one of a set of allegories of the
four continents. Solimena was commissioned to paint such a series in fresco
on the ceiling of a bedroom in the
Palazzo Reale, Naples, decorated for
the wedding of Charles III to Maria
Amalia of Saxony in 1738 (B. De
Dominici: *Vite dei pittori e scultori ed
architetti napolitani,* Naples, 1844, vol.
IV, p. 449). These paintings were later
destroyed. It has generally been assumed that engravings for the conti-

nents in ovals, by Pierre Jacques Gaultier after Solimena (cf. De Dominici: *Vite dei pittori,* p. 491) and several sets of paintings of the continents attributed either to Solimena or to his workshop, are connected with this commission for the Royal Palace, though Solimena could well have made paintings of this subject independently, either earlier or later. A number of versions or replicas of Solimena's continents survive. There is a set in the Galleria Doria-Pamphili, Rome (assigned to Solimena's studio by E. Sestieri: *Catalogo della Galleria ex-Fido commissaria Doria Pamphili,* Rome, 1942, p. 119, though Ferdinando Bologna: *Francesco Solimena,* Naples, 1948, p. 273, describes the *Asia* and *Europe* as autograph *bozzetti* for the Royal Palace and assigns the other two to his studio). There is a set of replicas in the foyer of the Teatro San Ferdinando, Naples (F. Bologna: *Francesco Solimena*). A *Europe* and an *Africa* are in the Leeds City Art Gallery; a poor replica of the *America* is in the Musée des Beaux Arts at Pau, and others are recorded as having passed through the salerooms. The painting exhibited differs slightly from that in the Galleria Doria Pamphili, which lacks the alligator, and in which the main figure wears a vest, which may have been added at a later date.

Iconographically the picture conforms with the image of America prescribed by Ripa, showing her with alligator, parrot, and arrow. However, the pose and gesture of the main figure, and also of the recumbent man, are strongly reminiscent of the corresponding figures in Andrea Pozzo's allegory of America, painted in 1691-94 on the ceiling of S. Ignazio, Rome, which Solimena would surely have seen when in Rome in 1700.

Literature: *Paintings and Sculptures of the Italian Baroque,* exhibition catalogue, Heim Gallery, London, 1973, no. 12.

Jean François de Troy
French, 1679-1752.
The son and grandson of well-known painters, de Troy trained in Paris and then at the French Academy in Rome, where he remained from 1699 to 1706. He became one of the most accomplished of French Rococo painters, equally at home with large scale mythological subjects, portraits, small genre pictures, and more purely decorative work, notably tapestry designs, of which he did several for the Gobelins. In 1738 he returned to Rome as director of the Academy.

Jean François de Troy

129 *Christopher Columbus Landing in America*

Oil on canvas. Before 1718. Signed: *Peint et inventé par Jean De Troy Fils peintre ordinaire du Roy A Paris.* 17 x 31⅞ inches (43 x 81 cm.). Provenance: Mme. Orly, from whom it was acquired in 1903 by Peyre, who bequeathed it to the Museum in 1905. Paris, Musée des Arts Décoratifs.

In this early eighteenth-century evocation of the discovery of America, the Indians fall in adoration before the cross which is set up by Columbus's men. It is thus linked with the several Baroque allegories of the evangelization of America. Some years later the theme was to be given poetic expression in France in Mme. du Boccage's epic, *La Colombiade, ou la foi portée au Nouveau Monde* (Paris, 1758).

Is is supposed that this sketch and another of a naval battle (now lost) were painted in 1716 as projects for decorations in the Sala del Consiglio of the senate in the Palazzo Ducale, Genoa, which de Troy failed to carry out because his aged father was reluctant to be separated from him. Both scenes were engraved in 1718 by the comte de Caylus (later to become famous as a student of classical antiquities). But their relationship to the paintings for the Sala del Consiglio by Francesco Solimena [128] has never been satisfactorily established. Solimena was commissioned, probably in 1708, to execute four paintings of historical scenes connected with the city of Genoa. The first two reached Genoa between 1715 and 1717 and the last—*The Landing of Christopher Columbus*—in 1728. All were destroyed by fire in 1777, and no visual record of them appears to survive. There is, however, a drawing by Solimena (in the Cooper-Hewitt Museum, New York) of *The Landing of*

Christopher Columbus with a composition rather more elaborate than that by de Troy but enclosed within a frame of exactly the same unusual shape as that in the latter's sketch. Solimena may have made this drawing some considerable time before completing his painting of 1728. A small painting of a ship and four men on a beach, inscribed *Solimena Napoli 1715* (Musée des Beaux Arts, Rennes) and later engraved by Jean Barbault with the title *Christophe Colomb arrivant en Amérique* was probably made in connection with the commission for Genoa (cf. N. Volle and P. Rosenberg: *Jean Barbault,* exhibition catalogue, Musée départmental de l'Oise, Beauvais and elsewhere, 1975, no. 65). R. P. Wunder argues "that the 1718 date on Caylus's engraving [after de Troy] is sufficient evidence to prove that de Troy cribbed directly from Solimena, who, in his finished work, had simplified his scheme." But the evidence is far from conclusive: the figures in Solimena's drawing and in his painting at Rennes bear very little similarity to those in de Troy's sketch. It must therefore be assumed that both Solimena and de Troy worked out compositions to fill panels of the same shape independently of one another. Unless further documentation is discovered, the reason why the Genoese Senate should have commissioned projects for the decoration of the main room in the Palazzo Ducale from both Solimena, who was one of the most celebrated artists of the day, and de Troy, a young and, at that date, very little known French painter, must remain a mystery.

Literature: G. Brière in L. Dimier: *Les peintres français du XVIIIᵉ siècle,* Paris-Brussels, 1930, vol. II, p. 38; *L'Art français et l'Europe,* exhibition catalogue, Orangerie, Paris, 1958, no. 44; R. P. Wunder: "Solimena Drawings in the Cooper Union" in *Art Quarterly,* XXIV (1961), pp. 151-164; *Cent Chefs-d'oeuvre,* exhibition catalogue, Musée des Arts Décoratifs, Paris, 1964-65, no. 15; *Watteau et sa génération,* exhibition catalogue, Galerie Cailleux, Paris, 1968, no. 10.

IX
Americainerie

Cléveland presents one of the fullest accounts of America as it appeared in the imagination of a European in the early eighteenth century. This long geographical novel, published in seven volumes between 1728 and 1738, was written by the Abbé Prévost, better known nowadays as the author of one of the most brilliant stories of its time, *Manon Lescaut,* which ends in an imaginary America—a waterless desert a few miles from New Orleans! *Le Philosophe anglais, ou Histoire de M. Cléveland* recounts the adventures of a "natural son of Oliver Cromwell," who follows his beloved, Lady Fanny Axminster, from England to St. Helena, Jamaica, Santa Domingo, Virginia, and through the central American plains beyond the Alleghenies. In the course of his travels he visits three Utopias—a theocratic Protestant settlement, an Indian tribe living in a state of nature, and an ideal republic in a mountain fastness. He encounters both cannibals and friendly natives. Of the latter he wrote: "They are tawny without being black or olive coloured. Their skin is dark brown. They wear no clothes except around their middles. In their eyes there is a fire which indicates the depth of their souls. Although there is generally something wild in their looks, one could not say that it was ferocious nor that their outward appearance could cause alarm. Most of them were armed with bows and arrows and some had their heads bizarrely decorated with feathers in their hair."[1]

Figures such as those described by Prévost could be seen in many a delicately decorated rococo interior, balancing precariously on crests of scrollwork. They were painted on ceilings and over doors, modelled in porcelain, and woven in silks. Out of doors they might support the florid decoration of a carriage, like that designed by Bernard Picart for the duke of Osuna [130]. Several were to be found dancing on the parterres of princely gardens in Germany and Italy. Others appeared as oarsmen in a water fête in Dresden and in a regatta in Venice [152]. More elegant than their seventeenth-century predecessors, these Rococo Indians have acquired a more sprightly, light-footed bearing. Braves have been transformed into beaux and cannibal women into coquettes, man-eaters of a different kind!

The renovation which accompanied Alexandre-François Desportes' work on the *Indes* tapestries is typical [133]. Everything becomes prettier and lighter—and much less serious. Eckhout's Tapuya Indians are replaced by playful monkeys or conventional figures from the stage or opera in feather skirts. The birds, beasts, fishes, and plants are there as before, but everything has been subtly subordinated to an overall demand for exoticism—for an "Americainerie" which bears the same relationship to the natural products of the New World as does "Chinoiserie" to the arts of China.

Allegories of the continents—in which American Indians made their most frequent appearances in Rococo art—continued to be devised according to complex programmes, often with political motives. The great staircase ceiling which Giovanni Battista Tiepolo painted in the Residenz at Wurzburg is a case in point: ostensibly it represents the fame of the patron, Prince-Bishop Carl Philipp von Greiffenklau, trumpetted to the four corners of the earth and even to the gods on Olympus. Yet this preposterous notion plays only a minor role in Tiepolo's sparkling vision, which seems, rather, to reflect the world view of the Enlightenment—including the most voluptuous of all personifications of America [134]. In the hands of lesser artists, allegories of America, as of Africa, seem to have been intended mainly to satisfy a craving for exoticism combined with eroticism—hot climates and sultry passions. And it is a sign of the inconographically less exacting times that the attributes of the two southern continents were often confused, as by Johann Wolfgang Baumgartner [137].

The German modellers of porcelain statuettes of the continents were, however, careful to make America *salonfähig,* so that she could take her place beside courtly courting couples, Harlequin and Columbine. Allusions to cannibalism, previously so prominent, were played down if not entirely omitted: indeed the whole subject was treated increasingly lightly. In 1719 Defoe had described American cannibals with spine-chilling vividness in *Robinson Crusoe,* one of the most widely diffused of all eighteenth-century books. But in Voltaire's *Candide* of 1759 they are no more than a joke.[2]

1. Quoted by Gilbert Chinard: *L'Amérique et le rêve exotique,* Paris, 1913, p. 289.
2. Voltaire: *Romans et Contes,* ed. R. Groos (La Pleiade), Paris, s.d. pp. 181-182.

Bernard Picart

French, 1673-1733.
Picart was born in Paris and trained as a draughtsman, engraver, and miniature painter by his father, Etienne Picart. From 1696 to 1698 and from 1710 until his death, he worked in the Netherlands. Although he made some decorative designs (see below), he is best known for his fine engravings after works by French seventeenth-century artists and numerous book illustrations, most notably those in *Cérémonies et coutumes religieuses de tous les peuples du monde*, a vast eleven-volume compendium, of which the first volume was published in Amsterdam in 1723 [172].

Bernard Picart

130 *Design for a Coach*

Pen and ink and grey wash. ca. 1710. Signed: *B.Picart fecit*. 7⅛ x 6³⁄₁₆ inches (18 x 15.7 cm.). Provenance: Marie-Gaspard Grimod, comte d'Orsay. Paris, Musée du Louvre, Cabinet des Dessins.

This is one of a group of three designs for a ceremonial coach, probably intended for an ambassador. Indians with feather head-dresses, skirts, armbands, and anklets are assimilated into its early rococo decorations among tritons and *amorini*. In 1713 Picart published a set of engravings of the coach he designed for the Spanish ambassador, the duke of Osuna, for his entry into Utrecht.

Rosalba Carriera

Italian, 1675-1757.
Her pastels, especially portraits, made Carriera one of the most celebrated artists in eighteenth-century Europe. Apart from very successful visits to Paris in 1721 and Vienna in 1730, she spent all her life in Venice. Her work perfectly reflects elegant Rococo Venetian taste at this period.

Rosalba Carriera

131 *America*

Pastel on paper. ca. 1720. 17⅛ x 13¹³⁄₁₆ inches (43.5 x 34 cm.). Provenance: Laurence Currie, sold London, Christie's, 17 December 1926, lot no. 134; James Hazen Hyde.

Giambattista Tiepolo

136 *The World Pays Homage to Spain*
Oil on canvas. ca. 1762. 41⅛ x 71½
inches (104.5 x 181 cm.). Provenance:
Pagliano family, Venice; Edward
Cheney; Alfred Capel Cure; Francis
Capel Cure; Contini Bonacossi; Sam-
uel H. Kress, 1935.
Washington, D.C., National Gallery of
Art, Samuel H. Kress Collection, 1943.
(Exhibited in Washington only.)

This sketch corresponds in general
design to the throne-room ceiling in the
Royal Palace, Madrid, and is probably
that mentioned by Tiepolo in a letter
to an unidentified correspondent of 13
March 1762: "I am just now finishing

the *Modello* for the Great Work, how
vast, one need only reflect that it measures a hundred feet . . . ." Tiepolo
wrote to the Spanish ambassador in
Venice on 28 September 1761, thanking him for the measurements and plan
for the throne-room decorations. He
left for Spain at the beginning of April
1762 and the ceiling fresco in the
throne-room was finished in 1764. It
was his last great work.

Although it has usually been called
The World Pays Homage to Spain,
the subject of the ceiling seems to be
the homage of the Spanish provinces
to their monarchy. In 1772 Antonio
Ponz wrote that the ceiling included
various "fabulous and allegorical fig-

ures" signifying the "power, greatness,
religion and other qualities of the
Spanish monarchy," and, above the
cornice, "figures dressed in their national costumes and with their particular products," symbolising "the
provinces of Spain and the Indies" (cf.
A. Ponz: *Viaje de Espana* [1772], ed.
Casto Maria del Rivero, Madrid, 1947,
p. 522). Differences between the sketch
and the ceiling suggest that Tiepolo
may have modified his original design
in order to make this meaning clearer.
In both, America is represented by a
feather-crowned and feather-skirted
figure somewhat similar to that on the
Würzburg ceiling. But in the place of
the high-pooped ship in the corner of

Bernard Picart

French, 1673-1733.
Picart was born in Paris and trained as a draughtsman, engraver, and miniature painter by his father, Etienne Picart. From 1696 to 1698 and from 1710 until his death, he worked in the Netherlands. Although he made some decorative designs (see below), he is best known for his fine engravings after works by French seventeenth-century artists and numerous book illustrations, most notably those in *Cérémonies et coutumes religieuses de tous les peuples du monde,* a vast eleven-volume compendium, of which the first volume was published in Amsterdam in 1723 [172].

Bernard Picart

130 *Design for a Coach*
Pen and ink and grey wash. ca. 1710. Signed: *B.Picart fecit.* 7⅛ x 6³⁄₁₆ inches (18 x 15.7 cm.). Provenance: Marie-Gaspard Grimod, comte d'Orsay. Paris, Musée du Louvre, Cabinet des Dessins.

This is one of a group of three designs for a ceremonial coach, probably intended for an ambassador. Indians with feather head-dresses, skirts, armbands, and anklets are assimilated into its early rococo decorations among tritons and *amorini.* In 1713 Picart published a set of engravings of the coach he designed for the Spanish ambassador, the duke of Osuna, for his entry into Utrecht.

Rosalba Carriera

Italian, 1675-1757.
Her pastels, especially portraits, made Carriera one of the most celebrated artists in eighteenth-century Europe. Apart from very successful visits to Paris in 1721 and Vienna in 1730, she spent all her life in Venice. Her work perfectly reflects elegant Rococo Venetian taste at this period.

Rosalba Carriera

131 *America*
Pastel on paper. ca. 1720. 17⅛ x 13¹³⁄₁₆ inches (43.5 x 34 cm.). Provenance: Laurence Currie, sold London, Christie's, 17 December 1926, lot no. 134; James Hazen Hyde.

New York, Cooper-Hewitt Museum of Design, Smithsonian Institution, Gift of the Trustees of the Estate of James Hazen Hyde.

This allegorical figure of America, wearing a jewelled hair fillet decorated with plumes and carrying an arrow, with a quiver on her back, forms part of a set of *Continents*, of which *Europe* and *Asia* are also in the Cooper-Hewitt Museum of Design.

Literature: *The Four Continents from the Collection of James Hazen Hyde,* exhibition catalogue, The Cooper Union Museum, New York, 1961, no. 82.

René Frémin

French, 1672-1744.
Frémin was a pupil of François Girardon and Antoine Coysevox, won the first prize at the Ecole académique in Paris in 1694, and spent the next four years at the French Academy in Rome. In Rome he executed two bronze reliefs for the Cappella di S. Ignazio in the Gesù. After returning to Paris he became a member of the Académie Royale in 1700 and from 1705 to 1717 worked at Versailles, the Trianon, and Marly, mainly on garden sculpture. In 1721 he accepted an invitation to Spain from Philip V and stayed there until 1738, working on the vast and elaborate lead statues for the gardens of the royal palace of La Granja. His last years were spent in Paris with lodgings in the Louvre and with the title of *écuyer conseiller secrétaire* to Louis XV.

René Frémin

132 Bust of America
Marble. ca. 1738-1744. Height 34 inches (86 cm.). Provenance: Nicolas Beaujon, Hôtel d'Evreux, Paris (sold *Vente* Beaujon, 25 April 1787, no. 162); ... A. Fauchier-Magnan, St. James, Neuilly-sur-Seine.
New York, Wildenstein & Co. Inc.

During his period in Spain, Frémin executed a full-length statue of America for the garden of the royal palace of San Ildefonso near Segovia.

Literature: A. Masson: "La galerie Beaujon" in *Gazette des Beaux Arts,* 6e, XVIII (1937), p. 55; *idem: Un mécène bodelais Nicolas Beijon,* Paris, 1937, p. 105.

Gobelins Tapestry Factory, after Alexandre-François Desportes

133 Les Nouvelles Indes: The Camel
France (Paris). Tapestry of dyed wool, dyed silk, and gold yarn. 1740-1741. 163½ x 132 inches (415 x 345 cm.). Inscription: *Desportes Pxit Cozette exit.* Provenance: Garde Meuble de la Couronne, Paris.
Paris, Mobilier Nationale.

In 1735 the director of the Gobelins Factory commissioned Desportes to paint a series of tapestry cartoons to replace those used since 1687 for weaving *Les Indes* [114]. The new series was called *Les Nouvelles Indes,* and the cartoons by Desportes were shown at the Paris Salons of 1738, 1739, and 1741. Desportes, who as a young man

had worked on the original series, retained many of their features but also made numerous additions and alterations to answer the changes in taste which had come about in half a century. In the panel exhibited, variously called *Le chameau* or *Le cheval pommelé* (the camel or the dappled horse), he retained the llama and the fishes in the foreground of the panel in the original series, entitled *L'Indien à cheval*, but replaced the Indian on horseback from which it took its name with a camel ridden by a monkey, gave greater prominence to the black man holding the horse on the left, and lent the whole a richer effect by adding parrots and another exotic bird in the tree, a flamingo and pineapple plant, a bird of paradise, and, in the distance, a group of ostriches among palm trees. He thus further enriched the mixture of flora and fauna of the four continents at the very moment when the naturalist Buffon was demonstrating that South American animals were not only different from, but inferior to, those of the Old World.

The cartoons for *The Camel* served both for the single panel and for the left half of another, wider panel, with a leopard attacking a horse on the right. The panel exhibited was woven under the direction of Pierre-Francois Cozette (1714-1801) on a low-warp loom. The series was later woven with different borders and with some subjects in reverse under Jacques Neilson from 1754 onwards (examples are in Palazzo del Quirinale, Rome; Archbishop's Palace, Prague; Kunstgewerbemuseum, Schloss Charlottenburg, Berlin, and elsewhere).

Literature: M. Fénaille: *Etat général des tapisseries de la manufacture des Gobelins,* Paris, 1907, vol. IV, p. 40 ff.; H. Göbel: *Die Wandteppiche und ihre Manufakturen,* Leipzig, 1928, vol. II, i, pp. 147-148; M. Benisovich: "The History of the *Tenture des Indes*" in *The Burlington Magazine,* LXXXIII (1943), pp. 216-225; T. Bodkin:

"Les Nouvelles Tentures des Indes" in *The Burlington Magazine,* LXXXIV (1944), pp. 65-66; M. Jarry: "Dessins et études provenant de l'atelier Desportes . . ." in *Bulletin de la Société de l'histoire de l'art français,* 1957, pp. 39-45; idem: "Les Indes, série triomphale de l'exotisme" in *Connaissance des Arts,* May, 1969, pp. 62-69.

Giambattista Tiepolo

Italian, 1696-1770.

Tiepolo was one of the greatest, perhaps the greatest, of all eighteenth-century European painters. He was born in Venice, trained under a minor late baroque painter, Gregorio Lazzarini, began to work independently in 1715, became a member of the Venetian painters' guild in 1717, and executed his first major commission—the decoration of the staircase and gallery of the archbishop's palace in Udine—in 1725-28. Other commissions for extensive schemes of fresco painting followed, and soon his fame, especially for the decoration of ceilings, spread beyond the frontiers of the Venetian Republic. In 1750 he was invited to Würzburg by the Prince-Bishop Carl Philip von Greiffenklau, for whom he painted in the Residenz the ceilings of the Kaisersaal and the staircase. The latter incorporates an allegory of America (see below). He referred again to America quite prominently on the ceiling of the throne room in the Royal Palace in Madrid (1762-64), which depicts the *Apotheosis of Spain.*

Giambattista Tiepolo

134 *America*

Red and white chalk on blue paper. 1751-1752. 15½ x 10³⁄₁₆ inches (39.3 x 25.7 cm.).

Stuttgart, Staatsgalerie, Graphische Sammlung.

Literature: P. Molmenti: *G. B. Tiepolo. La sua vita e le sue opere,* Milan, 1909, p. 239; Eduard Sack: *G. B. und D. Tiepolo,* Hamburg, 1910, no. 308; Detlef von Hadeln: *Handzeichnungen von G. B. Tiepolo,* Munich, 1927, pl. 138; *Tiepolo. Zeichnungen von Giambattista, Domenico und Lorenzo Tiepolo . . .,* exhibition catalogue, Graphische Sammlung, Staatsgalerie, Stuttgart, 1970, no. 90.

Giambattista Tiepolo

135 *Man with an Alligator*

Red and white chalk on blue paper. 1751-1752. 16⅜ x 10³⁄₁₆ inches (41.5 x 25.7 cm.).

Stuttgart, Staatsgalerie, Graphische Sammlung.

This and [134] are both preparatory drawings for the painting on the staircase ceiling of the Residenz at Würzburg. Tiepolo, together with his two sons, Domenico and Lorenzo (who assisted him), arrived in Würzburg in early December 1750. He began work almost immediately in the Kaisersaal in the Residenz, and before this was completed the prince-bishop commissioned him to paint the ceiling of the staircase, for which he made sketches before April 1752 and which he completed by 8 November 1753, when he left Würzburg and returned to Venice. The subject of the staircase ceiling (probably inspired by that of nearby Schloss Pommersfelden, where Johann Rudolf Byss in 1717 had painted the four continents paying homage to the Elector Lothar Franz von Schönborn) is the fame of the Prince Bishop Carl Philip von Greiffenklau trumpeted to the gods on Olym-

pus and the four corners of the world. Out of this rather unpromising programme Tiepolo created a sumptuous vision of the world, sparkling with Venetian light and colour. For the personification of America he resorted to the stock iconographical pattern, showing her as a naked figure with a feather head-dress and gold ornaments, seated on a gigantic alligator. The drawing [135] is very close to the work as painted and includes the head of a page-boy in sixteenth-century Venetian

costume, who holds a cup (presumably of chocolate), as in the fresco. The other drawing on this sheet is a study for the kneeling figure to the right of America on the ceiling. The second drawing is a study for the group of a man carrying a dead alligator beside a moustachioed man with an Indian head-dress, also to the right of the main figure in the section of the ceiling devoted to America. The drawing also shows the furled parasol crowned by a crescent which is one of the several

Eastern elements which Tiepolo included in this part of the ceiling. The child's head on this sheet seems to be a study for one of the several *amorini* fluttering in the sky.

Literature: P. Molmenti: *G. B. Tiepolo*, p. 240; Eduard Sack: *G. B. und D. Tiepolo*, no. 318; Detlef von Hadeln: *Handzeichnungen von G. B. Tiepolo*, Munich, 1927, pl. 138; *Tiepolo. Zeichnungen von Giambattista, Domenico und Lorenzo Tiepolo* . . ., exhibition catalogue, Graphisches Sammlung, Staatsgalerie, Stuttgart, 1970, no. 80.

Giambattista Tiepolo

136 *The World Pays Homage to Spain*
Oil on canvas. ca. 1762. 41⅛ x 71½
inches (104.5 x 181 cm.). Provenance:
Pagliano family, Venice; Edward
Cheney; Alfred Capel Cure; Francis
Capel Cure; Contini Bonacossi; Sam-
uel H. Kress, 1935.
Washington, D.C., National Gallery of
Art, Samuel H. Kress Collection, 1943.
(Exhibited in Washington only.)

This sketch corresponds in general
design to the throne-room ceiling in the
Royal Palace, Madrid, and is probably
that mentioned by Tiepolo in a letter
to an unidentified correspondent of 13
March 1762: "I am just now finishing
the *Modello* for the Great Work, how
vast, one need only reflect that it measures a hundred feet . . . ." Tiepolo
wrote to the Spanish ambassador in
Venice on 28 September 1761, thanking him for the measurements and plan
for the throne-room decorations. He
left for Spain at the beginning of April
1762 and the ceiling fresco in the
throne-room was finished in 1764. It
was his last great work.

Although it has usually been called
The World Pays Homage to Spain,
the subject of the ceiling seems to be
the homage of the Spanish provinces
to their monarchy. In 1772 Antonio
Ponz wrote that the ceiling included
various "fabulous and allegorical figures" signifying the "power, greatness,
religion and other qualities of the
Spanish monarchy," and, above the
cornice, "figures dressed in their national costumes and with their particular products," symbolising "the
provinces of Spain and the Indies" (cf.
A. Ponz: *Viaje de Espana* [1772], ed.
Casto Maria del Rivero, Madrid, 1947,
p. 522). Differences between the sketch
and the ceiling suggest that Tiepolo
may have modified his original design
in order to make this meaning clearer.
In both, America is represented by a
feather-crowned and feather-skirted
figure somewhat similar to that on the
Würzburg ceiling. But in the place of
the high-pooped ship in the corner of

the sketch, Tiepolo painted on the ceiling a long low galley loaded with the produce of the Indies, Indians, and, in their midst, Columbus, who points with both hands to his cargo while looking up towards the personification of Spain.

Literature: P. Molmenti: *G. B. Tiepolo,* p. 26; E. Sack: *G. B. und D. Tiepolo,* pp. 139, 223; A. Morassi: *G. B. Tiepolo: His Life and Work,* London, 1955, p. 35; M. von Freeden und C. Lamb: *Tiepolo. Die Fresken der Würzburger Residenz,* Munich, 1956, p. 57; E. Battisti: "Postille documentarie su artisti italiani a Madrid" in *Arte antica e moderna,* 9 (1960), p. 79; A. Morassi: *A Complete Catalogue of the paintings of G. B. Tiepolo,* London, 1962, p. 67; *Paintings from the Samuel H. Kress Collection, Italian Schools* XVI-XVIII *Century* (London, 1973), pp. 150-152.

Johann Wolfgang Baumgartner

Austrian-German, 1712-1761. Baumgartner was born at Kufstein in Austria, close to the Bavarian frontier. He began as a glass painter in Salzburg, back-painting on glass panels. He seems to have practiced this on his travels in Italy, Austria, Hungary, Styria, and Bohemia. He settled in Augsburg in 1733 and was admitted to full citizenship in 1746. Here he gave up painting on glass and worked increasingly in oils and fresco, developing a fluid rococo style of great delicacy, also providing designs for engravers. Although he was active in Augsburg mainly as a religious painter, his allegories of the continents (see below) are probably his best-known works.

Johann Wolfgang Baumgartner

137 *America*

Oil on canvas. ca. 1750-1760. 9⅞ x 15 inches (25 x 38 cm.). Provenance: Hofrat Sigmund Röhrer, Unterschondorf, 1924.
Augsburg, Städische Kunstsammlung—Deutsche Barockgalerie.

This is one of a set of continents, from which Europe is missing, apparently executed as sketches either for large-scale paintings or for prints. Johann Philipp Koch of Augsburg issued a mezzotint of the *Africa* inscribed: *Baumgartner pinx. I.P.Koch exc.A.V.* and may also have made prints of the others. The painting exhibited owes little to the iconographical tradition for allegories of America save the alli-

gators and has been mistaken for a representation of Africa (in the *Reallexikon*). It includes an elephant tusk and what appears to be a camel, while the nude figure in the centre combines African facial features with an American Indian complexion. Baumgartner did, however, stress the riches of the New World in sparkling jewellery. He also incorporated mysterious bales and a galleon, presumably waiting to ship the bales to Europe. But his sketch seems to have been inspired mainly by a desire for exoticism, not untouched by eroticism.

Literature: A. Feulner: *Die Sammlung Hofrat Sigmund Röhrer im Besitze der Stadt Augsburg,* Augsburg, 1926, p. 2; *Süddeutsches Rokoko,* exhibition catalogue, Augsburg, 1947, no. 139; H. Tintelnot: *Die barocke Freskomalerei in*

Deutschland, Munich, 1951, p. 150; N. Lieb: *Führer durch die Städische Kunstsammlungen Augsburg,* Augsburg, 1953, p. 48; *Schönheit des 18. Jahrhunderts,* exhibition catalogue, Zurich, 1955, no. 8; N. Lieb and H. Müller: *Augsburger Rokoko,* Augsburg, 1956, p. 17; *Rococo Art from Bavaria* (commemorative catalogue of exhibition, Victoria and Albert Museum, 1954) London, 1956, no. 71; *Der barocke Himmel,* exhibition catalogue, Staatsgalerie, Stuttgart, 1964, p. 57; H. Schindler: *Barockreisen in Schwaben und Altbayern,* Munich, 1964, p. 57; E. Köllman, K.-A. Wirth et al. in *Reallexikon sur Deutschen Kunstgeschichte,* vol. v, Stuttgart, 1967, col. 1190; *Deutsche Barockgalerie Augsburg,* Augsburg, 1970, pp. 31-32.

Christoph Thomas Scheffler

German, 1699-1756.

Scheffler was the son of a painter, Johann Wolfgang Scheffler, from whom he received his initial training as an artist. After working under the great Bavarian Late Baroque painter Cosmas Damian Asam, he became a novice at the Jesuit college in Landsberg but left without taking orders and devoted the rest of his life to painting altarpieces and fresco decorations, mainly for Jesuit churches in Bavaria and the Rhineland. His frescoed ceiling in the Jesuit church at Dillingen is his masterpiece.

Christoph Thomas Scheffler

138 *The Jesuit Mission in America*

Pen, grey ink, black chalk, and grey wash, heightened with white on blue-grey paper. 1749-1750. $10^{11}/_{16}$ x $14^{3}/_{8}$ inches (27.1 x 36.5 cm.). Inscription: *America / V: Pater Josephus Anchieta, Pater Ignatius Acebediy.*
Stuttgart, Staatsgalerie, Graphische Sammlung.

This is a preliminary design for the American section of the fresco representing the work of the Jesuit Missions in the four parts of the world, painted on the ceiling of the nave in the Jesuit church at Dillingen (Bavarian Swabia) by Christoph Thomas Scheffler in 1750. It shows in the centre the Jesuit Apostle of Brazil, José de Anchieta (1534-1591), preaching in front of the church of Nossa Senhora da Ajuda, Bahia, which he erected (1569, remnants survive). Ascending the steps on the left, the Jesuit missionary to Paraguay, Anton Sepp, carries a copy of the image of the Virgin in the Bavarian church of Altötting; on the right the sub-prior of the Brazilian Mission, Ignatius Azevedo (1525-1570), who was drowned off the Canaries when the ship in which he was travelling was captured by Dutch pirates, sinks into the sea, clutching a copy of the image of the Virgin in the Alte Kapelle at Regensberg.

Litterature: W. Braun: *Christoph Thomas Scheffler,* Stuttgart, 1939, pp. 60-63, 91; *Der Barocke Himmel,* exhibition catalogue, Staatsgalerie, Stuttgart, 1964, no. 109.

142 Meissen Factory, *America*. Wadsworth Athenaeum.

António González Velázquez

Spanish, 1729-1793.

He was a member of a prominent family of artists working in Madrid: his father, Pablo, was a sculptor; his brother Alejandro was an architect, and his brother Luis a painter. As a youth he went to Rome, where he studied under the Neopolitan painter Corrado Giaquinto, to whose style he remained faithful throughout his career. He returned to Spain in 1752, painted frescoes in churches at Saragossa and Madrid, was appointed court painter in 1764, and served as honorary director of the Madrid Academy, 1765-85. His work influenced the young Goya.

António González Velázquez

139 *Christopher Columbus Presenting the New World to the Catholic Monarchs*

Oil on canvas. ca. 1760-1765. 37¾ x 61½ inches (96 x 156 cm.). Provenance: Le Comte de Silguy, 1864.
Quimper, Musée des Beaux Arts.

This is a sketch for a ceiling in the Royal Palace, Madrid, painted by António González Velázquez certainly before 1765 and probably before 1762-64, when G. B. Tiepolo depicted Columbus and the people of the Hispano-American colonies in his *Apotheosis of Spain* on the ceiling of the throne room. The allegory of Religion in the sky emphasizes the evangelizing aspect of the *Conquista* which had long been stressed in Spain. But it may also have a more topical significance, alluding to the ecclesiastical policy of Charles III, who came to the throne in 1759 and in 1765 sent an order to the *Audiencia* of Santo Domingo declaring his power to intervene "in everything regarding the spiritual government of the Indies" by virtue of his position "as vicar and delegate of the Holy See deriving from the bull of Alexander VI" (cf. Richard Konetzke: *America centrale e meridionale I La colonizzazzione ispano-portoghese*, Milan, 1968, p. 219).

Literature: *Catalogue du Musée des Beaux Arts, Quimper,* Quimper, 1873, no. 170; J. A. Gaya Nuño: *La Pintura Española fuers de España,* Madrid, 1958, p. 107 (as by Teodoro Ardemans); *Trésors de la peinture espagnole,* exhibition catalogue, Musée des Arts Decoratifs, Paris, 1963, no. 112; *Goya and His Times,* exhibition catalogue, Royal Academy of Arts, London, 1963-64, no. 15; F. J. Sánchez Cantón: *Escultura y Pintura del Siglo XVIII* (Ars Hispaniae, vol. XVII), Madrid, 1965, pp. 134-139.

140 *Tea-Pot*

Germany, Meissen Porcelain Factory. Porcelain, painted with enamel colours and gilt. ca. 1730. Height with cover 4 7/16 inches (11.3 cm.). Provenance: James Hazen Hyde, New York, 1959. New York, The Metropolitan Museum of Art, Gift of the Estate of James Hazen Hyde.

An Indian with a feather head-dress and the palm-trees often associated with America are here joined by chinoiserie figures in a charming expression of the early eighteenth-century taste for exoticism. The Chinese figures are close in style to those by Johann Gregor Höroldt, who joined the Meissen factory as a painter in 1720 and was largely responsible for its early success.

141 *Tea-Pot and Tea-Caddy*

Germany, Bayreuth Pottery. Brown glazed earthenware with decorations in silver. ca. 1725-1750. Height of tea-pot 5 11/16 and of caddy 4 11/16 inches (14.5 and 12 cm.). Provenance: James Hazen Hyde, New York, 1959. New York, The Metropolitan Museum of Art, Gift of the Estate of James Hazen Hyde, 1959.

But for the inscription *America,* the significance of the allegory on the tea-pot might be difficult to ascertain, though elephants were not infrequently associated with Brazil. The figures on the caddy were probably intended to represent Asia.

142 *America*

Germany, Meissen Porcelain Factory.
Porcelain on gilt bronze base. ca. 1745.
Overall height 14 inches (35.5 cm.),
including base of 3½ inches (8.9 cm.).
Provenance: J. P. Morgan, New York,
1917.
Hartford, Connecticut, Wadsworth
Atheneum, Gift of J. P. Morgan.
Colorplate 4.

This figure belongs to the larger of two
sets of Continents produced by the
Meissen factory from similar models
in the 1740s. References to these sets
in the factory records are somewhat
confusing, but the model for the larger
version of *America* seems to have been
the joint work of Kändler, Eberlein,
and Reinike. Johann Joachim Kändler
(1706-1775) was the factory's chief
modeller from 1733 and the creator of
most of its finest figures. The general
design of *America* may well be due to
him. Johann Friedrich Eberlein (d.
1749) was his assistant from 1735.
Peter Reinike (1715-1768) was trained
as a sculptor and worked at Meissen
from 1743, assisting Kändler and also
making models independently, including exotic figures of Turks and China-
men and animals. The *Europe* in the
larger set of Continents is by him, and
he seems to have been responsible for
the smaller version of *America*,
modelled 1746-47. Another example
of the large *America* on a different,
rocky, platform is in the Porzellan-
sammlung, Dresden. Examples of the
small version are in the Bayerische
Nationalmuseum, Munich, and the
Cooper-Hewitt Museum, New York.

Literature: Carl Albiker: *Die Meissner
Porzellantiere im 18. Jahrhundert,* Berlin,
1959, pp. 27-29 (for the model).

Paul de Lamerie

English, 1688-1751.

De Lamerie was born at 'sHertogen-bosch, the child of French Huguenot parents who had sought refuge from religious persecution in Holland. By 1691 they had moved to London, where in 1703 he began to serve his apprenticeship as a silversmith to another Huguenot refugee, Pierre Platel. In 1712 he was admitted to the Goldsmiths' Company and began to work as an independent silversmith, soon establishing himself as one of the most notable in the city. His workshop produced silver vessels in a variety of styles, from the austerely simple to the very ornate, from the bold late Baroque to the delicately intricate Rococo.

Paul de Lamerie

143 *Tea-Kettle on Lampstand*

Silver. 1745. Marked with the London hall-mark and date letter for 1745, and with de Lamerie's maker's mark. Provenance: Mr. William A. McMahan, New York; Mr. Arthur Leidesdorf, New York; sold Christie's, London, 28 March 1973, lot 122.
New York, Hartman Rare Art.

The kettle is made to a general design (probably of French origin) which was popular in mid-eighteenth-century England. Several examples have chinoiserie figures embossed on the body of the vessel. The substitution of an Indian child with feather head-dress, bow, and arrow is very unusual, if not unique. Somewhat similar Indian children do, however, appear as supporters for silver salt cellars made by Thomas Germain in Paris in 1757-58 [144, 145].

François-Thomas Germain

French, 1726-1791.

The son of Thomas Germain, the great French eighteenth-century silversmith, Germain took over his father's workshop on his death in 1748, being appointed *sculpteur orfèvre* to Louis XV the same year. He continued, with little change, his father's Rococo style and was very successful and productive, until his personal extravagance led to bankruptcy. In 1765 he was dismissed from his royal and other appointments. He never recovered from this and died in obscurity.

François-Thomas Germain

144 *Double Salt Cellar*

Silver. 1757-1758. Height 9⅞ inches (25.1 cm.). Marked with date letter *R* (for 1757-58) and the maker's mark of F.-T. Germain. On three silvergilt interior parts, the mark V (for 1760-61). On the bottom the Portuguese royal arms.

145 *Pair of Salt Cellars*

Silver. 1760-1761. Height: 7 9/16 inches (19.2 cm.). Marked with date letter *R* (for 1757-58) and the maker's mark for F.-T. Germain.

145 *Pair of Salt Cellars*

Silver. 1760-1761. Height: 7%16 inches (19.2 cm.). Marked with date letter *R* (for 1757-58) and the maker's mark for F.-T. Germain.

Provenance: Portuguese Royal Collection.
Lisbon, Museu de Arte Antiga.

These formed part of the large quantity of domestic silver supplied by Germain to the Portuguese Crown during the decade following the Lisbon earthquake of 1755 to replace the lost royal treasures. Putti similarly dressed in American Indian feathers were modelled at this period also in porcelain [147], and one appears on an English silver tea-kettle [143].

Literature: G. Bapst: *Etudes sur l'orfèvrerie française au XVIIIᵉ siècle, Les Germain, Orfèvres-Sculpteurs du Roy,* Paris and London, 1887, pp. 147-148; *Les tresors de l'orfèvrerie du Portugal,* exhibition catalogue, Musée des Arts Décoratifs, Paris, 1954-55, nos. 415, 417.

146 *Centrepiece: The Four Continents*
Germany, Ludwigsburg Porcelain Factory. Porcelain with polychrome and gilt decoration. ca. 1760. Marked with the two interlaced "C's" under a ducal coronet applied to Ludwigsburg porcelain between 1758 and 1793. Height 12¼ inches (31 cm.). Provenance: James Hazen Hyde.
New York, Cooper-Hewitt Museum of Design, Smithsonian Institution, Gift of the Trustees of the Estate of James Hazen Hyde.

This centrepiece has been attributed to Johann Göz (1732-1762), who was "chief-repairer" and probably also modeller at Ludwigsburg from 1759 to 1762.

Literature: *The Four Continents from the Collection of James Hazen Hyde,* exhibition catalogue, The Cooper Union Museum, New York, 1961, no. 25; H. Backlin-Landman and E. Shapiro: *The Story of Porcelain*, New York, 1965, p. 29.

147 *America and Europe*
England, Chelsea Porcelain Manufactory. Porcelain. ca. 1765. Marked with a gold anchor applied to porcelain made at the Chelsea factory between ca. 1758 and 1769. Height 9½ inches (24.1 cm.). Provenance: James Hazen Hyde, New York, 1959.
New York, The Brooklyn Museum, Bequest of James Hazen Hyde.

Although the mark reveals that this piece was made after 1758, the model may well have been the same as that for "a very beautiful groupe of figures representing Europe and Asia" included in the 1755 sale of products of the Chelsea factory (cf. William King: *Chelsea Porcelain*, London, 1922, p. 97).

148 *America*

Spain, Alcora Porcelain Factory. Porcelain, with polychrome and gilt decorations. ca. 1770. Height 9¹¹⁄₁₆ inches (24.5 cm.). Provenance: James Hazen Hyde.
New York, Cooper-Hewitt Museum of Design, Smithsonian Institution, Gift of the Trustees of the Estate of James Hazen Hyde.

The monstrous ladle among the attributes of *America* is probably the result of a misunderstood engraving showing *America* with a Brazilian club.

Literature: *The Four Continents from the Collection of James Hazen Hyde,* exhibition catalogue, The Cooper Union Museum, New York, 1961, no. 56.

Johann Adam Huber

German, fl. 1762-1779.
Huber was a decorator of porcelain and held various appointments at the Nymphenburg Porcelain factory, though he is mainly known for his work as a *Hausmaler,* or independent, free-lance decorator working outside the factory. In this way Huber decorated many Nymphenburg vessels, usually jugs, in his own studio.

Johann Adam Huber

149 *American Indians* (or *Allegory of America*)

Enamel colours on a Nymphenburg porcelain tankard mounted in pewter. Signed and dated with the initials *I.A.H. / 1778 / D.17.8bh* and marked with the impressed shield of the Nymphenburg factory. Height 8 inches (20.3 cm.). Provenance: James Hazen Hyde, New York, 1959.
New York, The Metropolitan Museum of Art, Gift of the Estate of James Hazen Hyde.

A tankard of the same form painted by Huber with similar rococo scrolls framing European landscapes is reproduced in Gustav E. Pazaurek: *Deutsche Fayence- und Porzellan-Hausmaler,* Leipzig, 1925, vol. II, p. 376.

150 *America*

Germany, Fulda Porcelain Factory. Porcelain. ca. 1780-1788. Marked in underglaze blue with crowned *FF* applied to porcelain made at Fulda. Height 9⅜ inches (23.8 cm.).
Provenance: James Hazen Hyde, New York, 1959.
New York, The Metropolitan Museum of Art, Gift of the Estate of James Hazen Hyde, 1959.

Literature: Clare Le Corbeiller: "Miss America and her Sisters" in *Metropolitan Museum of Art Bulletin,* XIX (1961), p. 209.

Antoine Vestier

French, 1740-1824.
Vestier was trained under the enamel painter Antoine Révérend, whose daughter he married in 1764. He then studied in the studio of J.-B. Pierre and visited Holland and England in 1776. In 1786 he became a member of the Académie in Paris. He worked mainly as a portrait painter and miniaturist. Though he signed himself *pictor regis* in 1788, he painted some of the more notable portraits of revolutionaries during the following decade.

Antoine Vestier

151 *L'Amérique*

Black chalk heightened with white on tinted paper. ca. 1778-1780. 20¼ x 14¾ inches (51.5 x 37.5 cm.).
Paris, Cailleux.

Comparison with the marble bust of Guimard by Gaétan Merchi in the Bibliothèque de l'Opèra, Paris (signed and dated 1779; see E. de Goncourt: *La Guimard,* Paris, 1893, pp. 142-146, 318, 319) suggests that this drawing is of her in the ballet "La fête de Mirza."

This was by the great ballet master Noverre and had its premiere in November 1779 at the théâtre de l'Académie royal de Musique à Paris. A similar drawing of her by Vestier is in The Metropolitan Museum of Art, New York. Though successful, Noverre's ballet was coolly received in the *Correspondence Littéraire* (letter for December 1779), where various entertainments inspired by the taking of Grenada in the West Indies were more warmly welcomed.

Literature: *Vestier, Colson, Trinquesse,* exhibition catalogue, Palais des Etats de Bourgogne, Dijon, 1969, no. 49.

Innocente Alessandri

Italian (Venice), 1741-1803.
Alessandri was one of the most productive of late eighteenth-century Venetian print makers and publishers. A pupil of Francesco Bartolozzi, he began to work independently in 1761. By 1770 he had gone into partnership with Pietro Scattaglia (d. 1803), and in the following decades they issued prints of current events in Venice as well as of portraits and other paintings by contemporary Venetian artists.

Innocente Alessandri

152 *The Americans*

Engraving. 1784. 11¾ x 18 inches (29.8 x 45.6 cm.). Inscribed: *Gli Americani / Bissona fatta construire dalla Serenissima Signoria di Venezia per la Regatta alla Maestà di Gustavo III Re di Svezia.*
Provenance: Emanuele Cicogna, who gave it to the Museum in 1865.
Venice, Gabinetto delle Stampe e Disegni del Museo Civico Correr.

This is one of a set of eight prints of *bissone*, or festival barges, which took part in the regatta staged in Venice 8 May 1784 in honour of the visit of Gustavus III of Sweden. There were eighteen *bissone* in all, the others representing such diverse subjects as Dutchmen, Quakers, spring, autumn, sturgeon fishing, and Aeneas in Elysium. Gustavus III, travelling incognito as the conte di Haga, spent a few days in Venice on his return journey from Rome to Stockholm and was very lavishly entertained (cf. R. Gallo: *I Pisani ed i palazzi di S. Stefano e di Stra,* Venice, 1945, pp. 89-97). He is said to have been particularly pleased by the regatta, which he called "the most beautiful spectacle to be seen anywhere in Europe." The *bissone*—said to have been designed by Cloder and Bian, who are otherwise unrecorded—were similar to many which had been created for earlier eighteenth-century Venetian regattas and imitated elsewhere. (For an American barge designed for a festival in Dresden in 1719 by Alessandro Mauro, who had also worked in Venice, see E. Hempel: *Der Zwinger zu Dresden,* Berlin, 1961, p. 54.) The prints published by Alessandri and Scattaglia were advertised in the Venetian newspaper *Nuovo Postiglione,* 22 May 1784.

Literature: G. Dalla Santa: *Il Viaggio di Gustavo III Re di Svezia negli Stati Veneti e nella Dominante 1784* (per Nozze Stucky Chiggiato), Venice, 1902, p. 24; G. Lorenzetti: *Le Feste e le maschere Veneziane,* exhibition catalogue, Ca' Rezzonico, Venice, 1937, pp. 19, 46.

Bissona fatta construire dalla Serenissima Signoria di Venezia per la Regatta alla Maestà di Gustavo III Re di Svezia

Jean-Baptiste-Marie Huet

French, 1745-1811.
A member of a family of artists working in Paris, Huet was the son of Nicolas Huet, a flower painter who specialised in the decoration of carriages,
and the nephew of Christophe Huet,
who is best known for his chinoiseries
and arabesques. In 1768 he was *agréé*
at the Académie, of which he became a
full member in 1769. His paintings are
generally of animals and delicate pastoral scenes, but he is remembered
mainly for the numerous designs which
he provided from 1783 onwards for the
decoration of *toiles de Jouy* printed at
Christophe-Philippe Oberkampf's factory, including an allegory of the four
continents (see below), two celebra-
tions of American independence [214],
an apotheosis of Louis XVI and, a little
later, the fall of the Bastille.

Jean-Baptiste-Marie Huet

153 *The Four Continents*
Pen and grey wash. ca. 1785-1790.
40⅛ x 36⅜ inches (102 x 92.5 cm.).
Provenance: Barbet de Jouy, who pre-
sented it to the Museum in 1896.
Paris, Musée des Arts Décoratifs.

This drawing provided the design for a
plate-printed cotton, or *toile de Jouy*,
made at Oberkampf's factory at Jouy,
near Versailles. Europe is shown in the
centre, Asia (above and below) with
two figures by an altar and a camel,
Africa (bottom left and upper right)
with ostrich, lion, elephant, and snake,
America (top left and bottom right)
with two Indians, alligator, and monkeys, one of which climbs a palm-tree.
The design is made in such a way that
the main motifs interlock: thus an
American macaw perches on a tree
above Europe. Many examples of the
cottons printed with this design survive
(e.g. in The Metropolitan Museum of
Art, New York), but it does not seem to

have been as popular as that, also designed by Huet and printed at Jouy, of *America Paying Homage to France* [214].

Literature: A. Guérinet, ed.: *Les nouvelles collections de l'Union Centrale des Arts Décoratifs, 9e série, J.-B. Huet, dessins pour la Manufacture de Jouy,* Paris, s.d. vol. I, pl. 38-39; P. Vignon: *Toiles de Jouy anciennes,* Paris, 1913, pl. 50; H. Clouzot: *Histoire de la manufacture de Jouy et de la toile imprimée au XVIIIe siècle,* Paris, 1928, pl. 16; *Quatre siècles de colonisation française,* exhibition catalogue, Bibliothèque Nationale, Paris, 1931, no. 436.

154 *The Triumph of Spain in America*
Spain. Wood-block printed cotton. Eighteenth century. 16 x 51½ inches (40.6 x 130.5 cm.). Provenance: James Hazen Hyde, New York.
New York, The Metropolitan Museum of Art, Gift of the Estate of James Hazen Hyde.

The main motif shows two figures carrying an unusually fully clad personification of America on a litter with the legend: *Triunfa España en las Americas.*

155 *Wallpaper Screen*
France. Wallpaper printed in distemper colours from wood-blocks. Early nineteenth century. Each panel 67⅞ x 28½ inches (172 x 72.2 cm.). Inscriptions: *L'Hiver; L'Europe; L'Amérique; L'Eté*. Provenance: Paul Rosenberg, who gave it to the Museum in 1931.
Chicago, The Art Institute of Chicago, gift of Paul Rosenberg.

The personification of America devised in the sixteenth century survived into the early decades of the nineteenth, with bare bosom, pearl necklace, feather head-dress, cincture and leg bands, bows and arrows, and parrot. On this screen she has lost only the symbol of cannibalism. The screen consists of six panels, representing winter, summer, and the four continents (*Asia* and *Africa* are not exhibited). Europe is shown with symbols of the arts, sciences, and warfare. America is the denizen of a halcyon world of exotic nature with tropical trees and, lurking in the undergrowth behind her, what appears to be an alligator. The manufacturer of the wallpaper has not been identified, but it was probably printed in Paris ca. 1810-30. (Odile Nouvel has kindly suggested that it may have been produced by the Manufacture Mader, founded in 1823 by J.-C. Xavier Mader, who had previously worked for Joseph Dufour.)

X
A Distant Clime

The primeval American landscape, now so carefully preserved in the Yellowstone and Yosemite parks, had little appeal for Europeans until late in the nineteenth century. Early descriptions of it are extremely uninviting, as in Oliver Goldsmith's vision of the "distant clime" of Georgia:

> Those matted woods where birds forget to sing,
> But silent bats in drowsy clusters cling;
> Those poisonous fields with rank luxuriance crown'd,
> Where the dark scorpion gathers death around;
> Where at each step the stranger fears to wake
> The rattling terrors of the vengeful snake;
> Where crouching tigers wait their hapless prey,
> And savage men more murderous still than they;
> While oft in whirls the mad tornado flies,
> Mingling the ravag'd landscape with the skies.
>
> ("The Deserted Village," 1770)

Promotional literature put out to encourage emigration naturally presented a rather different picture, sometimes supplementing the written word with views or plans of neat new towns [159], but this was no enticement for European artists.

The depiction of the American scene was therefore left to amateurs. Some were explorers, such as the Franciscan father Louis Hennepin, whose *New Discovery of a Vast Country in America* (1698) contains the first depiction of Niagara; some were government officials, such as Thomas Pownall [162]; some were soldiers, such as Thomas Davies, whose neat, fresh, engagingly naive watercolours were plainly made for his own enjoyment [163, 164]. Only one professional landscape painter, John Webber, went to America before the end of the eighteenth century. He was taken on Captain Cook's last expedition, in order to supply "the unavoidable imperfections of written accounts," and the wash drawings he made in the far north are the finest American landscapes painted before the nineteenth century [165]. Although made as scientific records, Webber's glimpses of silent seas and unscaled mountain heights rising from vast empty shores convey an extraordinary feeling for atmosphere akin to that of John Robert Cozens's Alpine views. Early in the next century the coast still further north was to be painted by Ludwig Choris, artist to a Russian expedition [169].

But whether painted by professionals or amateurs, these early North American landscapes, in which picturesque or dramatic views of rivers, lakes, and waterfalls predominate, might almost seem to have been inspired by Buffon's characterisation of the New World. "Lands which have been long inhabited," Buffon wrote, "are easily distinguished from new countries, where the soil appears in a rude state, where the rivers are full of cataracts, where the earth is either overflowed, or parched up with

179

drought, and where every spot on which a tree will grow, is covered with uncultivated woods."[1] It was remarks such as these that lay behind Goldsmith's account of Georgia. They gave little encouragement to the landscape painter.

1. George Louis Le Clerc comte de Buffon: *Natural History* (Paris, 1749), London, 1792, vol. I, p. 13.

Abraham Storck (Sturckenburg or Sturck)

Dutch, 1644-after 1704.
The son of a painter, Jan Jansz. Sturck or Sturckenburch, Abraham Storck was born in Amsterdam, where he seems to have spent his entire life. His recorded paintings range in date from 1650 to 1695 and show the influence of his slightly older contemporaries, especially Willem van de Velde the Younger, Ludolf Bakhuizen, and Jan Beerstraaten. Apart from some topographical views of Amsterdam, they are all marine subjects, mainly Dutch and Italianate harbour scenes and sea battles.

Abraham Storck (Sturckenburg or Sturck)

155A *Dutch Whalers*
Oil on canvas. ca. 1688. Signed: *A Storck 1688.* 21½ x 28 inches (54.7 x 71 cm.). Mr. and Mrs. Douglass C. Fonda, Jr., Nantucket.

America appeared to Europeans as a land of climatic extremes, and, although their vision was dominated by the landscape of the sultry tropical zone, the icy north also played a part in it. The picture exhibited is one of the few in which Dutch and English artists visualised whaling ships off the barren coast of Greenland or north-east America—the regions to which they sailed after the Dutch whaling station at Spitzbergen was closed in the 1640s. At about the time it was painted, however, New Englanders were taking the lead from Europeans in whaling and the processing of whale oil.

Wolfgang William Romer or Römer

Dutch-English, 1640-1713.
Born in The Hague, Romer became a soldier and had risen to the rank of colonel by 1688, when he went to England with the prince of Orange on his accession as William III. He served as an engineer with William III's army in Ireland in 1690-92 and on a Mediterranean expedition in 1693. In 1697 he accompanied the earl of Bellamont, governor of New England, to New York. He directed the fortification of Boston harbour in 1701-03 but had returned to England by 1708.

Wolfgang William Romer or Römer

156 *Map of Colonel Römer's Journey from New York to Albany*

Pen, ink, and watercolour. 1700.
17⅜ x 23¼ inches (44 x 59 cm.). Inscription: *A Mappe of Colonel Römers voyage to ye 5 Indian Nations going from New York to Albany thence west. . . .* Provenance: Acquired by the British Museum in 1828 as part of the topographical collection in the Library of George III.
London, The British Library, Map Library.

In 1700 Lord Bellamont, governor of New England, sent Colonel Romer with Major Van Brugh and Henrick Hansen to survey the still little known land between Albany and the western Finger Lakes and select the site for a fort on Lake Ontario. Romer was then sixty, and it must have been a strenuous journey for a man of his age. Nor was it made any easier by the Indians of the Five Nations, who refused to co-operate (cf. E. B. O'Callaghan and R. Fernow, ed.: *Documents relative to the Colonial History of the State of New York,* New York, 1856-87, vol. IV, pp. 802-806). But he explored the country around Lake Oneida and along the Oswega River to Lake Ontario. The map exhibited is one of two which re-

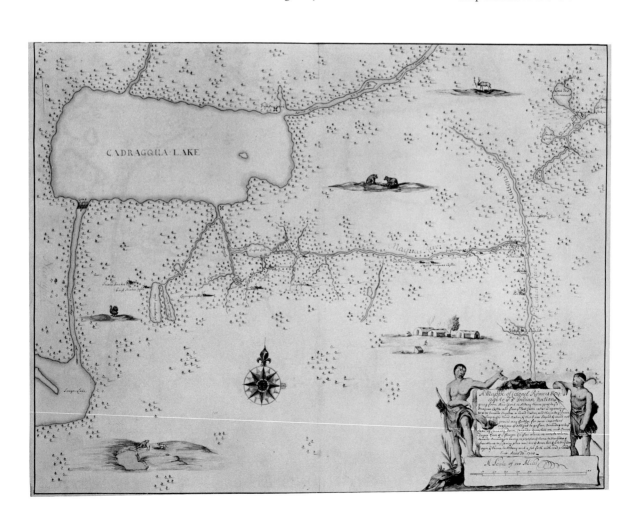

cord this (the other is in the Public Record Office, London, CO 700, New York, 13 A; cf. W. P. Cumming, S. E. Hillier, D. B. Quinn, and G. Williams: *The Exploration of North America 1630-1776*, London, 1974, p. 62). It indicates local wild-life—turkeys, beavers, and bears—as well as Indian settlements and geographical features. Though clearly based on a chart made in the course of the journey, it was probably drawn after Romer's return to New York.

Literature: R. H. Major and J. Holmes: *Catalogue of the Manuscript Maps, Charts and Plans, and of the Topographical Drawings in the British Museum,* London, 1861, vol. III, p. 524.

Johann Baptist Homann
German, 1664-1724.
Homann was one of the leading German engravers and publishers of maps and founded the Homännischen Landkarten-Offizin in Nuremberg, which survived until 1848. In 1698 he went to Leipzig to engrave the maps for Christophorus Cellarius: *Notitia orbis antiqui* (1701-06), and after his return to Nuremberg he engraved the maps for *Atlas novus, hoc est, Geographia universa* (1710) by the Jesuit P. Heinrich Scherer. He issued some 200 maps, richly decorated with historical or ethnographical illustrations. In 1715 he became a member of the Royal Prussian Societät der Wissenschaften.

Johann Baptist Homann

157 *Map of Virginia, Maryland and Carolina*

ca. 1714. 19³⁄₁₆ x 22¾ inches (48.7 x 57.8 cm.). Inscription: *Virginia Marylandia et Carolina in America septentrionali Britannorum industria excultae repraesentatae a Ioh.Bapt. Homann S.C.M. Geog. Norinbergae cum privilega sac.Caes.Majeste.* Savannah, Georgia Historical Society.

This sheet is from the 1759 reprint of Homann's *Atlas Geographicus Major,* first issued ca. 1714.

Literature: W. P. Cumming: *The Southeast in Early Maps,* Princeton, 1968, pp. 180-181.

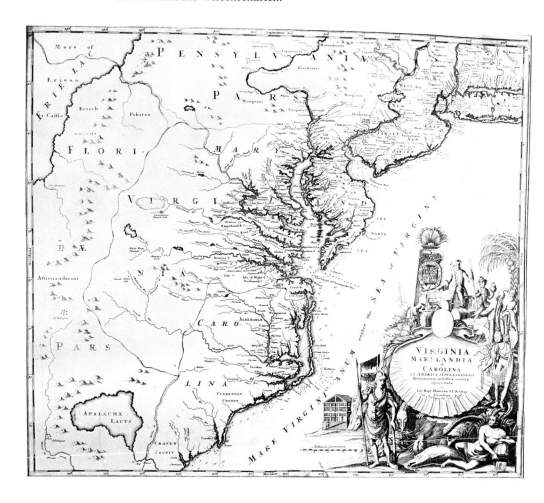

Jean-Baptiste Michel Le Bouteaux

French, fl. ca. 1720.
Little is known about this artist, except that he appears to be the same Le Bouteaux described in the caption of [158] as the assistant director of the concession of Law's Camp in New Biloxi.

Jean-Baptiste Michel Le Bouteaux

158 *View of the Camp of John Law's Concession in New Biloxi, Louisiana*

Pen, ink, and wash. 1720. 19½ x 35⅜ inches (49.5 x 89.8 cm.). Signed and dated. Inscription: *VEUE DU CAMP DE LA CONCESSION DE MON-SEIGNEUR LAW AU NOUVEAU BILOXY. COSTE DE LA LOUISI-ANNE / dessignie par Jean baptiste Michel / Le bouteaux / Le dixᵉ De-cembre 1720 / De l'ordre de Mʳ Elias / St. Huteus directeur / general.* Arm of cross inscribed *Concession de Mon-seigʳ LAW.* Captions translated as follows: *A. Storehouse 80 feet long and 25 feet wide. B. Tent of Mr. Elias St. Huteus, director general. C. Tent of Mr. Le Vens, second director. D. Tent of Mr. Le Bouteaux, assistant director. E. Tent of Mr. Navarre, surgeon. F. Tent of Mr. Le Saint, chaplain. G. House of R. P. Maximin, chaplain. H. Tent of Mr. Labro, tobacco inspector. I. The main road formed at its end by the workers' barracks, in the middle of which are the tents of the foremen and assistant foremen. L. Camp of the concession of His Grace the Duc de Guiche. M. Guards' quarters. N. Officers' tents. O. House of Boucher, charged with the care of the ditch carrying salt water to the evaporator. P. The forge, the armorer, and the cutler. Q. The furnace. R. Barracks of the apothecary and the apprentice surgeons. S. Hospital. T. Launch on support with a 28 foot keel and 30 feet from stem to stern. V. Barge used for towing the launches which anchor in the roadstead. X. Stakes driven for playing a game. Y. Spring having very good water which was directed towards Old Biloxi for the Director of the company. Z. Large cross at the entrance to the camp which indicates the Lord Proprietor of the concession. &. Pit in the sandy riverbank used for warming the sick. Since this drawing, the chapel has been enlarged and guards' quarters placed in line with the house of R. P. Maximin.* Provenance: Ayer Collection.
Chicago, Newberry Library, Ayer Collection.

Although Louisiana had been claimed for France by La Salle in 1685, no permanent French colony was established there until the le Moyne brothers founded Port Biloxi in 1699. In 1712 the financier Antoine Crozat—brother of the famous collector and patron of Watteau—took responsibility for the settlement of Louisiana in return for a fifteen-year monopoly on its trade. By 1717, however, Crozat had given up hope of ever realising a profit and relinquished his rights. The Council of Regency then placed the colony under the charge of John Law (1671-1729), the Scottish adventurer who fled to France on being condemned to death for killing "Beau" Wilson in a duel and established the Banque Générale (the first bank of any kind in France). In 1717 he launched his "Mississippi scheme"—later known as the "Mississippi Bubble," the headquarters of which was at the camp depicted in this drawing. It lay east of the projected but never built fort at New Biloxi, across the bay from Old Biloxi. Made on 10 December 1720, the drawing appears to be an accurate representation of the camp. Here the settlers sent by Law disembarked and remained until boats were constructed to take them up the Mississippi. The large warehouse in the background is characteristic of early French buildings in Louisiana. (It is a timber frame building erected on ground sills, with its steep hipped roof covered with wood shingles.)

John Law's Mississippi Bubble burst in 1720, when the truth about conditions in Louisiana became known. Not only were impressed emigrants being sent—one category of whom was later immortalised in Prévost's *Manon Lescaut*—but the limited and as yet undeveloped resources were quite inadequate for the large number being dumped there. Early in 1721 five hundred of them died at Biloxi.

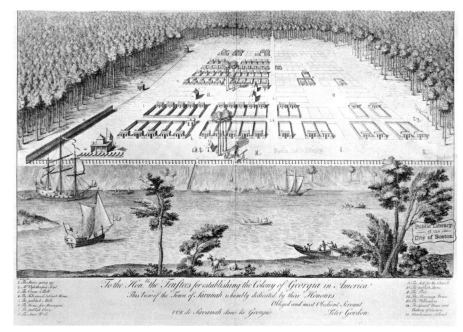

To the Hon.ble the Trustees for establishing the Colony of Georgia in America. This View of the Town of Savanah is humbly dedicated by their Honours. Obliged and most Obedient Servant Peter Gordon. VUE de Savannah dans la Georgie.

Pierre Fourdrinier

French, fl. ca. 1720-1758.
Fourdrinier was an engraver of French extraction working in London. He illustrated a wide range of books, from collected editions of Racine, Moliere, and Shakespeare to R. Wood's *Ruins of Palmyra* and *Ruins of Balbek* (1753 and 1757, after drawings by G. B. Borra).

Literature: *The French in America,* exhibition catalogue, Detroit, 1951, no. 164; W. P. Cumming, S. E. Hillier, D. B. Quinn, and G. Williams, *The Exploration of North America 1630-1776*, London, 1974, p. 157.

Pierre Fourdrinier

159 *A View of Savannah*
Engraving. 1734. 15¾ x 21¾ inches (40 x 55 cm.).
Boston, The Trustees of the Public Library of the City of Boston.

This bird's-eye view was drawn by Peter Gordon soon after General James Edward Oglethorpe (1696-1785) had chosen the site and laid out the plan of Savannah in 1733. The original town-plan of wards around squares still survives, although the core of the present city is largely a creation of the early nineteenth century, after the fires of 1796 and 1820, which destroyed nearly all the original buildings. An interesting panoramic view by Firmin Cearveau of the city southwards from City Hall (1837, Georgia Historical Society) shows some of the original wooden buildings of the eighteenth century.

Literature: *American Printmaking The First 150 Years*, Smithsonian Institution, Washington, D.C., 1969, no. 21.

Matthias Seutter

German, 1678-1757.

Seutter was a pupil of Johann Baptist Homann [157] at Nuremberg and set up his own publishing house for maps, mainly coloured maps, in his native Augsburg. He issued two large collections of maps, *Atlas Novas*, Vienna, 1728 and *Atlas Minor*. He also issued engravings to be mounted on globes.

Matthias Seutter

160 *Plan of New Ebenezer*

Engraving, coloured. 1747. 19½ x 11¾ inches (49.5 x 29.9 cm.). Inscription: *Plan von New Ebenezer verlegt von Matth.Seutter. Kayser: Geogr. in Augspurg.*
Savannah, Georgia Historical Society.

Not long after General James Edward Oglethorpe founded Savannah in 1733 [159], the Trustees for Establishing the Colony of Georgia settled a group of Germans from Salzburg further up the Savannah River at a place they named Ebenezer. This plan of New Ebenezer appeared in the thirteenth part (1747) of the "Urlsperger Tracts," a work begun by Samuel Urlsperger at Halle in 1734, entitled *Ausfürliche Nachricht von den Saltzburgischen Emigranten.* The 1735 has the additional title of: *Der Ausführlichen Nachrichten Von der Koniglich Groso-Britannischen Colonie Saltzburgischen Emigranten in America.*

The two inserts below the *Plan of New Ebenezer* are a map of Georgia and part of Carolina, including a detail of Great St. Simon's Isle, and a detailed plan of the mill house and mill creek near Ebenezer.

Literature: P. Smith: *Early Maps of Carolina,* exhibition catalogue, Library of the University of South Carolina, 1930, p. 14.

William Pierie

English, fl. 1759-1777.

Nothing is known of Pierie, except that he joined the Royal Regiment of Artillery in 1759, became a matross or cadet the next year, second lieutenant in 1768, first lieutenant in 1771, and resigned his commission on 3 October 1777. He probably received, like other artillery officers, some training in draughtsmanship at the Royal Military Academy, Woolwich, under either Gamaliel Massiot or Paul Sandby, who was appointed drawing master there in 1768. He may be identical with a "Captain Pierie" who exhibited a landscape at the Society of Artists in London in 1775.

William Pierie

161 *Map and Views of Boston*

Pen, ink, and watercolour. Signed and dated: *. . . in the Year 1773, by Lt. Wm. Pierie of the Rl. Regt. of Artillery.* 22 x 34⅞ inches (56 x 88.5 cm.). Provenance: Acquired by the Museum as part of the topographical collection in the Library of George III, 1828. London, The British Library, Map Library.

The views surrounding this map still show Boston as a peaceful colonial city, though it had already been the scene of the "Massacre" of 5 March 1770. The "Tea Party" took place towards the end of the year in which it was drawn. Pierie's watercolours are somewhat similar to those of the better known Thomas Davies, who was an officer in the same regiment. But they are more obviously practical and still less influenced by the conventions of eighteenth-century landscape painting.

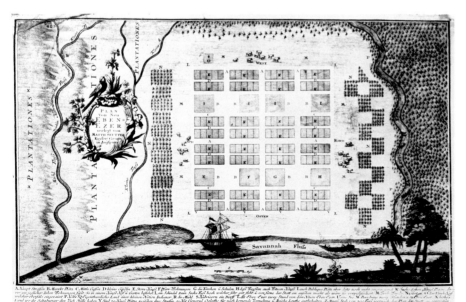

VIEW of BOSTON the Capital of NEW ENGLAND; from Col. HATCH's House on the Road to DORCHESTER.

VIEW FROM DORCHESTER NECK at Station A.

VIEW FROM CHARLESTOWN at Station B.

VIEW of CASTLE WILLIAM at Station C.

VIEW of CASTLE WILLIAM at Station D.

VIEW of CASTLE WILLIAM &c. DORCHESTER NECK & the Light House, &c. sailing out of the HARBOUR.

Literature: *Catalogue of the Manuscript Maps, Charts, and Plans, and of the Topographical Drawings in the British Museum,* London, 1861, vol. III, p. 537; *The American War of Independence 1775-83,* exhibition catalogue, the British Library, 1975, no. 68.

Thomas Pownall

English, 1722-1805.
Pownall was known as "Governor Pownall" and is famous for his *The Administration of the Colonies* (1764), in which he proposed that all British possessions in America be united into one Dominion and pointed out the reluctance of colonists to be taxed without their own consent. He was lieutenant-governor of New Jersey from ca. 1753 until he became governor of Massachusetts in 1757. In 1759 he was transferred to South Carolina, as his manners were thought unsuited to "the gravity of New England puritans." He returned to England from America in 1760. As a member of Parliament he urged the government to treat with the colonists after war broke out in 1775.

Thomas Pownall

162   *A View of the Great Cohoes Falls, on the Mohawk River; / The Fall about Seventy feet; the River near a Quarter of a Mile broad*

Engraving. ca. 1761. 18⅛ x 24⅛ inches (45.4 x 59.8 cm.). Inscription: *Sketch'd on the Spot by his Excellency Governor Pownall. Painted by Paul Sandby, & Engraved by Wm. Elliot. / London. Printed for John Bowles at No. 13 in Cornhill, Robert Sayer at No. 53 in Fleet Street, Thos. Jefferys the Corner of St. Martins Lane in the Strand, Carington Bowles at No. 69 in St. Pauls Church Yard, and Henry Parker at No. 82 in Cornhill.*
Collection of Mr. and Mrs. Paul Mellon.

Governor Pownall made a number of sketches when in North America, some of which were later engraved by William Elliot (1727-1766) from paintings done after them by Paul Sandby (1725-1809). The Great Cohoes Falls are situated just above the mouth of the Mohawk River. They greatly impressed early travellers in North America. Pownall described their sound as being "like the roar of a storm at sea heard from the land in the dead of night," in *A topographical description . . . of North America,* 1776. Because of the falls, travellers were forced to enter the river by an overland route from Albany.

Literature: W. P. Cumming, S. Hillier, D. B. Quinn, G. Williams: *The Exploration of North America 1630-1776,* London, 1974, p. 64.

A View of the Great Cohoes Falls, on the Mohawk River; / Vue de la Grande Cataracte de Cohoes, sur la Rivière des Mohawks;

Thomas Davies

English, ca. 1737-1812.

Davies was a professional soldier, eventually rising to the rank of lieutenant-general, and a talented amateur watercolour painter, working in the style of Sandby, whom he may have known as a draughtsman to the Board of Ordnance. He crossed the Atlantic for the first time in 1757 and served in the Canadian campaign. After Quebec was in British hands, he was sent to explore the St. Lawrence and Lake Ontario, and during this period he made many watercolours. Then he was in England for several years and exhibited at the Royal Academy for the first time in 1771, but left for North America in 1773 and saw action in the Revolutionary War, probably at Bunker Hill and certainly at Manhattan.

He was last in America in 1786-89, when he may have been senior artillery officer in Canada.

Thomas Davies

163 *Montreal, 1762*

Watercolour. 1762. 13¹⁵⁄₁₆ x 21¹⁄₁₆ inches (35.3 x 53.5 cm.). Provenance: Earl of Derby; sold Christie's 19 October 1953; Frank T. Sabin, London. Ottawa, The National Gallery of Canada.

The *verso* is inscribed (not by the artist): "A View of Montreal in Canada taken from the Isle St. Helena in 1762," with the following inserted: "so-called Citadelle Hill / now removed." The buildings shown in the watercolour include, from left to right, the Récollet church, the Grey Nuns' convent (?), the Parish Church, and the fort.

Literature: The National Gallery of Canada, *Annual Report of the Board of Trustees for the Fiscal Year 1954-55*, Ottawa, 1955, p. 33; J. R. Harper: "Three Centuries of Canadian Painting" in *Canadian Art* (Nov.-Dec. 1962), p. 411; W. E. Greening: "Some Early Recorders of the Nineteenth Century Canadian Scene" in *Canadian Geographical Journal* (April, 1963), pp. 124-125; D. G. G. Kerr and R. J. Robinson: *Canada, a Visual History*, Toronto, 1966, p. 21; *Thomas Davies*, exhibition catalogue, The National Gallery of Canada, Ottawa, 1972, no. 18.

Thomas Davies

164 *Great "Seneca" Falls, Lake Ontario*

Watercolour. Inscription by the artist: *A View of the Casionchiagon or Great Seneca Falls Lake Ontario North America taken on the spot 1766 T. Davies Pinxit.* 13⅜ x 20⅜ inches (34.6 x 51.7 cm.). Provenance: Earl of Derby; sold Christie's 19 October 1953; Frank T. Sabin, London. Ottawa, The National Gallery of Canada.

The *verso* is inscribed (not by the artist): "Casionchiagon, or Little Seneca's River on Lake Ontario." An earlier view by Davies of these falls, the uppermost of three on the Genesee River at the present Rochester, New York, is in the Public Archive of Canada, Ottawa. The region was in the territory of the Seneca Indians.

John Webber

English, 1752-1793.
Webber's father was a Swiss sculptor who had emigrated to London. John Webber was trained under J. G. Wille in Paris, J. L. Aberli in Berne, and at the Royal Academy in London. In 1776 he was appointed draughtsman to Captain Cook's last voyage—"for the express purpose," as Cook later wrote, "of supplying the unavoidable imperfections of written accounts, by enabl-

---

Literature: The National Gallery of Canada, *Annual Report of the Board of Trustees for the Fiscal Year 1954-55,* Ottawa, 1955, p. 33; R. H. Hubbard: *The Development of Canadian Art,* Ottawa, 1963, *Thomas Davies,* exhibition catalogue, The National Gallery of Canada, Ottawa, 1972, no. 25.

ing us to preserve, and to bring home, such drawings of the most memorable scenes of our transactions, as could only be executed by a professed and skillful artist." Webber later superintended the engraving of his drawings as illustrations to the three volumes of Cook's *Voyage to the Pacific Ocean,* 1784. He was elected an associate the following year and a full member of the Royal Academy in 1791.

John Webber

165 *Sandwich (Prince William) Sound, 1778*

Pen, ink, and wash. 1778. 19⅜ x 26 inches (49 x 66 cm.).
London, British Library, Department of Manuscripts.

Captain Cook's third and last expedition sailed from London in July 1776, and his two ships, the *Resolution* and *Discovery,* first sighted the northwest coast of America on 7 March 1778. They anchored in King George's Sound, or Nootka Sound, on Vancouver Island, and from there sailed north, reaching Prince William Sound (named Sandwich Sound by Cook) in May. Here they encountered a different type of native from the Nootka Indians, though whether they were of Eskimo or Athapaskan stock is not known. They evidently lived away from the shores, for no description of their settlements is given by Cook. But many visited the two ships. "Some ventured on board the Ship," Cook wrote in his Journal on 14 May 1778,

> but not before some of our people went into their boats. Amongst those that came on board was a good looking middle aged man who we afterward found to be the Chief; he was cloathed in a dress made of the Sea beaver skin and on his head such a Cap as is worn by the people of King Georges Sound, Ornamented

with sky blue glass beads about the size of a large pea; these he seemed to set ten times more Value upon than our white glass beads which they probably thought was only crystal which they have among them. They however esteemed beads of all sorts and gave whatever they had in exchange for them, even their fine Sea beaver skins. But here I must observe that they set no more value upon these skins than others, neither here nor at King Georges Sound, till our people put a Value upon them, and even then at the last place they would sooner part with a dress made of these than one made of the skins of wild Cats or Martins. These peoples were also desirous of iron, but it must be pieces eight or ten inches long at least, and three or four fingers broad for small pieces they absolutly rejected; consequently they got but little from us, as it was now become rather a scarce article. The points of some of their spears or lances, were of Iron shaped into the form of a Bear spear, others were of Copper and a few of bone which the points of their darts, arrows &ca were made of. I could not prevail on the chief to trust himself below the upper deck, nor did he and his companions remain long on board, but while they were it was necessary to look after them as they soon betrayed a thevesh dispossission.

Literature: J. C. Beaglehole, ed.: *The Journals of Captain James Cook on his Voyages of Discovery: The Voyage of the Resolution and Discovery 1776-1780*, Cambridge, The Hakluyt Society, 1967, Part I, p. ccxiii.

L'ENTRÉE AU PORT DE BOSTON
DANS L'AMERIQUE.

Dominic Serres

English, 1722-1793.
Born at Auch (Gascony), Serres ran away to sea and eventually became master of a vessel trading with the West Indies. In about 1758 he was taken prisoner and brought to England, where he settled, working as an artist specialising in marine subjects. He was a founding member of the Royal Academy, of which he was appointed librarian in 1792. He became marine painter to George III.

Dominic Serres (attributed to)

166 *Staten Island from Fort Hamilton, New York*
Black ink and watercolour over graphite. ca. 1791. 9³⁄₁₆ x 23³⁄₁₆ inches (23.3 x 58.8 cm.).
Greenwich, National Maritime Museum.

The Stars and Stripes indicates that this was painted after the War of Independence, and it has been dated 1791. Serres is known to have worked from drawings by other artists (e.g. his two views of Quebec in the Public Archives of Canada, Ottawa), and he may have made this watercolour in that way.

Claude Joseph Vernet

French, 1714-1789.
A landscape painter, Vernet specialised in views of Mediterranean ports and worked both in Italy and the south of France. He was commissioned by Louis XV to paint the ports of France. He also specialised in painting shipwrecks.

Claude Joseph Vernet (after)

167 *The Port of Boston*
Etching. ca. 1790. Signed: *Vernet pinxit. F. A. Annert Sc.* 5¾ x 8⅛ inches (14.5 x 20.7 cm.).
Inscription: *L'Entrée au Port de Boston dans L'Amérique.*
Washington, D.C., Library of Congress.

This is one of a pair of wholly imaginary views of American ports by Friedrich Albrecht Annert (1759-1800) after Vernet, the other being an equally fantastic view of the port of Philadelphia.

George Bulteel Fisher

English, 1764-1834.
Fisher was a distinguished artillery officer in the Peninsula War and was later knighted. An amateur artist, he exhibited at the Royal Academy in London between 1780 and 1803 as an "Honorary Exhibitor."

George Bulteel Fisher (after)

168 *The Falls of Montmorenci*
Aquatint. 1796. Signed: *G. B. Fisher delint.* and *J. W. Edy Aquantinta.* 20¹⁄₁₆ x 28 inches (51 x 71 cm.).
Inscription: *View of the River St. Lawrence, Falls of Montmorenci from the Island of Orleans.*
Provenance: Acquired by the British Museum in 1828 as part of the topographical collection in the Library of George III.
London, British Library.

This acquaint was issued with others by John William Edy (ca. 1780-1820) after George Bulteel Fisher in *Six Views of North America from Original Drawings made on the spot, by Lieutenant Fisher, of the Royal Artillery,* London, 1796. A watercolour of the Falls of Montmorenci near Quebec, signed and dated by George Bulteel Fisher in 1792, is in the Victoria and Albert Museum, London.

Fisher described the falls when frozen as "the most beautiful filigree work that can be conceived." He also drew them from the Island of Orleans —"altogether one of the most striking and pleasing scenes which this country affords." The other aquatints in the volume represent "Cape Diamond, Plains of Abraham and Part of the Town of Quebec," the "Falls of Chaudière," a "View of the St. Ann's or Grand River," and "St. Anthony's Nose on the North River."

Literature: *Catalogue of Maps, Prints, Drawings, etc. forming the Geographical and Topographical Collection attached to the Library of His late Majesty King George the Third,* London, 1829, p. 230; *The British Museum: Catalogue of Printed Maps, Charts and Plans,* vol. v, London, 1967, col. 314; R. Strong: *A Pageant of Canada,* exhibition catalogue, National Gallery of Canada, Ottawa, 1967, no. 161.

Ludwig Andrevitch Choris

Russian, 1795-1828.

Choris was of German-Russian parentage, trained as an artist in Moscow, and began his career as botanical draughtsman to F. A. Marschall von Bieberstein on a tour of the Caucasus. In 1815 he went as official artist on the Russian Pacific Ocean expedition led by Otto von Kotzebue (with the poet Adelbert von Chamisso as naturalist), exploring the west coast of America from the tropics, stopping in the region of San Francisco, where he made several drawings (Bancroft Library, University of California, Berkeley), and sailing along the coast of Alaska. He published lithographs after many of the drawings made on this expedition in his *Voyage pittoresque autour du Monde*, Paris, 1821-23. In 1826 he published a further volume, *Vues et paysages des régions équinoxiales*, and shortly afterwards returned to Central America, where he was murdered by robbers near Vera Cruz.

Ludwig Andrevitch Choris

169 *The Ice-bergs of Kotzebue Sound*
Watercolour. 1816. 10¼ x 17 inches
(25.4 x 43 cm.).
Provenance: David Bushnell Jr., 1925;
Belle Bushnell.
Cambridge, Mass., Peabody Museum of Archaeology and Ethnology, Harvard University.

This is one of the drawings made by Choris on the Russian-sponsored expedition led by Otto von Kotzebue with the purpose of finding a route from the Pacific to the Atlantic through the Bering Straits (i.e. the Northwest Passage from the other end). The main discovery was the sound still named after Kotzebue. On the shores of Alaska, Choris drew not only landscapes but also Eskimo carvings.

Literature: *The Painter and the New World,* exhibition catalogue, Montreal Museum of Fine Arts, Montreal, 1967, no. 20.

XI
The Noble Savage

"Atheistical, proud, wild, cruel, barbarous, brutish (in one word) diabolical"—these were adjectives used to characterise the Indians in 1682 by Mary Rowlandson, who had been taken prisoner by them.[1] "Affable, liberal, moderate" were those applied to them by the Jesuit missionary to the Hurons, Père Chauchetière, in 1694. "We see in the savages the fine remains of human nature which are entirely corrupted among civilised people. Indeed," he went on, "all our Fathers and the French who have lived among the savages reckon that life is passed more sweetly among them than among us."[2] These may seem extremist statements, yet they can be paralleled in many other writings of the seventeenth and eighteenth centuries, in plays, novels, and poems as well as in philosophical treatises, histories of America, and travel books. The hostile view was widespread, though by no means uniformly held, among the colonists.[3] And it was shared by others, notably Thomas Hobbes and, in the eighteenth century, Buffon, Voltaire, Raynal, and de Pauw. The favourable opinion was held especially by imaginative writers, one of whom described the Indians as being "above our level in the virtues which give real preeminence"[4]—in other words, noble savages.

Among the admirers of the Indians there were, however, important differences of opinion, especially regarding their laws, system of government, and religion—or lack of them. Reports were so diverse that the "savage people of America" could be cited both to prove and contradict the notion that these institutions were common to all mankind. John Locke found in the supposed atheism of the Indians support for his contention that there were no innate ideas even of the existence of God.[5] Alexander Pope, on the other hand, in the "Essay on Man" (much of which is indebted to Locke), brought forward, as evidence of the universality of hope for an after-life, the

> Indian whose untutor'd mind
> Sees God in clouds, or hears him on the wind;
> His soul, proud Science never taught to stray
> Far as the solar walk, or milky way;
> Yet simple Nature to his hope has giv'n,
> Behind the cloud-topt hill, an humbler heav'n;
> Some safer world in depth of woods embrac'd,
> Some happier island in the wat'ry waste,
> Where slaves once more their native land behold,
> No fiends torment, no Christians thirst for gold.
> To Be, contents his natural desire,
> He asks no Angel's wing, no Seraph's fire;
> But thinks, admitted to that equal sky,
> His faithful dog shall bear him company.

195

Similarly, as regards the Indian's "natural way of life," a wide range of views was possible even among admirers. To Louis Armand de Lahontan, for example, writing in 1703, it represented an ideal. The Indians had no kings because "nature knows neither distinctions nor pre-eminence in individuals of the same species;" no code of laws because "willing respect for natural law was the unique wealth" of their society; no religious creed because "man ought never to relinquish the privileges of reason which is the noblest faculty with which God has enriched him."[6] To Rousseau, on the other hand, no such simple view was possible, though it was largely from his study of reports on the Indians that he developed his ideas on a "state of nature" and the "best state for man," which he supposed to have been before the discovery of iron and the development of agriculture, when a patriarchal communistic society flourished.[7]

Correspondingly in the visual arts, the Indian was frequently idealised into a noble savage. Statuesque figures from de Bry's late sixteenth-century volumes [64, 65, 66, 67] were copied and imitated by innumerable book illustrators, making their most piquant reappearance in J.-L. Lafitau's comparative study of ancient Greek and Indian customs and religious rites.[8] John Verelst, who painted the "Indian Kings" visiting Queen Anne in 1710, showed them as English squires *en travestie* [170]. Other artists followed suit in their depiction of later Indian visitors to Europe. After the mid-century, however, the Indian was shown not as the equal of the civilised man but as his superior, as in Jean Jacques François Le Barbier's strange picture of *Canadian Indians at their Child's Grave* [181] or, more notably, in *The Indian Widow* by Joseph Wright of Derby—an exemplar of female virtue worthy to rank with the noblest of the Romans [184].

But such images, though memorable, are perhaps misleading. Unfavourable views of the Indian were also widely held, though their reflection in the visual arts was limited to caricatures of the revolutionary period [233, 237] and to a very few other works, such as the Californian drawings of Alexandre-Jean Noël [175]. A. de Batz, in an amateurish way, and Gustavus Hesselius with much greater technical ability, seem to have aimed at objectivity, and Hesselius painted two portraits of Indian chiefs, which, from an ethnographical point of view, are perhaps the most accurate before the nineteenth century [174]. But although Hesselius lived in America for more than forty years, he does not seem to have portrayed Indians again. Perhaps there was no demand for direct, straightforward portraits of them. John Webber and Sigmund Bacstrom, who accompanied expeditions to the northwest coast, made drawings of Indians as scientific records [178, 179, 188]. Yet large scale portraits, like those by Nathaniel Dance [183] and William Hodges [185], though commissioned for scientists, are more than a little coloured by preconceptions about the noble savage.

196

1. Benjamin Bissell: *The American Indian in English Literature of the Eighteenth Century*, New Haven, 1925, p. 8.

2. R. G. Thwaites: *The Jesuit Relations and Allied Documents*, Cleveland, 1896-1901, vol. LXIV, p. 130, quoted by G. Chinard: *L'Amérique et le rêve exotique*, Paris, 1913, p. 147.

3. R. H. Pearce: *The Savages of America*, Baltimore, 1953.

4. *Chrysal: or the Adventures of a Guinea*, London, 1760-1765, published anonymously but attributed to Charles Johnstone, cf. B. Bissell, *The American Indian*, p. 97.

5. John Locke: *An Essay Concerning Human Understanding* (1690), Book I, chapter 4, par. 8.

6. L. A. de Lahontan: *Supplément aux Voyages du baron de Lahontan où l'on trouve des dialogues curieux entre l'auteur et un sauvage de bon sens qui a voyagé*, The Hague, 1703, cf. Chinard, *L'Amérique et le rêve exotique*, pp. 157-187.

7. For Rousseau's complex attitude, see S. Landucci: *I filosofi e i selvaggi 1580-1780*, Bari, 1972, pp. 367-384.

8. J.-L. Lafitau: *Moeurs des sauvages américains comparées aux moeurs des premiers temps*, Paris, 1724.

ETOW OH KOAM, King of the River Nation.

John Verelst

English.

A member of a family of Dutch artists, several of whom worked in England, Verelst was probably the son of a flower painter, Cornelius Verelst. On his death he was described as a "noted face painter" in *The Gentleman's Magazine.* Numerous signed portraits by him, dated between 1706 and 1734, are recorded, mainly in English country houses.

John Verelst (after)

170   *Etow Oh Koam, King of the River Nation*

Mezzotint. 1710. 14 x 10¼ inches (35.5 x 26 cm.).
Inscription: *J. Verelst pinx. J. Simon fecit. Etow Oh Koam, King of the River Nation.*
Washington, D.C., Library of Congress, Prints and Photographs Division.

This is a portrait of one of the four Mohawk Indians who visited England in 1710. He was christened Nicholas and was probably either a Schacook or Mohican in origin, adopted by the Mohawks. The visit to England was organised by three colonial leaders, Colonels Samuel Vetch, Peter Schuyler, and Francis Nicholson, and had a double purpose: to convince the Indians of British might and to obtain the co-operation of Queen Anne's ministers for a massive attack on the French in Canada. Vetch wrote: "It will be requisite the Indians see as much of the Grandure and Magnificence of Brittan as possible, for the french endevour to possess them all with wonderfull notions of the Grandure and power of their master." The party consisted of Etow Oh Koam, Oh Nee Yeath Ton No Prow, Sa Ga Qua Prah Ton (grandfather of the famous Joseph Brant), and Te Yee Neen Ho Go Prow (who became a great leader of the Mohawks and visited England again in 1740).

Although only the last was a true Sachem, they were called in England the Four Indian Kings and were fêted as such.

They arrived at Portsmouth on 2 April 1710, went to London, were received by Queen Anne and the archbishop of Canterbury, shown the sights, taken to the theatre, and richly entertained until 22 May, when they set sail for America from Plymouth. The considerable interest they aroused is reflected in the full account of their activities printed in the newspapers. Richard Steele mentioned them in *The Tatler* (no. 171, May 1710); a year after they left Addison devoted an essay in *The Spectator* (27 April 1711) to a satire on English manners from the supposed point of view of one of them —and, as this was so frequently reprinted and translated, it kept their fame alive. Bernard Lens painted their portraits in miniature (British Museum), and several prints of them were published. John Verelst was commissioned to paint full-length portraits (now lost) for the queen, and from these Jean Simon (1675-1751), a French engraver working in London, made a set of mezzotints which were advertised in *The Tatler* in November and December 1710. The print exhibited belongs to this series, of which more than two hundred were shipped to America and distributed among friendly Sachems. The prints also provided the designs for wall-paintings in the main stairwell of the Macphaedris-Warner House, Portsmouth, New Hampshire.

Literature: J. Challoner Smith: *British Mezzotinto Portraits,* London, 1883, vol. III, no. 1095; C. T. Foreman: *Indians Abroad 1493-1938,* Norman, Okla., 1943, p. 36; Richmond P. Bond: *Queen Anne's American Kings,* Oxford, 1952; J. R. Fawcett-Thompson in *The Connoisseur,* LXX (1969), p. 49; Elwood Parry: *The Image of the Indian and the Black Man in American Art, 1590-1900,* New York, 1974, pp. 18-20.

SAUVAGE NEPISINGUE EN CANADA 1717.

171 *Nipissing Indian*
France. Pen and watercolour. 1717.
9⁵⁄₁₆ x 7⁵⁄₁₆ inches (23.6 x 18.6 cm.).
Inscription: *Sauvage Nepisingue en Canada 1717.*
Paris, Bibliothèque Nationale.

The Nipissing Indians were an Algonquin tribe living in the region of Lake Nipissing. But, despite its inscription, this drawing is clearly derived from one of John Verelst's portraits of the Indian "Kings" who visited Queen Anne in 1710 (see [170]) with merely fanciful variations. (Information kindly supplied by Dr. William C. Sturtevant.)

Literature: W. P. Cumming, S. E. Hillier, D. B. Quinn, G. Williams: *The Exploration of North America 1630-1776,* London, 1974, p. 14.

Bernard Picart
French, 1673-1733.

172 *The God of Hunting*
Pen and black ink and grey wash over traces of red chalk, heightened with white.
Signed and dated: *B. Picart f 1722.*
5⅞ x 8¼ inches (14.9 x 20.9 cm.).
Provenance: James Hazen Hyde.
New York, The Metropolitan Museum of Art, Gift of the Estate of James Hazen Hyde, 1959.

This is the preliminary drawing for plate 19 of the first volume describing the ceremonies and customs of "idolatrous peoples" in the great eleven-volume illustrated survey of *Cérémonies et coutumes religieuses de tous les peuples du Monde* published by Bernard Picart and Bruzen de la Martinière in Amsterdam in 1723. The scene is described in the text as follows:

> The Mexicans, especially those of Tlascalla, worshipped a god who had been a great hunter during his sojourn on earth. He was honoured by a solemn hunt which is here illustrated. While the image of the god was placed on an altar at the summit of a mountain around which many fires were lit, the devout hunters pursued wild beasts who, to escape the flames, took refuge on the top of the mountain. The animals were killed before the idol to which their hearts were sacrificed. The hunt ended with cheerful songs and cries of joy, after which the hunters took back the idol in triumph and the devotion of the day ended with a solemn festival.

The source for this extraordinary account is unidentified, and Picart's illustration appears to be original—unlike many of his other engravings in the same volume, which are derived from the publications of Montanus [39] and de Bry.

Cérémonies et coutumes is one of several works which reflect early eighteenth-century interest in comparative religion, which was taken up for various reasons—by orthodox churchmen, who studied the vagaries into which the devil had drawn the heathen, by deists, who sought a single faith underlying all the creeds, and by sceptics, who wished to show that all religions were equally false. In 1724 the Jesuit father Joseph-François Lafitau published an account of the religious beliefs and rites of the Indians, which he likened to those of ancient Greeks and ancient Egyptians, in order to disprove two arguments advanced by atheists: "that there is an almost complete world of nations which have no religion, and that the religion found elsewhere is the work of human prudence and an artifice of politicians." But the *Cérémonies et coutumes* by Picart and Bruzen de la Martinière, which left the reader free to draw his own conclusions from the mass of information and misinformation which it contained, seems to have been the more widely-read work: it was reprinted in 1743 and in a modified version in 1783.

A. De Batz

French.
Nothing is known of De Batz apart from his signed drawings, now in the Peabody Museum. One of these, depicting a temple and house of the chief of the Acolapissas, was made on 15 April 1731 and redrawn at New Orleans 22 June 1732. Others are dated up to 1735. He was probably an architect or engineer and may have been connected with the French Military Forces in Louisiana, where all his drawings were made. They are the earliest known to have been made in the Southern Country.

A. De Batz

173 *Choctaw Indians Equipped as Warriors and Carrying Scalps*

Pen and ink with watercolour.
ca. 1731-1735.
Signed lower left: *A. Debatz*. 8¼ x 15 inches (21 x 38 cm.).
Inscription: *Sauvages Tchaktas matachez en Guerriers qui portent des chevelures* and, below, *Petits sauvages* and, *negre*.
Provenance: Libreria Otto Lange, Florence; David I. Bushnell.
Cambridge, Mass., Peabody Museum of Archaeology and Ethnology, Harvard University.

The Choctaws became allies of the French, who tried to keep them at peace with the neighbouring Chickasaws, who were allies of the English. The English sought to foment war between them.

Literature: W. P. Cumming, S. Hillier, D. B. Quinn, G. Williams: *The Exploration of North America, 1630-1776*, p. 158.

Sauvages Tchaktas matachez en Guerriers qui portent des chevelures.

Gustavus Hesselius

Swedish, 1682-1755.
Hesselius was the first professional
European artist to settle in North
America. He was born at Folkäma,
Sweden, the son of a well-to-do family,
and in 1711 he emigrated with his
brother to the Swedish colony in Delaware but soon moved to Philadelphia,
where he spent the rest of his life. His
works include mythological and religious pictures, but he is best known for
his portraits of the colonial gentry of
Pennsylvania, Maryland, and Virginia.

Gustavus Hesselius

174 *Tishcohan*

Oil on canvas. 1735. 33 x 25 inches
(83.5 x 63.3 cm.). Provenance: John
Penn, whose descendant Granville
Penn, presented it to the Historical
Society of Pennsylvania, 1834.
Philadelphia, The Historical Society of
Pennsylvania.

This is one of two portraits of Indian
chiefs—the other represents Lapo-
winsa—painted by Hesselius for John
Penn, the son of William Penn by his
second marriage, for a fee of £16. Both
are unusually convincing portrayals of
individuals rather than generallised
types. Hesselius clearly took pains to
make a faithful record of the physiognomy of Tishcohan (whose name signified in the Delaware language "he
who never blackens himself," referring
to his failure to paint his body and
face with black pigment) and also of
the squirrel-skin tobacco pouch hung
round his neck—though he was rather
less successful in representing the
structure of his shoulders. An anthro-
pologist, John C. Ewers, has called
Hesselius's two pictures "probably the
first successful Indian portraits made
in North America." And, from an ethnographical point of view, they were
the last before the nineteenth century.

Lithographs after them were published
to illustrate Thomas L. McKenney and
James Hall: *History of the Indian
Tribes of North America*, Philadelphia,
1836-44.

The two chiefs were among those
who met with John and Thomas Penn
at Pennsbury on 9 May 1735. Two
years later they signed in Philadelphia
the treaty known as the "Walking Purchase," granting to the proprietors of
the colony land as far as a man could
walk in a day and a half from the
Neshanimy Creek. As the settlers
smoothed a path and employed a long-

distance runner, this tract was far
greater than expected by the Indians,
who denounced the treaty as a legal-
istic fraud.

Literature: W. J. Buck in *The Pennsylvania
Magazine of History and Biography*, VII,
no. 2 (1883), p. 215; C. Brinton: *Gustavus
Hesselius*, exhibition catalogue, Philadelphia Museum of Art, Philadelphia, 1938,
no. 9; John C. Ewers in *New York Historical Society Quarterly*, XXXIII (1949), p.
228; *Philadelphia Painting and Printing to
1776*, exhibition catalogue, Pennsylvania
Academy of the Fine Arts, Philadelphia,
1971, no. 14; Ellwood Parry: *The Image of
the Indian and the Black Man in American
Art, 1590-1900*, pp. 23-25.

Alexandre-Jean Noël

French, 1752-1834.
Noël was born at Brie-Comte-Robert and trained in Paris under Jacques-Augustin de Silvestre and Joseph Vernet. While still a student he accompanied the Abbé Jean Chappe d'Auteroche to Mexico in 1768 (see below). He exhibited at the Salon de la Correspondence in Paris in 1779 and 1780. In the last years of the century he visited Spain and Portugal and painted a series of views of their ports, some of which were engraved. Paintings by him were shown in the Paris Salons from 1801 to 1822.

Alexandre-Jean Noël

175 *The Funeral of the Abbé Chappe d'Auteroche*

Pen, ink, and watercolour. 1769.
Signed: *Noel.* 6¾ x 8⁷⁄₁₆ inches (17.1 x 21.3 cm.). Inscription: On the mount, probably in the artist's hand, *Anterement de M.Labbé Chappe d'Oteroche mort Le lᵉ D'Aout 1769 a St Joseph en Californie.* Provenance: Acquired for the Cabinet du Roi, 1778.
Paris, Musée du Louvre, Cabinet des Dessins.

This is one of a group of six drawings (all in the same collection) in which Noël depicted the Indians of Mexico and California. Usually he represented them as rather enfeebled creatures, very much as they had been described by Buffon and as they were viewed, in all probability, by the abbé Chappe, who was associated with the *philosophes.* However, this is less evident in the drawing exhibited than in others.

Chappe d'Auteroche (1728-1769) was an astronomer who had visited Russia in 1761 in order to observe the transit of Venus from Tobolsk. In 1768 he published an account of his journey and the people he met on it in a book which gave great offence to Catherine

the Great. In September 1768 he set off to observe the transit of Venus from California, taking with him Noël as draughtsman, a M. Pauly, "Ingénieur Géographe du Roi," and a clock-maker named Dubois to look after the scientific instruments. After experiencing some difficulty in obtaining passports, the party sailed from Cadiz and reached Vera Cruz on 6 May 1769. Chappe died in California on 1 August, having given his papers to Pauly, who returned with them to France (cf. *Voyage en Californie pour l'observation du passage de Vénus . . . par feu M. Chappe d'Auteroche rédigé et publié par M. de Cassini,* Paris, 1772). In the drawing exhibited, Pauly is presumably the well-dressed figure following the bier and the artist himself one of the two younger men behind the priest. Two of Noël's other drawings show the interiors of mission huts,

in which the natives seem to live literally under the shadow of the Church. He also made drawings of a fish and a lizard [51]. Noël exhibited *La mort de l'abbé Chappe* at the Salon de la Correspondence, Paris, in 1779 (cf. E. Bellier de la Chavignerie and L. Auvray: *Dictionnaire générale des artistes de l'école française,* Paris, 1885, vol. II, p. 162). A painting of this subject, commissioned by the Chappe family, was exhibited by Jean-Henri Marlet at the Paris Salon of 1817 (cf. C. Gabet: *Dictionnaire des artistes de l'école française,* Paris, 1831, p. 409).

Literature: M. H. Benisovich: "A French Artist in Mexico in 1769" in *The Art Quarterly,* XVII (1954), pp. 142-143; R. Lindon: "Le premier tableau peint à Etretat" in *Gazette des Beaux Arts,* 6ᵉS., LXXIV (1969), p. 366; L. Duclaux: *Inventaire général des Dessins, Musée du Louvre, Cabinet des dessins, Ecole française,* XII (Paris, 1975), p. 169.

Benjamin West

Pennsylvanian and English, 1738-1820.

West was born near Springfield, Pennsylvania, the son of a Quaker innkeeper. After learning the rudiments of art and working for some four years as a painter in Philadelphia and New York, he went in 1760 to Italy, where his style was formed in Rome, mainly under the influence of Anton Raphael Mengs. As an American he aroused curiosity in Rome, and the blind Cardinal Albani, supposing him to be an Indian, stroked his cheek—presumably to discover whether it was true that men of his race had no beard. In front of the Apollo Belvedere he is said to have exclaimed: "My God, how like it is to a young Mohawk warrior"—providing a corollary to the cliché comparison between Indians and antique statues. In 1763 he went to England, intending to make no more than a visit on his way back to America, but spent the rest of his long life there. He became a foundation member of the Royal Academy in 1768 and was appointed history painter to George III in 1772, a post he held throughout the American Revolution but lost in 1811. He was president of the Royal Academy from 1789 until his death, except for the years 1805-06.

In addition to painting subjects from the Bible and ancient history, West occasionally turned to American themes. He supplied illustrations for William Smith's *An Historical Account of the Expedition against the Ohio Indians, in the Year 1764* (London, 1766). His most famous work, very widely diffused through engravings, was *The Death of Wolfe* of 1770, which includes an Indian musing on the event (National Gallery of Canada, Ottawa). Scarcely less well-known and popular through engravings was his *William Penn's Treaty with the Indians* of 1771, which was exhibited at the Royal Academy the following year

(Pennsylvania Academy of the Fine Arts, Philadelphia). In 1784-85 he began a large group-portrait of *The Treaty of Paris Peace Commissioners* (unfinished; Henry Francis du Pont Winterthur Museum, Winterthur).

Benjamin West

177 *Colonel Guy Johnson*

Oil on canvas. ca. 1776. 79¾ x 54½ inches (202 x 138 cm.). Provenance: Dina E. Brown, Henfield; Andrew Mellon, who bequeathed it to the National Gallery, 1940.
Washington, D.C., National Gallery of Art, Andrew Mellon Collection, 1940.

Colonel Guy Johnson (1740-1788) was a colonial administrator who succeeded his uncle, Sir William Johnson, as superintendent of Indian affairs in 1774. To avoid hostilities developing between the British forces and the American colonists in 1775, he and about a hundred other loyalists, accompanied by a large part of the Mohawk tribe, went north to Canada. That November he sailed for England, taking with him a Mohawk war chief, Oteroughyanete, and Thayendanegea, better known as Joseph Brant, the grandson of one of the Indians who had visited England in 1710. On 26 January 1776 Johnson wrote to Lord George Germain, the secretary of state for the colonies: "The Indian chief who accompanied me, with his companion, are persons of character and influence in their country; they can more at large speak on any matters that may be required of them." Brant expressed various grievances of the Indians and, in return for promises to rectify them, declared: "I will lead three thousand braves to battle for the cause of England . . . and with our assistance, there can be but one end to the war—England will conquer." He was made much of in London, espe-

176 *Dancing Indian*
Italy, Doccia Porcelain Factory. Porcelain, on a marble plinth. ca. 1770. Height 12⅛ inches (30.7 cm.). Provenance: James Hazen Hyde.
New York, Cooper-Hewitt Museum of Design, Smithsonian Institution, Gift of the Trustees of the Estate of James Hazen Hyde.

The model was probably by Gaspero Bruschi (ca. 1701-1780), who was engaged as chief-modeller in 1735, when the Doccia Factory was founded by Marchese Carlo Ginori.

Literature: *The Four Continents from the Collection of James Hazen Hyde,* exhibition catalogue, The Cooper Union Museum, New York, 1961, no. 51.

cially by that inveterate lion-hunter James Boswell, and portrayed by George Romney. In early June 1776 Johnson and his two Indian companions embarked at Falmouth and reached New York at the end of July. (See C. T. Foreman: *Indians Abroad,* Norman, Okla., 1943, pp. 93-96.)

The portrait exhibited, though neither signed nor dated, was presumably painted during Johnson's visit to England. The figure of the Indian in the background has generally been identified as Joseph Brant, though he may have been intended to personify the Indians in general (his facial features do not correspond closely with those in the portraits of Brant by Romney and Stuart). He holds a pipe of peace in one hand, pointing with the other to a distant view of an Indian encampment and Niagara.

Literature: J. T. Flexner: *The Light of Distant Skies* (1954), New York, 1969, p. 54; Milton W. Hamilton: "Joseph Brant—'The Most Painted Indian'" in *New York History,* XXXIX (1958), pp. 122 ff.; Grose Evans: *Benjamin West and the Taste of his Times,* Carbondale, Ill., 1959, p. 46; Margaret Bouton: *American Painting in the National Gallery of Art,* Washington, D.C., 1959, p. 17; John Walker: *National Gallery of Art, Washington D.C.,* New York, 1963, p. 226; *The Painter and the New World,* exhibition catalogue, Museum of Fine Arts, Montreal, 1967, no. 85; Ellwood Parry: *The Image of the Indian and the Black Man in American Art, 1590-1900,* pp. 31-34.

John Webber
English, 1752-1793.

178 *A Man at Nootka Sound*
Pen, ink, and wash. 1778. Signed:
J. Webber del. 17⁵⁄₁₆ x 12 inches (44
x 30.5 cm.). Provenance: Admiralty,
London, 1784; Sir William Campbell
and heirs; Francis Edwards; David
Bushnell, 1925; Belle Bushnell, 1941.
Cambridge, Mass., Peabody Museum
of Archaeology and Ethnology, Har-
vard University.

Captain Cook's third and last expedition first sighted the northwest coast of
America on 7 March 1778. They
anchored in King George's Sound,
called Nootka by the natives, on Vancouver Island. (George Vancouver,
who later surveyed the northwest
coast, was at this time a seaman with
Cook's expedition.) The Nootka Indians lived in two villages on the shores
of the sound, and both the buildings in
these villages and their inhabitants
were described by Cook and drawn by
Webber. This drawing of a man was

probably made in April 1778. He
wears the type of cap described by
Cook in his account of the Nootka
natives as being "of the figure of a
truncated cone, or like a flower-pot,
made of fine matting, having the top
frequently ornamented with a round
pointed knob, or bunch of leathern
tassels, and there is a string that passes
under the chin, to prevent its blowing
off." Elsewhere Cook remarked that
"We have sometimes seen the whole
process of their whale-fishery painted
on the caps they wear." On his shoul-

der the man wears a heavy skin and is armed with a bow and arrows. The quiver opens lengthwise. The bands on his ankles conform with Cook's statement that "about their ankles they also frequently wear many folds of leather thongs, or the sinews of animals twisted to a considerable thickness."

Literature: David I. Bushnell, Jr.: "Drawings by John Webber of Natives of the Northwest Coast of America, 1778" in *Smithsonian Miscellaneous Collections*, vol. 80 (April 1928), No. 10, pp. 5-6; J. C. Beaglehole, ed.: *The Journals of Captain James Cook on his Voyages of Discovery: The Voyage of the Resolution and Discovery 1776-1780*, Cambridge, The Hakluyt Society, 1967, Part I, p. ccxiii, pl. 37.

paint; but the women puncture their faces slightly; and both men and women bore the underlip, to which they fix pieces of bone. But it is as uncommon, at Oonalashka, to see a man with this ornament, as to see a woman without it. Some fix beads to the upper lip, under the nostrils; and all of them hang ornaments in their ears.

Literature: David I. Bushnell, Jr.: "Drawings by John Webber of Natives of the Northwest Coast of America, 1778" in *Smithsonian Miscellaneous Collections*, vol. 80, April, 1928, No. 10, pp. 11-12. J. C. Beaglehole, ed.: *The Journals of Captain James Cook on his Voyages of Discovery: The Voyage of the Resolution and Discovery 1776-1780*, part I, p. ccxiii and pl. 52b.

John Webber

180 *Artifacts from the Northwest Coast*

Pen, ink, and wash. 1778. 20¾ x 14¾ inches (53 x 37.5 cm.). Inscription: *representations of animals used as decoys by the Americans of K. G. Sound.*
London, British Library, Department of Manuscripts.

This drawing depicts, at the top, two Nootka Indian masks of painted wood from Nootka Sound, Vancouver Island. The bird is a wooden rattle, also Nootka. At lower left is a wooden visor, which may be Aleut from Unalaska or Eskimo from the southern

John Webber

179 *A Woman of Unalaska*

Wash drawing. 1778. With frame 12 x 17 inches (30.4 x 43 cm.). Provenance: As for [178].
Cambridge, Mass., Peabody Museum of Archaeology and Ethnology, Harvard University.

Captain Cook's expedition reached Norton Sound and the island of Unalaska in September 1778, and early in October they anchored for several weeks in Samganoodha harbour, where there was a small village. Webber probably made this drawing there. Of the people of Unalaska, Cook wrote:

> These people are rather low of stature, but plump and well shaped; with rather short necks; swarthy chubby faces; black eyes; small beards; and long, straight, black hair; which the men wear loose behind them, and cut before, but the women tie up in a bunch. . . . Both sexes wear the same in fashion; the only difference is in the materials. The women's frock is made of seal skin; and that of the men, of the skins of birds; both reaching below the knee. This is the whole dress of the women. . . . They make use of no

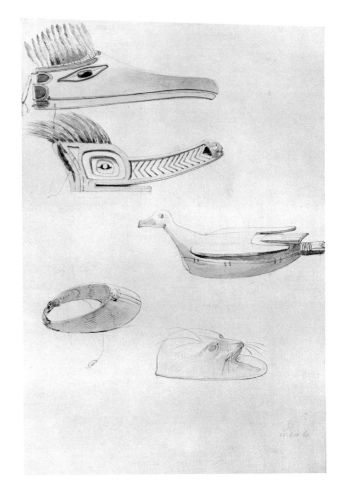

Bering Sea. Lower right is a wooden
hat in the form of a seal's head, used as
a decoy by Chugach Eskimo hunters of
Prince William Sound, Alaska.

Literature: J. C. Beaglehole, ed.: *The Journal of Captain James Cook on his Voyages
of Discovery: The Voyage of the Resolution and Discovery 1776-1780*, part I, p.
ccxiii; W. P. Cumming, S. Hillier, D. B.
Quinn, and G. Williams: *The Exploration
of North America 1630-1776*, p. 233.

Jean-Jacques-François Le Barbier the Elder

French, 1738-1826.
After winning the first prize for drawing at the Académie of his native
Rouen in 1754, Le Barbier went to
Paris and entered the studio of J. B.
Pierre. He travelled to Italy at his own
expense, returning before 1776, when
he was sent to Switzerland to draw the
most notable views of the country for
the Crown. There he met the poet and
painter Salomon Gessner, whose somewhat Rousseauist cult of nature seems
to have had a strong influence on him.
In 1781 he made his début at the Paris
Salon with his *"Canadian Indians at
the Grave of their Child"* (see below)
and other works. He became a full
member of the Académie in 1785 and
in the following year was commissioned to paint a series of cartoons of
the four continents for the royal
tapestry factory at Beauvais [195, 196].
These and his picture of Canadian Indians suggest special interest in America. But he is known to have depicted
only one other group of American subjects, a series of illustrations for Marmontel's *Las Incas* (Musée des Beaux-
Arts, Rouen). His other works were
mainly of classical or mediaeval subjects.

Jean-Jacques-François Le Barbier
the Elder

181 *Canadian Indians at their Child's
Grave*

Oil on canvas. Signed and dated: *Le
Barbier 1781*. 34⅜ x 24⅞ inches (87 x
63 cm.). Provenance: Gift of M. Darcel
to Musée de Rouen, 1867.
Rouen, Musée des Beaux Arts de
Rouen.

The parental and especially the maternal virtues of the Indians were extolled in eighteenth-century Europe
equally with their marital fidelity [184].

Thomas Raynal in *Histoire philosophique et politique des établissemens et du commerce des Européens dans les Deux-Indes* (Geneva, 1780, vol. IV, pp. 22-23) relates how Indian women were so overcome by the death of a child that bereaved Indian couples would mourn at the child's tomb, and the mother would let her milk flow upon it for many months after the child's death. This is the subject of Le Barbier's painting, and, despite its somewhat esoteric nature, it was engraved (by Ingouf, 1786) and even modelled—apparently for use as a clock-case [189]. However, one critic of the 1781 Salon, where the painting was exhibited, complained that it was preposterous of Le Barbier to have gone all the way to the Iroquois to learn lessons in virtue (*Galamatias anti-critique des tableaux du Salon . . .*, Neufchatel, 1781, p. 28).

Literature: Robert Rosenblum: "Caritas Romana after 1760: Some Romantic Lactations" in *Women as Sex Object*, ed. Thomas B. Hess and Linda Nochlin, New York, 1972, pp. 53-57.

Antoine Borel

French, 1743-after 1810.

182 *L'Enfant retrouvé*

Pen, ink, and wash. ca. 1784. Signed: *A.Borel invenit et delineavit.* 13⅜ x 16½ inches (34 x 42 cm.). Inscription: *L'Enfant retrouvé. Dans le Comté de U-ER en Amérique, un Sauvage a l'aide de son Chien retrouve un jeune Enfant, égaré dans les bois. il le remet dans les bras de son Pere et Mere, qui passent de la plus vive douleur a la joie la plus extrème. Voyez. Lettres dun Cultivateur Americain. Tome premier Page 199.*

Blérancourt, Musée National de la Coopération Franco-Américaine.

Borel began his career as a portrait painter but worked mainly as a draughtsman and etcher of illustrations to books and political allegories.

In this drawing and its companion piece, Borel illustrated St. Jean de Crèvecoeur's story of a settler's family whose lost child is found and returned to them by an Indian, with the aid of his sagacious dog. "Ah, my friend, that was a beautiful and striking scene to gaze on; the sudden laughter, the sweet tears, the cries of recognition, the eyes lifted to the sky, the simple words, the paternal joy," Crèvecoeur wrote. A "thousand different nuances" made it "too sublime for my feeble pen." The incident does not appear in the first edition of Crèvecoeur's famous book, published in England as *Letters from an American Farmer* in 1782. It was one of the additions he made to the French version, *Lettres d'un cultivateur américain* (Paris, 1784), which enjoyed considerable success on account of such touching scenes, as well as for its vivid descriptions of life in North America.

Literature: *Chateau de Blérancourt. Le Musée de la Coopération Franco-Americaine*, Paris, 1966.

L'ENFANT RETROUVÉ.

Dans le Comté de U-ER en Amérique, un Sauvage a l'aide de son Chien retrouve un jeune Enfant, égaré dans les bois. il le remet dans les bras de son Pere & de la Mere, qui passent de la plus vive douleur a la joie la plus extrème.

Voyez Lettres un Cultivateur Americain. Tome Premier Page 199.

Nathaniel Dance

English, 1735-1811.
Dance was trained as a portrait painter in London under Francis Hayman, then went in 1755 to Rome, where he spent the next ten years portraying young Englishmen on the Grand Tour, much in the style of Pompeo Batoni. Returning to England, he soon became one of the more fashionable portrait painters. He was a foundation member of the Royal Academy (1768). On inheriting a fortune he retired from professional practice in 1776, married a wealthy widow in 1783, and was created a baronet as Sir Nathaniel Dance-Holland in 1800.

Nathaniel Dance

183 *Attuiock, A Man from Labrador*
Pastel. Signed and dated: *N.Dance delit 1773*. 15 x 9½ inches (38 x 24 cm.). Provenance: Sir Joseph Banks, 1773, and by descent to present owner. Lent anonymously.

Attuiock was sent to London in 1773, together with his brother Tooklavinia, their wives, and a child. All died of smallpox except for Attuiock's wife, Caubvick, who is said to have carried the disease back to her native land. Sir Joseph Banks, the greatest English naturalist of his day, commissioned Dance to make two portraits of both Attuiock and Caubvick, keeping one pair himself and sending the other to J. F. Blumenbach in Göttingen (now in the University Museum, Göttingen). The work exhibited is inscribed on the back, probably in Bank's hand: "Esquimaux man who was brought over from Cape Charles on the coast of Labrador by Captain Cartwright in the year 1773. He was a Priest in his own country which is denoted by the thong of leather hanging down from his girdle. His name is Ettinock." Another portrait in oils of Caubvick was acquired by the surgeon and anatomist John Hunter and is now in the collection of the Royal College of Surgeons, London.

The interest taken in these Eskimo serves as a reminder that, although Newfoundland and Labrador were among the first parts of America to be discovered, they remained little known until late in the eighteenth century. The first accurate chart of the coastline was made by James Cook in 1758-65 (before he made his first Pacific voyage in company with Banks). Banks investigated the natural history of the region and discovered many new plants in 1766. And when next year Hugh Palliser, governor of Newfoundland, sent an Eskimo woman named Mykok to London, Banks commissioned John Russell to paint her portrait, which he sent to Blumenbach in Göttingen (now also in the University Museum, Göttingen).

Literature: A. M. Lysaght: *Joseph Banks in Newfoundland and Laborador 1766*, Berkeley and Los Angeles, 1971.

Joseph Wright, called Wright of Derby
English, 1734-1797.
Wright was born in Derby, trained as a portrait painter in London under Thomas Hudson, began to exhibit at the Society of Artists in 1765, toured Italy in 1773-75, and was elected an Associate of the Royal Academy in 1781. But, although he remained in touch with London, he spent most of his life in his native Derby, in contact with and often working for the industrialists and scientists whose enlightened ideals found expression in the formation of the Birmingham Lunar Society. He is best known for his moonlight scenes and for such paintings as *The Orrery* and *Experiment with an Air-Pump*.

Joseph Wright, called Wright of Derby
184 *The Indian Widow*
Oil on canvas. Signed and dated: *I.W. 1785.* 39½ x 49⅝ inches (101.6 x 127 cm.). Provenance: Bought at the sale of the artist's effects, Christie's, London, 6 May 1801, lot 64 by Mr. Borrow and remained in the collection of his descendants until acquired by Derby in 1960.
Derby Museums and Art Gallery.
Colorplate 5.

In a letter to William Hayley of April 1784, Wright mentioned his nearly finished *Indian Widow* as the "Companion" to his *The Lady in Milton's Comus* (Liverpool, Walker Art Gallery), but no comparable literary

source for the former can be traced. A passage in James Adair's *The History of the American Indians* (London, 1775, pp. 185-186), not previously mentioned in connection with Wright's picture, would appear to have provided the programme.

Their law compels the widow, through the long term of her weeds, to refrain all public company and diversions, at the penalty of an adultress; and likewise to go with flowing hair, without the privilege of oil to anoint it. The nearest kinsmen of the deceased husband, keep a very watchful eye over her conduct, in this respect. The place of interment is also calculated to wake the widow's grief, for he is intombed in the house under her bed. And if he is a war-leader, she is obliged for the first moon, to sit in the day-time under his mourning war-pole, which is decked with all his martial trophies, and must be heard to cry with bewailing notes. But none of them are fond of that month's supposed religious duty, it chills, or sweats, and wastes them so exceedingly; for they are allowed no shade or shelter. This sharp rigid custom excites the women to honour the marriage-state, and keeps them obliging to their husbands, by anticipating the visible sharp difficulties which they must undergo for so great a loss.

In a footnote to the passage Adair added: "The war-pole is a small peeled tree painted red, the top boughs cut off short; it is fixt in the ground opposite his door, and all his implements of war, are hung on the short boughs of it, till they rot."

When Wright exhibited his painting at Mr. Robin's Rooms in Covent Garden, London, in the spring of 1785, it was described as:

The Widow of an Indian Chief watching the arms of her deceased husband. This picture is founded on a custom which prevails among the savage tribes of America, where the widow of an eminent warrior is used to sit the whole day, during the first moon after his death, under a rude kind of trophy, formed by a tree lopped and painted; on which the weapons and martial habilments of the dead are suspended. She remains in this situation without shelter, and perserveres in her mournful duty at the hazard of her own life from the inclemencies of the weather.

Though vitiated by his attempt to prove that the American Indians were descended from the Jews, Adair's book contains much valuable ethnological information based on some forty years among the Indians of North America. The book was, however, unillustrated, nor did it provide a description of the widow's dress—and it was specifically "for want of knowing the dress of a Mourner" that the painting was unfinished when Wright wrote and asked for Hayley's help in 1784. The widow's dress is in fact imaginative, apart from the head-band and feathers. But, as Nicolson points out, the buffalo robe painted on the skin side, the quilled cords, and knife sheath hanging on the tree show some knowledge of Indian artifacts from at least as far west as the Great Lakes and seem to have been painted from authentic props. Indian objects had been brought back to England by soldiers who served in both the Canadian War and the Revolutionary War. One of them, Sir John Caldwell, had himself portrayed as an Ojibway chief ca. 1780 (both the painting and the items of dress have been preserved at Snitterton Hall, Derbyshire, since the late eighteenth century; cf. H. Honour: *The New Golden Land*, New York, 1975). Tomahawks of the type depicted could have been seen by Wright very easily, since they were extensively manufactured in the Midlands for export to America.

An engraving of the painting by J. R. Smith was published 29 January 1789. Wright sold a second version of it to a Mr. McNiven in 1792 (burnt). A copy is in the National Gallery of Art, Washington.

Literature: William Bemrose: *The Life and Works of Joseph Wright, A.R.A. commonly called 'Wright of Derby,'* London, 1885, pp. 18-19, 91; T. Crombie: "Wright of Derby's 'Indian Widow' " in *Apollo,* LXX (1959), p. 107; R. Rosenblum: "Wright of Derby: Gothick Realist" in *Art News,* March, 1960, p. 25; B. Nicolson: "Two Companion Pieces by Wright of Derby" in *The Burlington Magazine,* CIV (1962), pp. 113-117; R. Rosenblum: *Transformations in Late Eighteenth Century Art,* Princeton, 1967, p. 45; B. Nicolson: *Joseph Wright of Derby, Painter of Light,* London and New York, 1968, vol. I, pp. 148-149, 247.

William Hodges

English, 1744-1797.
Landscape painter and printmaker, Hodges studied under Richard Wilson in London. From 1772 to 1775 he was official landscape painter to Captain Cook's second voyage to the South Pacific, and most of his best work belongs to this period, e.g. *Tahiti* (National Maritime Museum, Greenwich). He skillfully adapted Wilson's style and technique to exotic subjects, combining the picturesque with an air of documentary fidelity. He worked in India from 1780 to 1784 and became a Royal Academician in 1787. But without exotic subjects to stimulate him his work declined. He abandoned painting for banking in 1795 and committed suicide two years later.

William Hodges

185 *Cherokee or Creek Indian*

Oil on canvas. ca. 1790. 29¾ x 24⅝
inches (75 x 62 cm.). Provenance: John
Hunter, the Hunterian Museum until
1800.
London, The Trustees of the Hunterian Collection and the President and
Council of the Royal College of Surgeons of England.

William Clift, the first conservator of
the Museum Collection of the Royal
College of Surgeons, who recorded in
his manuscript lists of 1816 and 1820
much traditional knowledge of the pictures in the collection, wrote that this
painting and a companion portrait of
another Cherokee by Hodges, also now
in the Royal College of Surgeons, were
painted by Hodges for Dr. John
Hunter (1728-1793), the famous surgeon and anatomist. "These two
American Indians were in London
about 1790-1791, after the termination
of the American war, and had, it appears, fought on the side of the English
during the struggle. I never heard their
names. They were at Sir Joseph Bank's
parties." It seems more than probable
that they were of the party of three
Cherokees and two Creeks brought to
England by William Augustus Bowles.

Literature: Sir A. Keith: *Hunterian and
other pictures in the Museum Collection
of the Royal College of Surgeons,* London,
1930, no. 5; William Le Fanu: *A Catalogue
of the Portraits and other Paintings, Drawings and Sculpture in the Royal College
of Surgeons of England,* Edinburgh and
London, 1960, no. 245; J. W. Fawcett-
Thompson in *The Connoisseur,* CLXX
(1969), pp. 49-53; William C. Sturtevant:
"A French Report on Cherokees from
Nootka as British Agents in the Haitian
Revolution" in *The Cherokees in Historical Perspective,* ed. Duane King, Knox-
ville, University of Tennessee Press, in
press.

186 *American Indian and Family*
England (?). Oil on canvas. Before
1793. 23⁹⁄₁₆ x 19 inches (60 x 48 cm.).
Provenance: John Hunter, 1793.
London, The Trustees of the Hunt-
erian Collection and the President and
Council of the Royal College of Sur-
geons of England.

This painting formed part of the collection of paintings of racial types
formed by the famous surgeon and
anatomist, Dr. John Hunter. It also
included two portraits of Cherokee
[185] and a portrait of a woman from
Labrador. The Indian family seems to
come from the region of the Great
Lakes. According to Dr. William C.
Sturtevant, they are probably Iroquois,
though they could also be Algonquin,
Ojibwa, or Menomini; details of costume and the gourd dipper in the lower
left corner are accurately depicted (private communication). But the forest
background with the somewhat
strange shelter appears to be imaginary. Thus it seems likely that the picture was painted in England, either
from field sketches or with Indians
taken there in the late eighteenth century as models.

Literature: William Le Fanu: *A Catalogue
of the Portraits and other Paintings, Drawings and Sculpture in the Royal College
of Surgeons of England,* Edinburgh and
London, 1960, no. 247.

Thomas Hardy
English, fl. 1778-1798.
Little is known about Thomas Hardy,
except that he exhibited portraits at
the Royal Academy in London between 1778 and 1798 and at the Society of Artists in 1790. His best known
portrait is that of Josef Haydn, 1791,
now in the Royal College of Music,
London.

184 Joseph Wright, *The Indian Widow*. Derby Museums.

Thomas Hardy (after)

187 *William Augustus Bowles*

Mezzotint. ca. 1791. 16⅝ x 11⅜ inches (42.3 x 29 cm.). Inscription: *Painted by T. Hardy . . . Engrav'd by I. Grozer . . . William Augustus Bowles . . . Chief of the Embassy from the Creeke & Cherokee Nations. Published as the Act directs, March 26, 1791. by T. Hardy, No4 Great Marlborough Street.* New York, The Metropolitan Museum of Art, Rogers Fund, 1912.

This mezzotint by Joseph Grozer (fl. 1782-1797) is after a portrait in oils by Thomas Hardy exhibited at the Royal Academy in 1791 and now in the possession of the National Trust at Upton House, Oxfordshire. William Augustus Bowles (1763-1805) was born in Frederick County, Maryland, and after a short time with the British army was deprived of his commission for insubordination. He then joined some Creek Indians, learned to speak their language, and lived with them for twenty years, marrying the daughter of one of their chiefs. He commanded the Creeks in General Arthur Campbell's battle with Don Bernardo Gálvez on May 9, 1781, in defense of Pensacola. Nine years later he and two Creek and three Cherokee chiefs went to England to promote a mad-cap scheme for an invasion of Mexico. They were made much of in London, took a box at Covent Garden, visited St. Paul's, dined with the Lord Mayor at the Mansion House, and were received by Lord Grenville, secretary for foreign affairs.

Sir John Hunter seems to have commissioned William Hodges to paint two of the Indians [185], and a sensational and very favourable account of Bowles was published by a "Capt. Bayston of the provincial American Troops" as *Authentic Memoirs of William Augustus Bowles, Esquire, Ambassador from the United Nations of Creeks and Cherokees to the Court of*

London, London, 1791. A very different account was given of him by James Seagrove, the commissioner of Indian affairs in America:

This Bowles is an American, of low, mean extraction . . . he was obliged, on account of his villainy, to fly from home and follow the British army, where he was despised and treated as a bad man and a *coward* . . . He endeavoured to impose on the King of England, by telling him that you [the Creek Indians] wished to make him, Bowles, your beloved man; that it was your desire to make war against the United States and

Spain; but the King of England, finding him an imposter, drove him out of his land, but treated the Indians that were with him kindly, on their own account. . . .

Bowles and his party returned empty-handed to America. Almost immediately Bowles turned to piracy and was captured by General Alexander McGillivray and taken to New Orleans in irons. In 1792 he was sent to Spain. He died at Havana in a dungeon in Morro Castle in 1805. (See C. T. Foreman: *Indians Abroad 1493-1938,* Norman, Okla., 1943, pp. 101-106.)

Sigismund Bacstrom

Dutch, fl. 1772-1797.
Bacstrom was a protégé of Sir Joseph Banks, naturalist and patron of Stubbs and other artists (see [183]), who appointed him his secretary in his abortive project to accompany Cook on his second voyage in 1772. In 1791 Bacstrom joined, as surgeon, a ship which Theophilus Pritzler and Alderman Curtis were sending round Cape Horn to the South Seas, Nootka Sound, the East Indies, and the Cape. He left the ship at Nootka Sound (Vancouver Island) and later served as surgeon on several other ships, visiting China, India, the Cape, America, and elsewhere before returning to England in November 1796 (cf. Warren R. Dawson: *Calendar of Banks Letters*, 1958, pp. 26-27). He wrote an account of his travels (never published) and made a number of drawings, many of which, together with Bacstrom's autograph catalogue of all the drawings he made on his voyage, are in the collection of Mr. and Mrs. Paul Mellon.

Sigismund Bacstrom

188 *Hangi, a Chief's Daughter, at Tattesko*

Watercolour. ca. 1793. Signed: *S.Bacstrom, ad viv: del:*. 10¹¹⁄₁₆ x 8⁷⁄₁₆ inches (27 x 21.4 cm.). Inscription: *Hangi a Chief's Daughter at Tattesko near Bocarelli Sound, N: W: Coast of America.*
Collection of Mr. and Mrs. Paul Mellon.

Among the surviving drawings by Bacstrom are several of Indians on the northwest coast of America, some signed and dated 1793 with an additional note "fecit 1797," indicating that Bacstrom made these finished versions after his return home from drawings done on the spot.

Hangi a Chief's Daughter at Tattesko near Bocarelli Sound N.W. Coast of America.

S. Bacstrom ad viv:del:

Joseph-Charles Marin

French, 1759-1834.

A pupil of Clodion, Marin is best known for small terracottas of bacchantes, nymphs and satyrs, and other elegantly erotic subjects of the type made famous by his master. He almost equalled Clodion's elegance and sophistication. He exhibited at the Salon from 1791 onwards but did not achieve great success or any official recognition until 1796. In 1801 he was awarded the Prix de Rome, for which he had been competing for twenty years, and in 1805 became Professor de l'Académie. Chateaubriand, then French ambassador in Rome, commissioned him to execute a monument to Pauline de Beaumont in S. Luigi dei Francesi. He returned to France in 1810 and taught for several years in Lyon but died in Paris, in penury.

Joseph-Charles Marin

189 *Canadian Indians at their Child's Grave*

Terracotta. ca. 1795. Height 12⅛ inches (32 cm.). Provenance: Bernardin de Saint-Pierre family; Pierre Decourcelle; sold Galerie G. Petit, Paris, 29-30 May 1911, no. 194.
Paris, Heim Gallery.

In the 1795 Salon it was described as "Les Canadiens au tombeau de leurs enfants d'après l'estampe gravée par Ingouf." The engraving by Ingouf was after the painting by Jean-Jacques-François Le Barbier [181].

Marin's terracotta was evidently a model for a clock-case, the movement for which would have displayed an enamelled disc with hour and minute divisions through the arched aperture, with an arrow indicating the time. This type of dial achieved some popularity during the Directoire.

Literature: J. J. Guiffrey, ed.: *Collection des livrets des anciennes expositions depuis 1673 jusqu'en 1800*, Paris, 1871, p. 69; S. Lami: *Dictionnaire des sculpteurs de l'Ecole Francaise au XVIIIe siècle*, Paris, 1911, vol. II, p. 110; J. L. Vaudoyer: "Le collection de M. Pierre Decourcelle" in *Les Arts*, 1911, no. III, p. 18; M. Quinquent: *Un élève de Clodion—Joseph Charles Marin, 1759-1834*, Paris, 1948, pp. 56-57; A. Pigler: *Barockthemen*, Budapest, 1956, vol. II, p. 560.

XII
Libertas
Americana

No event on the other side of the Atlantic was ever so closely watched by Europeans as the Revolution. "It is a great and sublime spectacle that America puts on for us today," a Frenchman remarked to Benjamin Franklin in 1778.[1] By that date the "shot heard round the world" had been echoing, especially through France, for three years. Already in the late summer of 1775 a "great lady" in Paris asked Horace Walpole if he "was not a Bostonian."[2] The denizens of the enlightened and highly civilised salons he frequented were all "Bostonians"—he did not meet a single Frenchman who opposed the cause of the colonists. With the publication of the Declaration of Independence, the victories of the American armies, and their final triumph, enthusiasm mounted higher still. The *philosophes* applauded to a man, recognising in the new republic the promised land of the Enlightenment. It would provide "an asylum from fanaticism and tyranny for all the peoples of Europe," Denis Diderot prophecied. A. Turgot and M. Condorcet were equally optimistic. Poems were written and songs were sung in honour of the Americans. "Bravo, Messieurs les Insurgents," one of them began, politely.[3]

Much of the initial support for the United States in France was because of Benjamin Franklin, whose plain, open, sharp-eyed, humorous features seemed to personify enlightened ideals. From the moment of his arrival in 1776, he was fêted. Writers vied with each other in composing epigrams on him. One called him "the double genius of the arts and liberty." Another ingeniously combined references to his scientific experiments and political ideals: "he snatched the lightning from heaven and the sceptre from tyranny" [205]. His portrait was painted by Jean Baptiste Greuze, Joseph-Siffred Duplessis, and many others, drawn by Jean-Honoré Fragonard and sculpted by Jean Antoine Houdon [190]. He appeared in numerous engravings and even on snuff-boxes, coffee-cups [207], watches, dishes, handkerchiefs. His face was "as well known as that of the moon," he told his daughter. He became—or rather European artists made him—almost a symbol of America. No other American was so frequently portrayed in Europe, though various likenesses of Washington and the dashing John Paul Jones were circulated. Washington was, however, the subject of one of the finest of all late eighteenth-century portrait statues—the full-length life-size marble by Houdon in the State Capitol at Richmond, Virginia—and Houdon also modelled and carved busts of him [192], John Paul Jones [191], Thomas Jefferson, and later of Robert Fulton [193] and Joel Barlow [194], creating a group of works which constitute the finest tribute by any European artist to the "new men" of the United States.

France was, of course, directly involved in the Revolutionary War from 1778. But enthusiastic acclaim for the United States also came from German writers and intellectuals. "We wished the Americans all success, and the names of Franklin and Washington began to shine in the firmament of politics and war," wrote Goethe some years later, remembering how "the brightest hopes spread over the whole world."[4] And so felt many others in Germany. Friedrich Maximilian Klinger's play *Sturm und Drang,* which gave its name to the dominant literary movement of the day, was set in America. Shortly afterwards the poet Friedrich Klopstock saluted the Revolution as the "Frühlingsmorgen der neugeborenen Freiheit"—the spring morning of new born liberty. A response was also heard as far away as Russia, where Alexander Radishev wrote in an "Ode to Freedom" in the early 1780s:

> Gaze on this boundless field,
> The armies of evil lie crushed,
> Crushed by a mighty foe,
> Not by mercenaries, nor red-coats
> But by an army of free men,
> Leaders all and unafraid.
> Washington, invincible warrior,
> You are and were unconquerable,
> Your guide being freedom.[5]

Corresponding expressions in the visual arts of France, Germany, and elsewhere in Europe are surprisingly rare and, with one or two notable exceptions, undistinguished. For the most part, visual images of the events in America were diffused in Europe by satirical prints and by engravings (published in Augsburg and Paris), which were shown in peep-shows carried around by travelling mountebanks. One of the latter, which purported to illustrate the destruction of a royal statue in New York [201], may perhaps have put ideas into some heads; but no such inferences were to be drawn from most European depictions of the Revolution and certainly not from those officially sponsored in France. Here the cap of American liberty nearly always appeared with the Bourbon lilies, as on the *Libertas Americana Medal* [218] and the widely diffused reproductions of it on *toile de Jouy.* They are close to one another and the Stars and Stripes on the America panel of the magnificent suite of Beauvais tapestries, of which a set was woven at the command of Louis XVI, probably for presentation to George Washington [195-199] (though the French Revolution intervened before they could be sent). Nor did this proximity of republican and monarchical symbols seem incompatible, or even incongruous, until the 1790s, when both acquired new meanings.

Paintings of the siege and taking of Yorktown were commissioned by the Crown, apparently as records of French victories, from Louis Nicholas van Blarenberghe [211, 212]. Jean-Baptiste Le Paon was commissioned to make cartoons for a series of tapestries commemorating French victories during the reigns of Louis XV and Louis XVI, including Yorktown, Pensacola, and, in the West Indian extension of the American war, Brimston Hill [209] and the taking of Grenada.[6] This attitude lingered on. Half a century later, when the ministers of Louis Philippe were seeking to arouse France from its *ennui,* a large painting of the surrender of the British at Yorktown was commissioned for the gallery at Versailles [226].

Officially inspired French works of art of the 1780s also reflected ministerial preoccupations with the freedom of the seas and the benefits to commerce which were expected to derive from participation in the Revolution. Until the founding of the United States, France was, of course, able to trade with North America only by way of England. "Independence of America" and "Freedom of the Seas" appear together on documents which Louis XVI hands to Franklin in a Niderviller porcelain group [215], and the same themes were the subject of relief carvings on an obelisk put up at the royal shipyard at Port Vendres [210]. Neptune appears in several allegories of the Revolution, sometimes with a broken rudder bearing the British coat of arms. And Mercury, patron of commerce, is still more conspicuous in such works [208]. Although thirst for glory and sympathy for the cause inspired many individual Frenchmen, including La Fayette, to go and fight in America, economic considerations played a larger part in securing official support.

In the early days of the French Revolution, H. G. R. Mirabeau recalled the enthusiasm with which the Declaration of Independence had been welcomed in Europe. But, he asked, "did the governments which joined them in fighting England dare to read all this manifesto and, having read it through, did they turn to their conscience? Is there at present in Europe even one single government, except Switzerland, Holland, and the British Isles, which according to this declaration would not have to be ousted?"[7] The American Revolution had been likened to the foundation of the Swiss Republic and United Provinces in a satirical print of the 1770s [202]. Their constitutional system, and the liberties they guaranteed, had for long been admired by political theorists. So had that of Great Britain. But with the Declaration of Independence the virtues formerly ascribed to the British constitution seem to have been transferred to America in the eyes of men like Brissot de Warville, as swiftly as in the summer of 1776 the English game of whist was renamed "Boston."

In England itself, the Revolution was seen by its many sympathisers not as an attempt to gain new freedom, but as a struggle by the colonists to preserve the rights enjoyed by every British subject since the Glorious Revolution of 1688. This is the burden of the parliamentary speeches of Edmund Burke, as of the drawing by his protégé, James Barry, in which John Locke, the great Whig political philosopher, mourns at the tomb of British

220

liberty [200]. But British attitudes are most clearly revealed in the thirteen "impolitical prints" shown in this section, of which only three are anti-American.

1. M. Grimm and D. Diderot: *Correspondence littéraire* (July, 1778) Paris, 1830, vol. x, p. 74. Franklin characteristically replied: "mais les spectateurs ne paient point."
2. Horace Walpole to William Mason, 6 September 1775.
3. Durand Echeverria: *Mirage in the West,* Princeton, 1957, p. 68. Much of my information on French attitudes toward the Revolution comes from this source.
4. J. W. von Goethe: *Dichtung und Wahrheit,* pt. iv, bk. 17, written 1812-1831 and published posthumously in 1833.
5. Max M. Laserson: *The American Impact on Russia, Diplomatic and Ideological 1784-1917,* New York, 1950, p. 53.
6. H. Doniol: *Histoire de la participation de la France à l'établissement des Etats Unis de l'Amérique,* Paris, 1892, vol. ii, p. ii.
7. M. M. Laserson, p. 36.

Jean-Antoine Houdon

French, 1741-1828.
The most famous French portrait sculptor of his day, Houdon was trained at the Academy schools in Paris under Michelange Slodtz but was influenced by both Jean-Baptiste Lemoyne and Augustin Pajou. From 1764 to 1768 he was at the French Academy in Rome, where he carved the colossal and impressively realistic *St. Bruno* for S. Maris degli Angeli. He returned to Paris in 1769 but found his first important patrons abroad, notably Catherine the Great of Russia, who bought his famous *Diana* (1780, Gulbenkian Museum, Lisbon). His remarkable series of portrait busts began with Diderot (1771) and Voltaire (1778) and included several Americans: Washington [192], Franklin [190], Jefferson (Museum of Fine Arts, Boston), Robert Fulton [193], John Paul Jones [191], and Joel Barlow [194]. Through Jefferson and Franklin he was commissioned to carve a full-length statue of George Washington (now in the rotunda of the Capitol, Richmond, Virginia) and went to the United States in 1785 to model him from life. He returned to Paris the following year. During the Revolution and Directorate he produced little and was forced out of his studio in 1795. But he returned to favour under the Empire, and his bust of Napoleon (1806) is among the finest. He exhibited for the last time in 1814.

Jean-Antoine Houdon

190 *Benjamin Franklin*

Marble. Signed and dated: *J.A.Houdon, 1780*. Height 23 inches (58.3 cm.).
Provenance: Benjamin Franklin; Jacques Donatien le Ray de Chaumont; Charles le Ray de Chaumont; Prince de Faucigny-Lucinge.
Kansas City, Nelson Gallery–Atkins Museum (Nelson Fund).

Benjamin Franklin (1706-1790) visited France in 1766 and 1769 and returned in 1776 to negotiate a treaty of alliance between France and the United States. He remained in France until 1785, when he went back to America with Houdon, who had been commissioned to carve the statue of Washington now in Richmond, Virginia. During these years Franklin became very well known indeed in Paris–the living symbol, almost, of his country–and his portrait was very frequently painted and sculpted by Greuze, Duplessis, and Fragonard, among many others.

Houdon exhibited a bust of Franklin at the Salon in 1779, together with busts of Rousseau, Molière, and Voltaire. In 1783 he exhibited a bust of him in the Salon de la Correspondance and again, in 1791, at the Salon. Three different types of busts of Franklin by Houdon survive. They are, first, in modern dress (marble, dated 1788 in Metropolitan Museum of Art, New York; plaster, in Staatliches Museum, Gotha; plaster, in City Art Museum, St. Louis; terracotta, in the Louvre, Paris; terracotta, in De Young Museum, San Francisco), second, in a senatorial robe over modern dress (plaster, Boston Athenaeum, Boston; plaster, in Musée des Beaux Arts, Angers) and third, in a senatorial robe *à l'antique*. Of the latter type the marble exhibited is the only known version. A copy in marble by Domenico Menconi is in the American Philosophical Society in Philadelphia.

Literature: L. Réau: "A Great French Sculptor of the Eighteenth Century, Jean-Antoine Houdon" in *The Connoisseur*, CXXI (1948), p. 78; "The Century of Mozart" in *Nelson Gallery and Atkins Museum Bulletin*, 1956, vol. I, no. 1, pp. 29, 78, no. 56, p. 79; *Nelson Gallery and Atkins Museum Handbook* (1959, p. 118), 1973, vol. I, p. 138; C. C. Sellers: *Benjamin Franklin in Portraiture*, New Haven, 1962, pp. 313-315, no. 15; H. H. Arnason: *Sculpture by Houdon*, exhibition catalogue, Worcester Art Museum, Worcester, 1964, pp. 54, 60-62; Jean Massengale: "A Franklin by Houdon rediscovered" in *Marsyas*, VII (1964-65), p. 3.

Jean-Antoine Houdon

191 *John Paul Jones*

Plaster. Signed and dated: *Houdon f 1780*. Height 27½ inches (69.7 cm.).
Provenance: Acquired ca. 1900 at the sale of the "Boston Museum" (a theatre in Boston) by Charles H. Taylor, who gave it to the Museum of Fine Arts, Boston, 1931 (see also below).
Boston, Museum of Fine Arts.

John Paul Jones (1747-1792), after various skirmishes off the coast of England and Scotland in April and May 1778, was called to Paris and given command of the French ship *Bon Homme Richard* for an expedition planned with Lafayette against a major English city. This expedition never took place, but Jones won some notable victories with the small squadron put under his command, and, when he returned to Paris in 1780, he was fêted as a great naval hero. It was for a festival in his honour at the French court that his bust was commissioned that year from Houdon by the Masons Lodge of the Nine Sisters. He is shown wearing his admiral's uniform, decorated with the cross he received from Louis XVI. This marble bust is now in the Naval Academy, Annapolis.

Houdon exhibited a plaster bust of John Paul Jones, painted to resemble terracotta, in the Salon of 1781, and a terracotta is mentioned in Houdon's sale in 1795. John Paul Jones ordered some eight plaster versions of the marble bust when in Paris between 1786 and 1788, for presentation to friends. He gave these to Washington, Franklin, Jefferson, Robert Morris, Lafayette, d'Estaing, Baron Grimm, and others. Although made later, these seem to have been dated 1780. The bust exhibited may be that given to Jefferson, whose heirs presented plaster busts by Houdon of Jones, Franklin, Washington, and Lafayette to the Boston Athenaeum in 1828. The bust

turned to Paris by Christmas. The statue of Washington, now in the Capitol at Richmond, Virginia, was not finished and shipped until 1796, but Houdon had meantime made several busts—in terracotta, plaster, marble, and perhaps bronze. All are *à l'antique,* but some are draped and some undraped. Of the draped type there are examples in a private collection, New York (marble), in the Louvre (terracotta), and at Versailles (marble, originally made for the Tuileries in 1801). Of the undraped type the original terracotta still survives at Mount Vernon, and a plaster, to which the exhibited bust is very close, was in Thomas Jefferson's collection and is now in the Boston Athenaeum. The exhibited bust is the finest marble bust of Washington by Houdon.

Literature: *Peintures et sculptures des écoles étrangères,* catalogue, Nationalmuseum, Stockholm, 1958, p. 262; H. H. Arnason: *Sculpture by Houdon,* exhibition catalogue, Worcester Art Museum, 1964, p. 90; B. Dahlback: *Nationalmusei arsbok Skulptörer,* Stockholm, 1964, pp. 91-111.

Jean-Antoine Houdon

193 *Robert Fulton*

Marble. Signed and dated: *houdon f an XII* (1803). Height 23¼ inches (58.9 cm.). Provenance: Admiral Decrès; by descent to Philippe Decrès; Percy A. Rockefeller; Jonce I. McGurk; Howard Young Gallery, New York. Detroit, The Detroit Institute of Arts, Gift of Dexter M. Ferry, Jr.

Robert Fulton (1765-1815), the inventor and painter, went to Europe in 1786, first to England and later to Paris, where he tried, with Joel Barlow's support, to sell his submarine project to the French government. Later he designed a successful steamboat and, after his return to the United States, the *Clermont,* which led to a

of Jones disappeared from the Athenaeum during the nineteenth century and was probably loaned to the theatre called the "Boston Museum" and thus included in the sale of its effects. Other examples of the plaster version survive in the Pennsylvania Academy of the Fine Arts, Philadelphia and in the National Academy of Design, New York.

Literature: *Boston Museum of Fine Arts Bulletin,* no. 193, October, 1934; M. M. Swan: *The Athenaeum Gallery 1827-1873. The Boston Athenaeum as an Early Patron of Art,* Boston, 1940, p. 166; H. H. Arnason: *Sculpture by Houdon,* exhibition catalogue, Worcester Art Museum, Worcester, 1964, p. 72. L. Réau: *Houdon sa vie et son oeuvre,* Paris, 1964, p. 34.

Jean-Antoine Houdon

192 *George Washington*

Marble. ca. 1785. Height 18⅛ inches (48 cm.). Provenance: Hj. Linder, who gave it to the Nationalmuseum, Stockholm, in 1918.
Stockholm, Nationalmuseum.

Through Thomas Jefferson, then American minister to France, a full-length statue of Washington was commissioned from Houdon in 1785, and in June that year Houdon and Benjamin Franklin sailed for America. At Mount Vernon he completed in a few weeks a life mask and a terracotta bust, from which he made plasters. He re-

new stage in marine transportation.

Houdon exhibited plaster busts of Fulton and Joel Barlow in the Salon of 1804. His marble bust of Barlow [194] is undated but was presumably made, like the exhibited bust of Fulton, in 1803. Both works are unusually fine examples of Houdon's late style and, in their straightforwardness and simplicity, vividly portray the new democratic ideal of America as seen by Europeans. A plaster version of the bust of Fulton is in the collection of Mrs. Sarah Hunter Kelley, New York.

Literature: Florence I. Smouse: "Houdon en Amérique" in *La Revue de l'Art,* XXXV (1914), pp. 227-228; G. Giacometti: *La vie et l'oeuvre de Houdon,* Paris, n.d. vol. I, pp. 108, 172, 175, 183, 203, vol. II, pp. 56-59; L. Réau: "Houdon sous la revolution et l'empire" in *Gazette des Beaux-Arts,* July-August, 1924, pp. 59-86; L. Réau: *L'art français aux Etats-Unis,* Paris, 1926, pp. 47-48; Paul L. Grigaut: "A Marble Bust of Robert Fulton" in *The Art Quarterly,* vol. XII, no. 3 (Summer, 1949), pp. 252-257; Paul L. Grigault: "Houdon's Marble Bust of Robert Fulton" in *Bulletin of the Detroit Institute of Arts,* vol. 28, no. 4, 1949, pp. 79-80; L. Réau: *Houdon sa vie et son oeuvre,* Paris, 1964, vol. I, pp. 162, 465-467, vol. II, p. 49; H. H. Arnason: *Sculpture by Houdon,* exhibition catalogue, Worcester Art Museum, pp. 125, 127; J. Montagu: *Jean Antoine Houdon,* Milan, 1966, pp. 3-4.

Jean-Antoine Houdon

194 *Joel Barlow*
Marble. 1803-1804. Height 22 inches
(55.8 cm.). Provenance: Joel Barlow
and by descent in Barlow family.
Washington, D.C., The White House.
(Exhibited in Washington only.)

Joel Barlow (1754-1812), the poet and
statesman, lived in Europe between
1788 and 1805, settling in Paris in
1792. He became a close friend there of
Robert Fulton, and Houdon exhibited
plaster busts of both Barlow and Fulton in the 1804 Salon in Paris. A plaster bust of Joel Barlow signed *houdon
an XII* (1803) and inscribed *J.Barlow
50 ans* has been in the Pennsylvania
Academy of Fine Arts, Philadelphia,
since 1812. The marble bust exhibited
is unsigned but is mentioned by Joel
Barlow in a letter to Houdon of 1808
and was in the possession of the Barlow family until recently acquired by
the White House. In 1912 ten plasters
were made from it and given to various
museums in both the United States and
Europe.

This is perhaps the finest of all Houdon's American portrait busts. In its
forthright, manly simplicity of bearing,
it conveys with great force and convic-
tion the character of the sitter—every
inch the "New Man" of Crèvecoeur's
famous definition.

Literature: *Robert Fulton*, exhibition catalogue, New-York Historical Society, 1909,
p. 15, no. 53; G. Giacometti: *Le Statuaire
Jean-Antoine Houdon et son Epoque*,
Paris, 1918-19, vol. II, pp. 67-68, vol. III,
p. 236; G. Giacometti: *La Vie et l'oeuvre
de Houdon*, Paris, 1929, vol. II, p. 8, 172,
vol. III, p. 8; C. H. Hart and E. Biddle:
*Memoirs of the Life and Works of Jean
Antoine Houdon*, Philadelphia, 1911, pp.
262-263, 310; F. Ingersoll Smouse: "Houdon en Amerique" in *Revue l'Art Ancien
et Moderne*, vol. XXXV, 1914, no. 205,
p. 288. L. Réau: *L'Art Francais aux Etats-
Unis*, Paris, 1936, p. 46; *Sculpture by
Houdon: Paintings and Drawings by
David*, exhibition catalogue, Century Association, New York, 1947, no. 3; H. H.
Arnason: *Sculpture by Houdon*, exhibition
catalogue, Worcester Art Museum, p. 122.

**Beauvais Tapestry Factory after Jean-
Jacques-François Le Barbier the Elder**
France (Beauvais).

195 *America*
Tapestry of silk and wool. 1789-1791.
144 x 180 inches (366 x 457 cm.).
Colorplate cover.

196 *Europe*
Tapestry of silk and wool. 1789-1791.
144 x 198 inches (366 x 503 cm.).

197, 198 *America*

Tapestry panels of silk and wool applied to two arm-chairs. 1789-1791. Height of back 38 inches, seat width 27 inches (96.5 x 68.5 cm.). Colorplate 6.

199 *Allegory of Commercial*
       Prosperity
Tapestry panels of silk and wool applied to a canapé. 1789-1791. Height of back 42 inches, seat width 78 inches (106.7 x 198 cm.).
Provenance: The Prince de Béarn, 1852; Gaston Menier, 1893.
Artemis S.A.

These tapestries, woven at the royal Beauvais factory, appear to have been intended as a gift from Louis XVI to George Washington but were never sent. In their designs they allude both to the independence of the United States and to the part played by the French in achieving it. No finer or more grandiose work of art was inspired by this subject. The tapestries

197, 198 Beauvais Factory, *America* Arm-chairs. Artemis S.A.

exhibited form part of a suite of the four continents, comprising four large panels and twenty-eight covers for the backs and seats of two canapés and twelve arm-chairs. (The Louis XVI style woodwork of the furniture is nineteenth-century.)

Jean-Jacques-François Le Barbier was commissioned in 1786 to paint cartoons of the four parts of the world for the Beauvais factory for the large fee of 10,000 *livres*. Some of his cartoons still survive (Mobilier Nationale, Paris). His designs for Africa and Asia are traditional, though he incorporated in the latter a somewhat incongruous Neo-classical building. But the other two continents received entirely new treatment. The conventional feather-crowned Indian girl now plays only a subsidiary role in the panel devoted to America. Instead, Liberty holds the flag of the thirteen stars and stripes, with the cap of liberty on top of its pole. Behind her sit Peace and Plenty. A dove flies down to the earth, and a phoenix rises from it. On the left, Fame hangs a portrait of George Washington on a Tuscan column (emblem of strength and martial prowess), while Minerva, thunderbolt in one hand and shield bearing the Bourbon lilies in the other, hovers over Britannia, accompanied by snarling leopards, with a broken sceptre and overturned cannons. The portrait of Washington is similar to that on the Duvivier medal completed in 1789 [222], and both seem to derive from a portrait by Charles Willson Peale rather than from Houdon's bust [192], as has been suggested. Minerva had already appeared attacking Britannia in a print after Antoine Borel, *L'Amérique Indépendante* [208]; and she holds the Bourbon shield while attacking the British leopard on the reverse of the *Libertas Americana* medal devised by Benjamin Franklin in 1783 [218]. Le Barbier seems to have been influenced by both

these prototypes. His figure of Britannia is, however, identical with that of one of the fallen *Curiatti* in his drawing of *Le Combat des Horaces et des Curiaces*, dated 1786 (cf. *Le Néo-Classicisme français, dessins des Musées de Province*, exhibition catalogue, Grand Palais, Paris, 1974-75, no. 89).

Le Barbier's design for the panel representing Europe alludes only obliquely to the United States—by celebrating the Peace of Paris. Minerva is here enthroned between the Muses of Painting, Sculpture, and Music, and the figure of Europe holding the escutcheons of the European states who recognised American independence. In the sky on the left flies a cupid, with tricolour feathers in his helmet, holding banners of victory. Casks and bales on the ground represent commerce, and a sail probably alludes to the freedom of the seas—a subject of great concern to the French at this time. Peace and trade seem also to be the subject of the tapestries on the back and seat of the canapé, which incorporate an American Indian with the fasces of unity, a French cockerel perched on top of a globe, a parrot, a monkey toying with a feather head-dress, much exotic fruit, domestic animals, ships on the sea, and casks on the shore.

A set of tapestries was woven from Le Barbier's cartoons in 1788-89. This is probably the suite of four panels now at Osterley Park, Middlesex—they are narrower than those in the set exhibited here and without borders. Whether or not they were originally accompanied by furniture covers is not known. Another set was woven at the command of Louis XVI between 1789 and 1791. It has for long been assumed that this was to be a gift for George Washington. By 1789 disappointment was felt in ministerial circles that French commerce had benefitted little from American independence, and that

England had resumed trade on a large scale with her former colonies. The tapestries may perhaps have been intended as a gentle hint. But before their weaving was completed, the time for royal gifts has passed in France: Louis XVI was virtually a prisoner in Paris.

In 1795 an army supplier, Abraham Alcan, took a set of the tapestry panels and seat covers in payment for a state debt of 20,000 *livres*—presumably the one of which part is exhibited here. Four panels of the Continents (presumably those now at Osterley Park) were sold in 1796 to an American dealer, because they bore "plusieurs signes de féodalité" (i.e. the Bourbon lilies), which rendered them unsuitable for the decoration of any official apartment in Republican France.

Literature: H. Doniol; *Histoire de la participation de la France à l'établissament des Etats-Unis d'Amérique*, Paris, 1892, vol. III, pp. vii-viii; vol. v, pp. i-ii; Jules Badin: *La Manufacture de tapisseries de Beauvais*, Paris, 1909, pp. 39, 66; J. H. Hyde: "L'iconographie des quatres parties du monde dans les tapisseries" in *Gazette des Beaux Arts*, LXVI (ii), pp. 253-272; H. Göbel: *Die Wandteppiche und ihre Manufakturen in Frankreich, Italien, Spanien und Portugal*, Leipzig, 1928, p. 231; G. Wingfield Digby: "A Set of Beauvais Tapestries alluding to the War of American Independence" in *The Burlington Magazine*, XCII (1950), pp. 251-254.

James Barry

Irish, 1741-1806.
Barry was brought to London from
Dublin in 1764 by Edmund Burke,
whose *Philosophical Inquiry into . . .
the Sublime and Beautiful* had appeared in 1757. Burke later paid for
him to travel to Italy, 1766-71. Barry
had high and noble ambitions as a
painter but achieved only one work on
the grand scale, *The Progress of
Human Culture*, a decorative cycle in
the Society of Arts, London, 1777-83.
He became a Royal Academician in
1773 but was expelled in 1799. He died
in poverty.

James Barry

200 *The Resurrection of Freedom*
Pen, ink, and wash over pencil. ca.
1776. 15¾ x 23⅝ inches (40 x 60 cm.).
Inscription: *Jas.Barry Invt.; Rome;
Athens;* and on the temple *Libert.
Ameri . . .* Provenance: Dr. J. Percy
(1817-1889), bought by Museum 1890.
London, Victoria and Albert Museum.

This is a study for the print entitled
*The Phoenix or Resurrection of Free-
dom* issued anonymously by Barry in
1776, attacking the government's
American policy. In this print a group
of men standing by a monument "to
the Memory of British Freedom" (a
recumbent figure mourned by Locke)
turn to a pastoral landscape, where a
man is ploughing and figures dance
near a trim classical temple bearing the
words *Libert. Ameri . . .* and crowned
by a phoenix, from whose wings
Liberty arises. Time scatters flowers on
fragments of sculpture labelled
"Athens," "Rome," and "Florence" in
memory of earlier republics. Underneath is inscribed: "Respectfully dedicated to the present minority in both
Houses of Parliament by an Artist. O
Liberty thou parent of whatever is
truly amiable and illustrious, associated

LA DESTRUCTION DE LA STATUE ROYALE A NOUVELLE YORCK.

Die Zerstörung der Königlichen Bild | *La Destruction de la Statue royale
Säule zu Neu Yorck*   *A Paris chez Basset Rue St Jacques .*   *a Nouvelle Yorck*

with Virtue thou hatest the luxurious and intemperate and hast successfully abandoned thy lov'd residence in Greece, Italy and thy more favoured England when they grew corrupt and worthless. Thou hast given them over to chains and despondency . . . ."

Thus the drawing and print express Burke's views on the American Revolution as put forward in his many parliamentary speeches. But Barry was also concerned to include some expression of the then prevalent idea that the arts flourished only in conditions of political freedom, and in the print he inscribed on a paper in the foreground the following words: "Every like loves like or 40 reasons why the shallow half characters were in art so peculiarly selected and patronized in this reign."

Literature: D. Irwin: *English Neoclassical Art,* London, 1966, p. 147; *La Peinture Romantique Anglaise et Les Préraphaélites,* exhibition catalogue, Paris, 1972, no. 2.

André Basset
French, ca. 1750-1800.

201 *The Destruction of the Royal Statue in New York*
Etching, hand coloured. ca. 1776. 12¹¹⁄₁₆ x 19⅛ inches (32.2 x 48.5 cm.). Inscription: *A Paris chez Basset Rue St. Jacques.*
Washington, D.C., Library of Congress, Prints and Photographs Division.

A series of "peep show prints" of New York, including this in reverse, was engraved and published by François Xavier Habermann, Augsburg, 1776 (Museum of the City of New York, cf. John A. Kouwenhoven: *The Columbia Historical Portrait of New York,* New York, 1953, p. 79). These so-called "peep show prints," with reverse let-

tering in the top margin, were published in Augsburg and Paris in the late eighteenth century to be displayed in mirrored boxes and carried around by itinerant showmen. The series to which the exhibited print belongs depicts various contemporary events—British troops entering the city, the Great Fire of 1776, etc.—but were presumably drawn from inadequate verbal descriptions, for they are largely imaginary. The statue of George III in the Bowling Green at the foot of Broadway, for example, was an equestrian statue by Joseph Wilton and not, as shown in the print, a standing figure. Nor did the buildings at the foot of Broadway resemble those in the print. The Statue of George III was torn down on July 9, 1776. It had been ordered from Wilton by the assembly of New York in 1768, together with a statue of William Pitt, earl of Chatham. They reached New York in 1770 and were erected the same year, and both were destroyed during the Revolution. The statue of Pitt stood at the intersection of Wall Street and Smith (later William) Street. Fragments of the statue of George III are preserved in the New-York Historical Society. For a reconstruction see Alexander J. Wall: "The Statues of King George III and the Honorable William Pitt erected in New York City 1770" in *The New-York Historical Society Quarterly Bulletin,* IV (July, 1920), p. 36 and George Gibbs: "Account of the Statue of George III . . ." in *The New-York Historical Society Proceedings,* 1844, pp. 168-175.

Carl Gottleib Guttenburg
German, 1743-1790.
Born at Wöhrd near Nuremberg, Guttenburg was trained there as a draughtsman under J. J. Preissler and as an engraver under D. A. Hauer. For six years he worked in Basle and then settled in Paris, where he spent most of the rest of his life. His works include engravings after Greuze, P. A. Wille, and Benjamin West's *Death of Wolfe.*

Carl Gottleib Guttenburg

202 *The Tea-Tax-Tempest, or the Anglo-American Revolution*
Engraving. 1778. 18⅛ x 22¾ inches (46 x 57.7 cm.). Inscription: *Angewitter entstanden durch die Auflage auf den Thee in Amerika. Orage causé par l'Impot sur le Thé en Amerique.*
Washington, D.C., Library of Congress, Prints and Photographs Division.

This famous engraving is an adaptation, in reverse, of a satirical print of 1774 by John Dixon entitled *The Oracle, Representing, Britannia, Hibernia, Scotia, as assembled to consult the Oracle, on the present situation of Public Affairs, Time acting as Priest. Dedicated to Concord.* This expressed the interest in America aroused by news of the Boston Tea Party, which reached England in the *London Evening Post* on 20 January 1774. In the print exhibited, Time, with a magic lantern, shows upon a curtain an allegorical representation of the revolution in America and points this out to four female figures representing the four continents. Europe, Asia, and Africa replace Britannia, Hibernia, and Scotia in Dixon's print. The American Revolution is represented by a tea-pot (like a coffee-pot) over a fire in which stamped documents are blazing. In early impressions, as in that exhibited, a cock, the emblem of France, is blowing at the fire with bellows, but this was removed in later impressions. The contents of the tea-pot are exploding, and a serpent (as used on one of the two American flags at the beginning of the war) and the cap of liberty on its staff are being shot from it into the air—the consequence of the Stamp Act and the tax on tea. Beneath the clouds of smoke a prostrate lion is partly visible, and below lies a flag with three leopards representing the British royal standard, torn, its staff broken. On the left three beasts of prey—a lion, a bear, and a puma or lioness—are fighting. Within the circle, on the right, American soldiers are advancing with a striped flag; before them comes an allegorical figure of America, her up-stretched hand about to grasp the cap and staff of liberty from the exploding tea-pot. Behind her is a mounted officer, followed by soldiers with fixed bayonets. On the left British soldiers are fleeing in disorder.

The example of Holland and Switzerland in their contest with tyrants is alluded to, as emblematic of the revolt of the colonies against England, in two medallions in the lower margin. One is inscribed *Auto da fe* and *Holland 1560*, the other *Wilhelm Tell, Switzerland. 1296.*

A reduced and slightly altered version of this print was published on 12 March 1783, after preliminary peace terms had been signed, by W. Humphreys. This suggested that it was the "little Hot Spit Fire Tea pot that had done all the Mischief."

Literature: M. D. George: *Catalogue of Political and Personal Satires ... in the British Museum*, London, 1935, vol. v, pp. 298-299; R. T. Haines Halsey: "Impolitical Prints" in *Bulletin of the New York Public Library*, vol. 43 (November 1939), no. 11, p. 823.

203 *An American Negro Holding an Englishman by the Shoulder*

France. Engraving coloured by hand. ca. 1778. 12⅞ x 9⁷⁄₁₆ inches (32.7 x 24.1 cm.). Inscription: See below. Paris, Bibliothèque Nationale, Cabinet des Estampes.

This anti-British caricature is concerned with the British blockade of American ports and the freedom of the seas—a matter of concern to the French because of international trade. The French inscription translates: "The American Negro holding an Englishman by the shoulder while showing him that their hope is as fragile as the head of this woman and the vessel that she bears. The child represents that from infancy we support our pennant and our navigation . . . ."

Giovanni Battista Nini

Italian-French, 1717-1786.
The son of an engraver and maiolica painter, Nini was born in Urbino, studied sculpture at Bologna, and began his career there as a print maker and engraver on glass. In 1739-40 he went to Spain, then settled in France. From 1760-61 he worked in a pottery in the Château de Chaumont, owned by Jacques Donatien Le Ray de Chaumont, who appointed him manager in 1772. Here he made the sharply modelled portrait reliefs for which he is famous: Louis XV (1770), Catherine the Great of Russia (1771), Marie Antoinette (1774), Benjamin Franklin (1777, see below), Louis XVI (1780), and Voltaire (1781). They were modelled in wax and cast in terracotta, often in large numbers.

Giovanni Battista Nini

204 *Benjamin Franklin*

Terracotta. 1777. Signed: *Nini F 1777*.
Diameter 4⁷⁄₁₆ inches (11.3 cm.). Inscription: *.B. Franklin.* and *.Americain.*
Provenance: James Parmelee.
Cleveland, The Cleveland Museum of Art, Bequest of James Parmelee.

This is an example of one of the most widely diffused portraits of Franklin, of which the first specimens were issued in June 1777. By the neat device of a coat of arms with a lightning rod and thunderbolt (on the tranche of the shoulder), it refers to his role as a scientist. The portrait has a somewhat complex history. In the spring of 1777 Franklin settled in a house at Passy lent him by J. D. Le Ray de Chaumont, an ardent *Américaniste* who contracted to supply the insurgents with gunpowder and other necessities. Le Ray de Chaumont was also owner of the Chaumont pottery and terracotta manufactory, where he sent a portrait of Franklin drawn by an English amateur, Thomas Walpole (1755-1840), son of a banker then living in Paris, and cousin of Horace Walpole. This drawing is lost, but it seems to have shown Franklin bare-headed and wearing spectacles, as Nini modelled him in the first projects for the relief. On the medallions, of which the one exhibited is an example, however, he omitted the spectacles and covered Franklin's head with a fur hat, not of the type he actually wore but derived from portraits of J. J. Rousseau. Whether intentionally or not, he thus provided a visual link between Franklin and the French *philosophes*, between the aims of the American Revolution and the European Enlightenment. A large number of the medallions were manufactured, and many survive, with slight variations in the form of the signature and the dots in the inscription. In 1778 Nini issued a second portrait derived from a drawing by Anne Vallayer-Coster.

Literature: C. C. Sellers: *Benjamin Franklin in Portraiture*, pp. 103-105, 343-347.

Le Negre Amériquain tenant un Anglois par l'épaule en lui montrant que leur espoire est aussi fragile que la tête de cette femme et le Vaisseau qu'elle porte,
l'Enfant représente que dès l'Enfance nous soutenons notre pavillon et notre navigation.

Jean Honoré Fragonard

French, 1732-1806.

One of the greatest French painters of his time, Fragonard was trained at the academy in Paris and later in Rome, 1755-61. During his last three years in Italy, he travelled extensively with the abbé de Saint Non (see below). Apart from a second visit to Italy in 1773, he spent the rest of his life in Paris. His finest works epitomise the frivolity, insouciance, and elegant eroticism of the *ancien régime*. He was ruined by the French Revolution, but J.-L. David obtained for him the post of conservateur of the Muséum des Arts.

Jean Honoré Fragonard

205 *Le Docteur Francklin couronné par la liberté*

Aquatint. 1778. 9⅞ x 7⅞ inches (24.9 x 20 cm.).
Paris, Bibliothèque Nationale, Cabinet des Estampes.

Early in 1778, when the Franco-American alliance was impending, Fragonard made a drawing for his friend Jean-Claude-Richard de Saint Non (1727-1791), who wished to give Franklin a demonstration of the new technique of aquatint engraving. This is an impression of the aquatint he made when Franklin came to lunch with him to learn the new technique. The drawing by Fragonard showed a bust of Franklin (after Caffieri) and a terrestrial globe, embraced by a winged youth. Liberty descends from the right towards it with a wreath extended in each hand. Saint Non made some adjustments to it, adding a liberty cap on a pole and rays of light over the figure of Liberty, the inscription "Amerique" on the globe, and to the scroll under the bust "Cons . . . tutions / du Gouvernment / de Pensilvanie / Art 1." On 17 April 1778 Saint Non wrote to Baron Gagnare de Joursanvault about the alterations and the circumstances under which the print had been made:

As for your hint on the print of Dr. Franklin, if you are aware of the iconography, you will recall that a cap held aloft on pole or baton is the emblem of Liberty, as a lamp is of Knowledge, or the scales of Justice; thus it is impossible to characterize it otherwise; the only trouble with the print is that that fatal cap is too deeply bitten by the acid and is too dark, while in the drawing it floats in the air; but I beg you to consider that this little piece has been made in the space of one morning and solely to convey to this celebrated man a conception of engraving in this technique, an idea of the process. I claim no more for it, and, after all, the merit is in the intention. You honor and reckon my talents too highly.

(For Fragonard's drawing, formerly in the collection of Lady Mendl, Paris, see A. Ananoff: *L'oeuvre dessiné de Jean-Honoré Fragonard*, Paris, 1961, vol. I, p. 181.)

Literature: R. Portalis & H. Beraldi: *Graveurs du dixhuitième siècle*, Paris, 1880-1882, vol. 3, pp. 491-492; L. Guimbaud: *Saint-Non et Fragonard, d'après des documents inédites*, Paris, 1928, pp. 166-167, 186-187; C. C. Sellers: *Benjamin Franklin in Portraiture*, pp. 284-285.

Jean Honoré Fragonard

206 *Eripuit Coelo Fulmen, Sceptrumque Tyrannis. Au Genie de Franklin.*

Etching. 1778. 18¾ x 14½ inches (sight) (47.6 x 36.8 cm.). Provenance: James Hazen Hyde.
New York, The New-York Historical Society.

Fragonard probably made the drawing, from which this print was etched by his sister-in-law Marguerite Gérard, in early 1778, for the Grimm-Diderot *Correspondence Littéraire* mentions in April 1778: "On a fait pour le portrait de M.le docteur Franklin un très-beau vers latin: *Eripuit coelo fulmen sceptrumque tyrannis*. C'est une heureuse imitation d'un vers de l'*Anti-Lucrèce: Eripuitque Jovi fulmen Phoebusque sagittas.*"

Publication of the print was announced in the *Journal de Paris* on 15 November 1778:

New print, dedicated to the Genius of Franklin. The ingenious author of this composition, M. Fragonard, Painter to the King, has sought to depict the Latin verse applied to *Franklin, Eripuit coelo fulmen, sceptrumque tyrannis*, which one reads at the base of the print.

Inspired by this verse, which summarizes the spirit and profound understanding of Franklin and his wisdom in the New World revolution, the painter has represented him at once turning aside the lightning with Minerva's shield, as his lighting rods have done, and with the other commanding Mars to attack Avarice and Tyranny; while America, nobly attendant on him and holding a fasces, symbol of the united provinces, calmly watches the overthrow of her enemies. The simple and rapid line of this composition is as clear and as facile as the verse, which the painter wanted to transform into a visual image. It is with this dignity that he has turned

his talents to celebrate true worth and great deeds.

This print, engraved by the Mlle. *Gérard*, after the drawing and under the direction of M. Fragonard, her brother-in-law, has the merit, dear to artists, of rendering in engraved line the spirit of the author. Here they have not aimed at that meticulousness, those beautiful works and those graces essential to the products of the burin; they have only sought to catch by the point the sure and

sensitive touches of the design, with a rapidity equal to that with which the drawing was executed, and it seems to us that they have succeeded.

A similar account of the print, cited as having been found in the "Gazette of Amiens," was published in the *Pennsylvania Packet* on 3 June 1780 and again in the *Connecticut Gazette* on 30 June 1780. Fragonard's original drawing, from which the print was made, is now in the White House (cf.

A. Ananoff: *L'oeuvre dessiné de Jean-Honoré Fragonard*, Paris, 1961, vol. 1, p. 180).

Literature: R. Portalis: *Les Dessinateurs d'illustration au dix-huitième siècle*, Paris, 1877, p. 244; Jeanne Doin: "Margarite Gerard" in *Gazette des Beaux-Arts*, 8 (1913), p. 430; L. Guimbaud: *Saint-Non et Fragonard, d'après des documents inédites*, Paris, 1928, p. 212; G. Grappe: *La Vie de Jean-Honoré Fragonard*, Paris, 1942, p. 213; C. C. Sellers: *Benjamin Franklin in Portraiture*, pp. 287-289.

207 Cup

France (Sèvres). Porcelain painted in enamel and gilt. ca. 1779. Marked with crossed *L*'s and *L.G.* (for Le Guay) in bluish enamel: *40* and a dash incised. Height 3 inches (7.6 cm.). Provenance: J. G. Joicey Collection.
London, Victoria and Albert Museum.

Etienne Henri Le Guay, who initialled and decorated the cup exhibited, was employed at Sèvres from 1749 to 1796. The profile portrait of Benjamin Franklin on the cup is a copy of a medallion profile portrait of him produced at Sèvres in unglazed porcelain in 1778. It was said to be a good likeness, e.g. by Franklin's sister (see C. Van Doren, ed.: *The Letters of Benjamin Franklin and Jane Mecom*, Princeton, 1950, p. 267). It was frequently copied and engraved, notably as the frontispiece to Franklin's *Political, Miscellaneous and Philosophical Pieces,* London, 1779. The cups made at Sèvres were accompanied by saucers decorated with emblems of the Franco-American alliance. A set of these cups and saucers was purchased by the comte de Saint-Simon in 1779 (see Pierre Verlet: *Sèvres, Le XVIII Siècle* Paris, 1953, p. 42).

Literature: C. C. Sellers: *Benjamin Franklin in Portraiture*, p. 368.

Antoine Borel

French, 1743-after 1810.
Borel began his career as a portrait painter but worked mainly as a draughtsman and etcher of illustrations for books and political allegories.

Antoine Borel

208 *Independent America*

Pen, ink, and wash. Signed and dated: *AB 1779*. 16¹⁵⁄₁₆ x 13¹³⁄₁₆ inches (43 x 35 cm.). Provenance: M. and Mme. Laugel, Paris; Mme. Th. Mallet, Paris. Paris, collection of M. Thierry Feray.

The United States, personified by an all but naked Indian woman, is presented by Mercury, patron of commerce, to France, who holds out a caduceus as a symbol of concord. Above, Fame trumpets the news abroad, and to the left the war goddess Bellona rests with her club by a crown, a pile of coins, and a snake. This appears to be a revised version of an allegory drawn by Antoine Borel and engraved by J. C. Le Vasseur in 1778, with a figure of Benjamin Franklin as a Roman senator in the centre. Borel wished to dedicate this print to Franklin, who declined the honour, for which he would have been expected to pay the artist. (See C. C. Sellers: *Benjamin Franklin in Portraiture,* New Haven and London, 1962, pp. 195-197.)

Jean-Baptiste Le Paon

French, 1738-1785.
Le Paon was a pupil of Francesco Casanova and specialised in battle paintings. He became *premier peintre* to the prince de Condé. Four decorative battle pieces in the *salon d'honneur* of the Ecole Militaire in Paris are by him, and also the overdoors in the library. In 1779 he painted for Lafayette a portrait of George Washington (now lost) and in 1782 a whole length painting of Lafayette at the siege of Yorktown, engraved by Noël Le Mire. Later (see below), he painted four scenes of the war in America for the Gobelins or Beauvais tapestry factory.

Jean-Baptiste Le Paon

209 *The Battle of Brimston Hill*

Pen, ink, and wash. ca. 1782. Signed: *Le Paon*. 17¾ x 13⅜ inches (45 x 34 cm.). Inscription: *Bataille de Brimston-Hill (11 Janvier 1782)*. Provenance: Georges Moussoir, Paris. Blérancourt, Musée National de la Coopération Franco-Américaine.

The battle of Brimston Hill, by which the French under the marquis de Bouillé took the island of Saint-Christophe (or St. Kitts) from the English between 16 January and 12 February 1782 (not 11 January as stated in the inscription), was an event in the war in the West Indies which developed out of that in North America. This drawing of it, together with another of the taking of Grenada three years earlier (also Blérancourt, Musée de la Coopération Franco-Américaine), are connected with cartoons for tapestries made by

Le Paon in 1783 for the Gobelins or Beauvais factories and also included the battles of Yorktown and Pensacola (Paris, Mobilier National). Engravings after Le Paon's drawings of these subjects were made and published in Paris by N. Ponce. By the Treaty of Paris in 1783, France returned Grenada to the British but retained Saint-Christophe.

Literature: *Chateau de Blérancourt, Le Musée de la Coopération Franco-Amércaine*, Paris, 1966, no. 37.

E. Bellier de la Chavignerie and L. Auvray: *Dictionnaire général des artistes de l'école française*, Paris, 1885, vol. II, p. 709). These are lost, and it is not known whether there were any decorations on the design for the obelisk corresponding with the drawings exhibited here. It is, however, improbable that de Wailly would have devised the latter before the Peace of Paris terminated the Revolutionary War. The reliefs were illustrated in engravings mysteriously signed (*Dessiné par Monet Peintre du Roi. Née sculp. 1786*) by two otherwise unknown artists and published in J.-B. de Laborde: *Description historique de la France*, Paris, 1787, vol. III, pp. 18-20.

Literature: L. L. de Grandmaison in *Réunion des Sociétés des beaux-arts des départements*, 1901, p. 400; A. Girodie in *Bulletin de la Société de l'histoire de l'art français*, 1929, p. 233; A. Giradie in *Bulletin des Musées*, 1930, p. 170; L. Hautecoeur: *Histoire de l'architecture classique en France*, Paris, 1952, vol. IV, pp. 152, 426.

Charles de Wailly

French, 1730-1798.
Trained in Paris under Blondel and later in Rome, de Wailly became one of the most notable architects of his day. His best known work is the Odéon in Paris (1779-85), which he designed in collaboration with Marie-Joseph Peyre. His later work is sometimes even more austerely Neoclassical.

Charles de Wailly

210 *Design for Relief Carvings*
Pen and ink and grey wash. Signed and dated: *De Wailly delineavit 1783.* 9⅞ x 12¹³⁄₁₆ inches (24.9 x 32.4 cm.). Inscription: *L'Amerique Independante. Une frégate du Roi aportant aux Américains rassemblés sur le rivage de Boston, le traité de l'indépendance* and *Bas relief de l'obelisque du Port Vendre. Côte du Port.*
Paris, Musée du Louvre, Cabinet des dessins, on loan to Blérancourt, Musée National de la Coopération Franco-Américaine.

These drawings are very slightly different versions for one of the relief panels on the base of an obelisk designed by de Wailly and erected in the town of Port de Vendres on the south-west coast of France. Two of the other panels (for which drawings are in the same collection) are entitled *La marine relevé* and *Le commerce protégé*—the navy exalted and commerce protected. All allude to the American Revolutionary War but reflect French official preoccupation with the freedom of trade and the seas as much as the liberty of the United States. The obelisk on which these reliefs were carved, and which still survives, was the only part of de Wailly's very grandiose scheme for the enlargement of Port-Vendres to be realised. In designing it he may have been influenced by drawings for obelisks to celebrate both the deeds of Louis XVI and the independence of America, commissioned in 1776 and 1777 by the abbé de Lubersac from Jean Touzé and Jean Duplessi-Bertaux. In the Paris Salon of 1781 de Wailly showed a series of designs for Port-Vendres, including "deux vues de l'obélisque élevée à la gloire de Louis XVI dans la principale place du port" and also "le modèle de l'obélisque" (cf.

Louis-Nicolas van Blarenberghe

French, 1716/19-1794.
Born in Lille, van Blarenberghe was appointed battle-painter to the French war department in 1769 by the Minister of War, the duc de Choiseul, for whom he decorated a famous snuff-box with microscopically detailed depictions of the duc's apartments. His larger paintings tend to resemble enlarged miniatures. In 1770 he painted fourteen views of European capitals as over-doors for the Ministry of Foreign Affairs (now the Bibliothèque de Versailles) and later, in 1779-90, a series of twenty-two gouaches of the sieges and battles in Flanders under Louis XV. The two gouaches exhibited formed an adjunct to this series. His work is very similar to that of his son Henri-Désiré (1741-1826).

Louis-Nicolas van Blarenberghe

211 *The Siege of Yorktown*

Gouache. Signed and dated: *Van Blarenberghe, 1784.* 23⅛ x 37 inches (59 x 94 cm.).
Versailles, Musée National du Château de Versailles. (Exhibited in Cleveland only.)

The siege and taking of the British military base of Yorktown between 6 and 19 October 1781, which led to the surrender of Lord Cornwallis, are depicted by van Blarenberghe with microscopic detail. He presumably worked from descriptions, probably both written and drawn, by officers of the topographical department in the comte de Rochambeau's expeditionary force. A gouache made by one of these officers of the taking of Grenada survives in the manuscript *Mémoires du comte de Bouillé sur la Guerre de l'Indépendance américaine* (formerly Marquis Pierre de Bouillé Collection). This is of the kind that was probably used by van Blarenberghe.

Replicas of *The Siege of Yorktown* and *The Taking of Yorktown* were given by Louis XVI to the comte de Rochambeau.

Literature: A. Girodie: *Exposition du Centenaire de La Fayette 1757-1834,* catalogue, Paris, 1934, pp. 68-69; *Treasures of Versailles,* exhibition catalogue, Art Institue of Chicago and elsewhere, 1962-63, nos. 124 and 125.

Louis-Nicolas van Blarenberghe

212 *The Taking of Yorktown*

Gouache. Signed and dated: *Van Blarenberghe, 1784.* 23⅛ x 37 inches (59 x 94 cm.).
Versailles, Musée National du Château de Versailles. (Exhibited in Cleveland only.)

François Godefroy

French, 1743-1819.
Godefroy was a print maker, trained under the painter J.-B. Descamps in Rouen and Jacques Philippe Le Bas in Paris. He produced numerous vignette book illustrations as well as single prints, including portraits and other subjects, such as *Exemple d'humanité donné par Mme la Dauphine* [Marie Antoinette] *le 16. 8bre 1773*. In 1790 he engraved with his son Adrien a collection of portraits of members of the National Assembly.

François Godefroy

213 *John Malcom*
Etching. ca. 1784. 11½ x 17³⁄₁₆ inches (29.2 x 43.5 cm.). Inscription: *Dessiné et Gravé par F. Godefroy de l'académie Imp^{le} et R^{le} de Vienne &c.* Washington, D.C., Library of Congress, Prints and Photographs Division.

On 27 January 1774 John Malcom or Malcomb, an unpopular commissioner of customs at Boston, was tarred and feathered, led to the gallows with a rope round his neck, and, on the way there, forced as a torture to drink enormous quantities of tea. His offence was in attempting to collect customs duties; it was not connected with the Boston Tea Party (cf. R. T. Halsey: *The Boston Port Bill*, London, 1904, pp. 77-82). For Malcom's memorial to the government of Massachusetts begging for relief and redress and his petition to the king for compensation and employment, cf. *Hist.MSS.Comm. Dartmouth MSS*, vol. I, p. 348; vol. II, pp. 192, 263. The incident was first depicted, satirically, by Carrington Bowles in two mezzotints published on 12 October 1774 in London and entitled: *A new method of Macarony making, as practised at Boston in North America*. A third version was issued by Bowles on 2 June 1775. Another, probably by P. Dawe, was published by Sayer and Bennett in London, 31 October 1774, as *The Bostonians Paying the Excise-man or Tarring & Feathering*. Cf. M. D. George: *Catalogue of Political and Personal Satires . . . in the British Museum,* London, 1935, vol. V, pp. 168, 169.

The print exhibited here was published in Nicolas Ponce and François Godefroy: *Recueil d'estampes representant les différents événemens de la guerre qui a procuré l'indépendance aux Etats Unis de l'Amérique . . .* Paris [1784?].

Dessiné et Gravé par F. Godefroy,
de l'Académie Impele et Rle Vienne &c.

JOHN MALCOM.

Le 25 Janvier 1774 la populace irritée pénétra sans armes dans sa maison. Il blessa plusieurs personnes à coups d'épée: mais les Bostoniens, modérés
malgré dans leur vengeance, le saisirent, le descendent par la fenêtre dans une charrette,ensuite il fut dépouillé, goudronné, emplumé, mené sur la place
publique, battu de verges,et obligé de remercier de ce qu'on ne le punissait point de mort;puis on le ramena chez lui sans autre mal.

ORIGINE DE LA REVOLUTION AMERICAINE.

Manufacture de Jouy, after Jean-Baptiste-Marie Huet

France.

214 *America Paying Homage to France*

Plate printed cotton. ca. 1784-1790. 35½ x 32⅝ inches (90 x 83 cm.). Inscription: *Manufacture Royale de . . . . A Jouy pres Versaile . . . .* Provenance: Gift of Mlle. Morris, 1926. Paris, Musée des Arts Décoratifs.

The central motif in this furnishing fabric is America, accompanied by Liberty (with her cap on a pole), a soldier carrying the flag of thirteen stars and stripes, and a kneeling black man, expressing gratitude to France—enthroned with an orb bearing the Bourbon lilies, and two soldiers in armour behind her. Around it there are islands (one inhabited by American Indians) and ships, signifying the freedom of the seas for commerce. This is one of two printed cottons alluding to American independence produced by Christophe-Philippe Oberkampf's factory at Jouy, probably at the instigation of Benjamin Franklin. In 1783 the factory issued a cotton, also designed by Huet, with the reverse of the *Libertas Americana* medal [218] as its central motif. The more elaborate cotton, of the pattern exhibited here, was first issued in 1783-84. It differs slightly from Huet's original design (Musée des Arts Décoratifs, Paris), where the figure of America has no drapery. On later specimens of the cotton, printed after the abolition of the French monarchy, the figure of France has no crown and the *fleurs de lys* have been removed from her orb. To judge from the number of surviving specimens, this cotton was very popular. It has recently been reprinted in France.

Literature: A. Guérinet, ed.: *Les nouvelles collections de l'Union Centrale des Arts Décoratifs, 9e série, J.-B. Huet*, Paris, s.d. vol. II, pl. 82; H. Clouzot and F. Morris: *Painted and Printed Fabrics, the History of the Manufactory at Jouy and other Ateliers in France 1760-1815*, New York, 1927, pl. 25; A. Girodie: *La Fayette 1757-1834*, exhibition catalogue, Musée de l'Orangerie, Paris, 1934, no. 57; E. McClung Fleming: "From Indian Princess to Greek Goddess, The American Image 1783-1815" in *Winterthur Portfolio*, III (1967), p. 45.

215 *Louis XVI and Benjamin Franklin*
France (Niderviller, Lorraine). Biscuit porcelain. ca. 1783-1785. Marked on base: *Niderville*. Height 12⅝ inches (32 cm.).
Providence, R.I., The Providence Athenaeum.

Louis XVI in Roman armour is here shown handing to Benjamin Franklin documents inscribed *Indépendence de l'Amérique* and *Liberté des Mers*. The group was made at the Niderviller porcelain factory in Lorraine, which was owned from 1770-71 until 1793 by Philibert, comte de Custine, who served with the French forces in the American Revolutionary War. The model is probably by Charles Gabriel Sauvage, called Lemire (1741-1827), who worked at the Niderviller factory from 1759 until 1808, when he joined the staff of the Sèvres Porcelain Factory. Two other specimens of the group are recorded, in The Metropolitan Museum of Art, New York, and the H. F. du Pont Winterthur Museum, Winterthur.

Literature: *L'Art,* 15 (1878), pp. 141-142; *The French in America,* exhibition catalogue, Detroit Institute of Arts, Detroit, 1951, no. 207; C. C. Sellers: *Benjamin Franklin in Portraiture*, pp. 320-321.

Pierre-Philippe Thomire
French, 1751-1843.
Thomire was the most famous Parisian bronze worker, or *fondeur ciseleur*, of the Louis XVI and Empire periods. He was trained as a sculptor under Pajou and Houdon, for whom he cast bronze portrait busts. By 1775 he was working for the Crown, and he collaborated with J.-L. Prieur on the bronze fittings for Louis XVI's coronation coach. He made many decorative bronzes for the royal palaces and in the 1780s also supplied gilt bronze mounts for Sèvres porcelain and furniture. But he flourished especially under the Empire, when he developed his business on a commercial scale. He was much patronised by Napoleon and received important commissions, e.g. toilet-service for Marie-Louise (1810 with Odiot) and the two cradles for the king of Rome (1811). He retired in 1823.

Pierre-Philippe Thomire

216 *Candelabra Commemorating American Independence*
Gilt bronze with biscuit de Sèvres plaques on a marble base. ca. 1785. Signed: *Thomire*. Height 28 inches (71.1 cm.). Provenance: King of Württemberg; French & Company. Washington, D.C., Corcoran Gallery of Art, William A. Clark Collection.

In 1785 Thomire was commissioned by the city of Paris to make a candelabrum for presentation to General Lafayette to celebrate the end of the American Revolution. This piece can no longer be traced, nor can the replicas he is said

to have made for Louis XVI and George Washington. But ten bronze candelabra referring to the victory of the United States, some signed by Thomire, are recorded. Each of them incorporates chained leopards, symbolising England, crowing cockerels for France, and sirens supporting ships, which allude both to Paris and the freedom of the seas (a ship has been the emblem of Paris since the Middle Ages). All have seven branches, of which the central one sometimes supports a statuette of an American Indian. They differ from each other mainly in the reliefs set in the drum-shaped base. On the example in the Louvre (Dreyfus Collection), they are of Sèvres biscuit porcelain and represent the beginning of hostilities in America, Peace casting down War, and the Treaty of Paris—though all the figures are in ancient Roman costume. Others, including those exhibited here, have reliefs of playing children made at Sèvres in imitation of Wedgwood jasper-ware.

Literature: J. Niclausse: *Thomire Fondeur-Ciseleur*, Paris, 1947, pp. 69-72, 121-122.

Augustin Dupré

217 *Allegory of the American Revolution*

Terracotta. 1783. Diameter 14⅜6 inches (37 cm.). Provenance: Godefroy Mayer.
Blérancourt, Musée National de la Coopération Franco-Américaine.

This is the large scale model for the reverse of a medal celebrating American independence engraved by Augustin Dupré [218]. The symbolical programme was devised by Benjamin Franklin, who wrote to Robert R. Livingstone, the American secretary of state for foreign affairs, on 4 March 1782 that he was planning to commemorate the capitulation of Lord Cornwallis by having a medal struck representing the United States in the figure of the infant Hercules strangling two snakes, which would also indicate the strength of the new nation. In the terracotta, as in the medal, Minerva with a shield bearing the Bourbon lilies struggles with the British leopard, while Hercules holds by the neck two snakes symbolising the armies commanded by Sir John Burgoyne and Lord Cornwallis. Franklin's idea was realised in a drawing by Esprit-Antonine Gibelin (1739-1813), also in the Musée de la Coopération Franco-Américaine, Blérancourt, inscribed: *Argumentum dedit Benjamin Franklin spiritus Antonius Gibelin exposit ac delineavit anno 1783* (the word *exposit*—set forth —has been written above *invenit*, which is crossed out, presumably to give Franklin full credit for the idea). This drawing differs from the terracotta in several details, notably the figure of Hercules, who is shown straddling a cradle. Although the terracotta has always been attributed to Augustin Dupré, it may well be by Gibelin, who worked as a sculptor and modeller of medals, though he is known mainly as

Augustin Dupré
French, 1748-1833.
One of the most distinguished French medallists of his day, Dupré learned the art of engraving metal in a gun factory in his native St. Etienne (Loire). He went to Paris ca. 1768 and was employed in another gun factory but soon attracted the patronage of the Spanish ambassador and began to work independently as a maker of decorative objects, including jewellery and, from 1776, medals. Benjamin Franklin, who commissioned from him the first of his medals celebrating the American

Revolution (see below), seems to have become a personal friend, possibly because they both had houses outside Paris at Passy. In 1791 he succeeded P.-S.-B. Duvivier [222] as engraver-general of French coins and in this capacity was responsible for the first French Republican decimal coinage, including the 5 *centime* piece with the head of liberty. He was a convinced Republican and for that reason was dismissed from his post by Napoleon in 1803. But he continued to engrave medals and also worked for the famous silversmith Martin Guillaume Biennais.

a painter (frescoes in Ecole de Mede-
cine and Ecole Militaire, Paris).

Literature: Godefroy Mayer: *Old Paintings, Drawings . . . relating to America*,
Paris, n.d. no. 460; André Girodie: *Exposition du centenaire de La Fayette*, exhibition catalogue, Musée de l'Orangerie,
Paris, 1934, p. 42; L. Bedourte: *Chateau
de Blérancourt, Le Musée de la Coopération Franco-Américain*, Paris, 1966, pl. 53.

Augustin Dupré

218 *Libertas Americana Medal*
Bronze. 1783. Signed: *Dupre F* on obverse (truncation of neck) and on reverse (above exergue line). Diameter
1⅞ inches (48 mm.). Inscription: Obverse, *LIBERTAS. AMERICANA. 4
Juil. 1776*; reverse, *NON SINE DIIS
ANIMOSUS INFANS.*
and 17 OCT. 1777
    19   1781
New York, The American Numismatic Society.

This medal was commissioned from
Dupré by Benjamin Franklin, who had
previously employed Pierre-Simon-
Benjamin Duvivier as medallist [222]
but complained of his charges. Struck
to commemorate the victories at Sara-
toga and Yorktown, the medal shows
on its obverse a head of liberty with a
diminutive liberty cap on a pole. The
reverse is as the preliminary model
[217], with the inscription taken from
Horace Book III, Ode iv, "Not without
the gods is the infant courageous."

Examples were struck in three
metals. On 5 April 1783 Franklin told
the American secretary of state for
foreign affairs that he was sending
two in copper for himself and one in
silver for the president of Congress.
He sent others to various members of
Congress. He gave a silver example to
each of the French ministers and also
to the Grand Master of the Order of
the Knights of Malta, who had fav-

oured the American cause. Two specimens in gold were given to Louis XVI
and Marie Antoinette. A writer in the
Correspondence Littéraire in April
1783 (probably Baron Grimm) described the medal and praised the "fort
belle tête, d'un trait pur, d'une expression franche et vigoureuse," ("very
beautiful head, pure in character, frank
and vigorous in expression"), remarking of the reverse that it was "too
pretty" and complaining of its medi-
ocre execution. The design of the reverse was copied by J.-B. Huet [153]
as the central motif for a cotton printed
at the Manufacture de Jouy. It seems
also to have influenced Jean-Jacques-
François Le Barbier's design for the
tapestry representing America woven
at Beauvais [195].

The obverse of this medal served as
the prototype for the obverse of the
U.S. Liberty Cap cents and half-cents
of 1793, the dies of which are believed
to have been cut by Joseph Wright of
Philadelphia. This basic design of a
flowing-haired Liberty with a liberty
cap was retained through the early part
of 1796.

Literature: F. M. Grimm and D. Diderot:
Correspondence Littéraire (April 1783),
Paris, 1830, vol. XI, pp. 360-361; J. F.
Loubat: *The Medallic History of the
United States*, New York, 1878, pp. 86-92;
W. S. Appleton: "Augustin Dupré and his
Work for America" in *Proceedings of the
Massachusetts Historical Society*, ser. 2, V
(1890), pp. 348-352; C. Saunier: *Augustin
Dupré, orfèvre, médailleur, graveur
général des monnaies*, Paris, 1894; L. For-
rer: *Biographical Dictionary of Medallists*,
Paris, 1894; L. Forrer: *Biographical Dictionary of Medallists*, London, 1904, vol. I,
p. 647; C. Saunier: "Les Médailles
françaises de l'indépendence américaine"
in *Les Arts*, no. 172 (1918), pp. 2-6; C.
Zigrosser: "The Medallic Sketches of
Augustin Dupré in American Collections"
in *Proceedings of the American Philosophical Society*, CI (1957), pp. 535-550;
Cornelius C. Vermeule, *Numismatic Art
in America*, Cambridge, Mass., 1971, pp.
9-10, 27-28.

Augustin Dupré

219 *Daniel Morgan Medal*

Bronze. Restrike after original of 1789.
Signed below exergue lines: *dupré f.*
(obverse), *DUPRE INV ET F* (reverse).
Diameter 2³⁄₁₆ inches (56 mm.). Inscription: Obverse, *DANIELI MORGAN
DUCI EXERCITUS* and *COMITIA
AMERICANA•*; reverse, *VICTORIA
LIBERATIS VINDEX* and *FUGATIS
CAPTIS AUT CAESIS/ AD COW-
PENS HOSTIBUS•/ XVII. JAN.
MDCCLXXXI•*
Washington, D.C., National Numismatic Collection, Smithsonian
Institution.

This is an official bronze restrike made
at the U.S. Mint of the medal engraved
by Dupré in Paris and paid for out of
funds voted by the U.S. Congress on 9
March 1781. The commission was
given to Dupré by Colonel David
Humphreys on the advice of Benjamin
Franklin in 1785. But it was not completed until 1789, when Thomas Jefferson modified the wording of the inscriptions, which had been devised in
consultation with the Académie des
inscriptions et belles-lettres. The obverse shows the conventional figure of
America dressed in feathers crowning
Daniel Morgan with a laurel wreath.
(A somewhat similar Indian greeted by
a personification of the Netherlands
appeared on a medal engraved by
Johann Georg Holtzhey and struck to
mark the arrival of John Adams as the
first United States envoy to the Netherlands in 1782.) The reverse shows the
victory of the United States army commanded by Daniel Morgan and Nathaniel Greene over Lord Cornwallis's
British force at Cowpens near Kings
Mountain, South Carolina, on 17 January 1781.

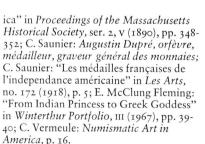

Literature: J. F. Loubat: *The Medallic
History of the United States*, New York,
1878, pp. xi-xxii, 40-45; W. S. Appleton:
"Augustin Dupré and his Work for America" in *Proceedings of the Massachusetts
Historical Society*, ser. 2, v (1890), pp. 348-
352; C. Saunier: *Augustin Dupré, orfèvre,
médailleur, graveur général des monnaies;*
C. Saunier: "Les médailles françaises de
l'independance américaine" in *Les Arts*,
no. 172 (1918), p. 5; E. McClung Fleming:
"From Indian Princess to Greek Goddess"
in *Winterthur Portfolio*, III (1967), pp. 39-
40; C. Vermeule: *Numismatic Art in
America*, p. 16.

Augustin Dupré

220 *John Paul Jones Medal*

Bronze. 1789. Signed on obverse and
reverse: *Dupré.F.* Diameter 2³⁄₁₆ inches
(56 mm.). Inscription: Obverse, *JO-*
ANNI PAULO JONES CLASSIS
PRAEFECTO and *COMITIA AMER-*
ICANA; reverse, *HOSTIUM NAV-*
IBUS CAPTIS AUT FUGATIS and *AD*
ORAM SCOTIAE XXIII. SEPT.
M.DCCLXXVIIII.
New York, private collection.

Congress voted funds for a medal of
John Paul Jones, which was commissioned from Dupré by Thomas Jefferson when he was *chargé d'affaires* of
the United States in Paris. The obverse
bears a portrait of Jones derived from
the Houdon bust [191], the reverse a
representation of his most famous
naval action in *Bonhomme Richard*
against H.M.S. *Serapis* off Flam-
borough Head in the North Sea on 23
September 1779. Jones was very anxious that this battle should be accurately depicted and on 29 August 1788
sent Jefferson an account of it, remarking that a medallist had already made
three medals of him, one showing the
combat between *Bonhomme Richard*
and *Serapis* without regard to the direction of the wind. A print which
Jones considered accurate was provided for Dupré's guidance.

Literature: J. F. Loubat: *The Medallic*
History of the United States, New York,
1878, pp. xix-xxi, xxviii, 97-112; W. S.
Appleton: "Augustin Dupré and his work
for America" in *Proceedings of the Massa-*
chusetts Historical Society, ser. 2, v (1890),
pp. 348-352; C. Saunier: *Augustin Dupré,*
orfèvre, médailleur, graveur général des
monnaies; C. Saunier: "Les médailles*
françaises de l'independance américaine"
in *Les Arts,* no. 172 (1918), p. 5; C. Vermeule: *Numismatic Art in America,* pp.
16-17.

Augustin Dupré

221 *The Diplomatic Medal*

Bronze. 1876 restrike after original of
1793. Signed on obverse: *DUPRE. F.*
(above exergue line) and *C. BARBER*
1876 (below). Diameter 2⅝ inches
(67 mm.). Inscription: Obverse, *TO*
PEACE AND COMMERCE and *IV*
JUL. MDCCLXXVI.; reverse, *THE*
UNITED STATES OF AMERICA.
Washington, D.C., National Numismatic Collection, Smithsonian
Institution.

This is an official bronze restrike made
at the U.S. Mint (from a die engraved
by Charles Barber in 1876 after the
original) of the last of the series of
medals on American subjects engraved
in Paris by Dupré. President Washington ordered the medal in 1790, and
Jefferson instructed William Short to
commission it in Paris from either
Duvivier or Dupré, favouring the
latter. The design was agreed to in collaboration with members of the
Académie des inscriptions et belles-
lettres. On the obverse Mercury, patron of commerce, presents a cornucopia to the personification of America, seated near bales and an anchor.

The reverse, which bears the great seal
of the United States, served as the
model for the heraldic eagle used on
U.S. silver and gold coinage from 1798
to 1807. Ironically, the medal was
completed the year before Jay's commercial treaty with England reduced
cordiality between France and the
United States to its nadir. Only eight
specimens of the medal were struck,
six in bronze as well as two in gold for
the marquis de la Luzerne, the first
French ambassador to Philadelphia,
and the marquis de Moustier, who succeeded him.

Literature: J. F. Loubat: *The Medallic His-*
tory of the United States, pp. x, xxix, 115,
117-118; W. S. A[ppleton]: Medal Commemorative of American Independence"
in *American Journal of Numismatics,* IX
(1875), pp. 65-66; W. S. Appleton: "Augustin Dupré and his Work for America"
in *Proceedings of the Massachusetts His-*
torical Society, ser. 2, v (1890), pp. 348-
352; C. Saunier: *Augustin Dupré, orfèvre,*
médailleur, graveur général des monnaies;
C. Saunier: "Les médailles françaises de
l'independance américaine in *Les Arts,* no.
172 (1918), p. 6; E. McClung Fleming:
"From Indian Princess to Greek Goddess"
in *Winterthur Portfolio,* III (1967), pp. 41-
42; C. Vermeule: *Numismatic Art in*
America, pp. 11-13.

Jacques Pilon of 1781 (Metropolitan Museum, New York). An example of the medal was exhibited at the Paris Salon of 1789, together with those of "Colonel William Washington" and Colonel John Eager Howard.

Literature: J. F. Loubat: *The Medallic History of the United States,* pp. xiii-xvi, xxviii, xxv, xlvii, 1-7; E. Bellier de la Chavignerie and L. Auvray: *Dictionnaire général des artistes de l'école française,* Paris, 1882, vol. 1, p. 509; H. Nocq: *Jean et Benjamin Duvivier,* Paris, 1911; C. Saunier: "Les médailles françaises de l'indépendance américaine" in *Les Arts,* no. 172 (1918), pp. 2-3.

Pierre-Simon-Benjamin Duvivier

French, 1730-1819.
Duvivier was the son and pupil of the most distinguished French medallist of the Louis XV period, Jean Duvivier (1687-1761). After his father's death he took over his apartment in the Louvre and in 1764 became a member of the Académie, exhibiting medals at the Paris Salons from 1765. On the accession of Louis XVI in 1774 he was appointed engraver-general of coins and royal medallist. Most of his work was for the court, but in 1780 he accepted a commission from Benjamin Franklin for a medal of Colonel de Fleury, one of the French officers who took part in the attack on Stony Point in 1779. Later he engraved medals of George Washington and Colonel Howard. He lost his post at the Mint to Augustin Dupré in 1791. In 1796 he engraved the last of his American medals—a representation of Castorland, the French settlement made by the Compagnie de New York on the Black River near Lake Ontario.

Pierre-Simon-Benjamin Duvivier

222 *George Washington Medal*
Bronze. 1789. Signed: Obverse, *Duvivier·Paris. F.*; reverse, *DUVIV.* (on breech of cannon). Diameter 2³⁄₁₆ inches (68 mm.). Inscription: Obverse, *GEORGIO WASHINGTON SUPREMO DUCI EXERCITUUM ADSERTORI LIBERTATIS* and *COMITIA AMERICANA*; reverse, *HOSTIBUS PRIMO FUGATIS* and *BOSTONIUM RECUPERATUM VII. MARTII MDCCLXXVI.*
New York, private collection.

This is one of the group of medals voted by the United States Congress and engraved in Paris, including also Augustin Dupré's Daniel Morgan and John Paul Jones medals [219, 220]. The reverse shows the taking of Boston on 7 March 1776. The portrait of Washington on the obverse is often said to be derived from Houdon's bust [192], but this is not so: it is closer to C. W. Peale's portrait, which also provided the model for the bust by Louis-

Philipp Friedrich von Hetsch

German, 1758-1838.
Born and trained in Stuttgart, capital of the Duchy of Württemberg, von Hetsch spent all his life there, apart from three years in Paris in the 1780s, when he knew J.-L. David, and two later visits to Rome. He became professor at the art school at Stuttgart and director of the Ducal picture gallery.

Philipp Friedrich von Hetsch

223 *Homage to Washington*
Oil on canvas. Signed and dated: *Hetsch 1793, Stoutgard.* 43⅝ x 35⅛ inches (110.5 x 89 cm.).
Private collection.

The subject of this unusual Neo-classical painting has been elucidated by H. W. Janson, who points out the extreme unlikelihood of such a tribute to Washington being painted in the Duchy of Württemberg unless commissioned in special circumstances. The banderole held by the two figures bears the inscription *Trenton 21 April 1789.* Washington passed through Trenton on that day on his triumphal progress from Mount Vernon to New York, where he was inaugurated president.

Louis-Charles-Auguste Couder

France, 1790-1873.
Couder was trained at the Ecole des Beaux-Arts in Paris under Jean-Baptiste Regault and Jacques-Louis David, exhibiting at the Salon in 1814 for the first time. He was much employed later as a religious painter for churches in Paris, e.g. Saint-Germain-l'Auxerrois, and, under Louis Philippe, for the large series of paintings illustrating French history for Versailles.

Louis-Charles-Auguste Couder

226 *The Battle of Yorktown*

Oil on canvas. ca. 1836. 9¹/₁₆ x 12³/₁₆ inches (23 x 31 cm.).
Blérancourt, Musée National de la Coopération Franco-Américaine.

This is a sketch for the painting, now at Versailles, which Couder exhibited at the Salon in 1837.

227 *The Deplorable State of America or Sc—h Government*

England. Engraving. 1765. 13¾ x 7¼ inches (34.9 x 18.4 cm.). Inscription: *Price 6d.* Provenance: As for [228]. Farmington, Connecticut, The Lewis Walpole Library.

This is one of several large satirical prints—all sympathetic to America— published in London in late 1765 or early 1766, based on stories in the London newspapers of the violent opposition in America to the Stamp Act introduced by Grenville in March 1765 as a means of making Americans contribute to the cost of the Seven Years War. It placed a duty on all legal documents, and because of the opposition in America resulting in wholesale cancellation of orders for goods and consequent distress in the manufacturing centres in England, the Act had to be

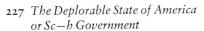

repealed. But in order to save face the government later passed the Declaratory Act, declaring its right to tax the colonists.

Britannia is shown seated, offering "Pandora's Box," i.e. The Stamp Act, to America, who appeals to Minerva, saying, "Secure Me, O Goddess, by thy Wisdom, for I abhor it as Death." Minerva replies, "Take it not." Liberty, prostrate on the ground, laments, "It is all over with Me" and is oppressed by a thistle, the emblem of Lord Bute, and attacked by a serpent, the symbol of treachery. Mercury, standing for trade, is leaving America. The king of France offers a heavy purse and says, "Take this, and let thy banefull Influence be poured down upon them." This is addressed to an irradiated boot, the emblem of Lord Bute. A wind is blowing violently against a tree dedicated "To Liberty," while a figure representing Loyalty shouts, "Heaven grant it may Stand." In the distance are ships, one with a broom at the masthead, signifying that it is for sale. Further away is a gibbet, alluded to as "Fit Entertainment for St—p M—n" and three Stamp Men or excisemen standing nearby say, "By G—d I'll rob first," "Ay, ay, necessity has no Law" and "We shall all Starve."

A long and detailed advertisement for this print appeared in the Boston *Gazette* for 11 November 1765.

Literature: F. G. Stephens: *Catalogue of Political and Personal Satires . . . in the British Museum*, vol. IV, p. 352; R. T. Haines Halsey: "Impolitical Prints" in *Bulletin of the New York Public Library*, vol. 43 (November 1939), no. 11, p. 800.

Benjamin Wilson

English, 1721-1788.
Born in Leeds, Wilson settled in London in 1750 and became a successful portrait painter. In 1759 he painted Benjamin Franklin (The White House, Washington, D.C.), with whom he had scientific interests in common. In 1760 he was awarded a gold medal by the Royal Society for his "curious experiments in electricity." He also painted theatrical conversation pieces, though his friend Garrick and his assistant Zoffany probably played a large part in the development of this *genre*. After 1770 he devoted himself increasingly to his scientific experiments.

Benjamin Wilson

228   *The Repeal, "or the Funeral of Miss Ame-Stamp"*

Engraving. March 18, 1766. 10¾ x 17⅞ inches (27.2 x 45.7 cm.). Provenance: Edward T. Truman sale, 1906; Alfred Bowditch; Augustus P. Loring.
Farmington, Connecticut, The Lewis Walpole Library.

This was probably the most popular of all the satirical prints issued in London during the American Revolutionary period, and Benjamin Wilson is said to have made £300 from it, though it sold for only sixpence. It was quickly pirated, and several versions, with slight variations, are known. Wilson gave several copies to his friend Benjamin Franklin, who wrote to his wife from London on 6 April 1766: "There are some Droll Prints in the box, which were given me by the Painter, and, being sent when I was not at home, were Packed up without my knowledge. I think he was wrong to put in Lord Bute, who had nothing to do with the Stamp Act. But it is the Fashion to abuse that Nobleman, as the Author of all Mischief."

The print was published three days after Parliament repealed the Stamp Act and depicts this event as a burial procession on the banks of the Thames, with a great deal of symbolism in the background. A somewhat similar mock funeral for the Stamp Act was reported in the *London Chronicle* of 18-20 March 1766:

Intelligence Extraordinary. We hear the same evening [of the Repeal] there was a splendid funeral procession to the Cocoa Tree [a London tavern frequented by the Tory Party] which was hung in black upon the death of the late Stamp Act. This Act after being embalmed was buried with all funeral honours. The chief mourner was the Gentle Shepherd [George Grenville, the prime minister under whom the Stamp Act was introduced]. The Rev. Anti-Sejanus [the Reverend Doctor W. Scott, a ministerial pamphleteer] who officiated, was so deeply affected as to be hardly able to get thro' the service. There being great rejoicing and ringing of bells throughout the town this evening, it was judged proper to perform the ceremony in the dead of night.

The print was accompanied by the following letterpress on a separate sheet:

Explanation to the REPEAL a PRINT Price Only Sixpence
The *Hero* of this *Print* is the gentle Mr *Stamper* [George Grenville] who is carrying to the Family Vault his favorite Child, in a Coffin, Miss AME-STAMP, about 12 months old. *Anti-Sejanus* [the Rev. Dr. W. Scott], who reads the Burial Service, is the first in Procession.—After him follow Two Pillars of the Law [Alexander Wedderburn and Sir Fletcher Norton], supporting Two Black Flags: on which are the usual Stamps, consisting of the *White Rose* united with the *Thistle*, supposed to have been originally contrived on the *Tenth* of *June*. The expressive Motto of Semper Eadem is observed: but the Price of the Stamp

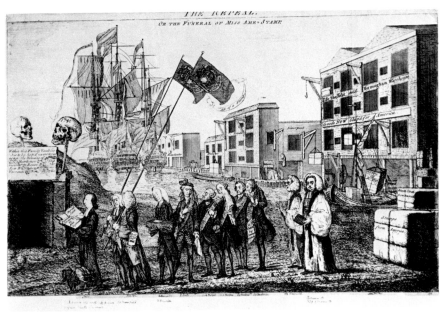

THE REPEAL.
OR THE FUNERAL OF MISS AME-STAMP.

Philip Dawe

English, ca. 1750–ca. 1785.
Dawe was an engraver and mezzotinter, trained under Henry Morland, with whose more famous son, George Morland, he became a close friend. In about 1760 he worked under Hogarth. He exhibited at the Free Society of Artists in London between 1769 and 1782. His work included reproductive prints, genre and mythological scenes, and numerous portraits, as well as political satires.

Philip Dawe (attributed to)

229 *The Bostonians in Distress*
Mezzotint. 1774. 17⅜ x 12⅞ inches (44 x 31.5 cm.). Inscription: *Plate II. London, Printed for R. Sayer & J. Bennett, Map & Print-sellers, No. 53 Fleet Street, as the Act directs, 19 Nov' 1774.* Washington, D.C., Library of Congress, Prints and Photographs Division.

This is the second of a series of five folio mezzotints published at intervals in London between late 1774 and early 1775 (see also [230]). They were based on letters from America published in the papers shortly before each print was issued and show both considerable knowledge of what was taking place and sympathy to the Americans, as in this print, which satirizes the treatment meted out to Boston after the Tea Party. The port was virtually blockaded as a result of the Boston Port Act, 1774, the first of the series of laws which Americans called the Coercive or Intolerable Acts and which led directly to the Revolution. The hunger and distress caused by the closing of the port aroused widespread indignation, and gifts of food were sent from all over the continent, including, as noted in the English press, "two hundred and seven quintals of codfish" from Marblehead.

is changed to Three Farthings, which the Budget explains; and the small Numbers, which are pointed at, are too contemptible to deserve notice by the Majority. The Chief Mourner, Sejanus [Lord Bute] follows Mr. Stamper. Then two remarkable personages Weaver [the Duke of Bedford] and Lord *Gawkee* [the Earl Temple]; after them Jemmy Twitcher [the Earl of Sandwich] with his Friend and Partner, Lord H— [Halifax]. Two B—s [Bishops] conclude the Procession. Upon the Fore Ground are two large Bales of Black Cloth and Stamps returned from America. The unhappy Gang are separated from the joyous Scene which is opposite, on the other side of the river Thames: where, along the Shore, are Open Warehouses for the Goods of different Manufacturing Towns now shipping for America. In the River are three First-rate Ships, the Rockingham, the Grafton,

and the Conway. Among the Goods shipping off, is a large Case, which is wrote upon a Statue of Mr. Pitt: this is heaving on board a Boat Number 250. There is another Boat nearer the First rates, taking Goods in also, and is numbered 105. N.B. The two Skeleton Heads, upon the Vault, were Monsters born in the Rebellions of the years 1715 and 1745.
To be had at the Print Shops at the Royal Exchange and all others in London and Westminster.

Literature: Edward Edwards: *Anecdotes of Painters,* London, 1808, p. 149; Samuel Redgrave: *Dictionary of Artists of the English School,* London, 1878, p. 477; F. G. Stephens: *Catalogue of Political and Personal Satires . . . in the British Museum,* vol. IV, pp. 368-373; W. G. Strickland: *A Dictionary of Irish Artists,* Dublin and London, 1913, vol. II, p. 545; R. T. Haines Halsey: "Impolitical Prints" in *Bulletin of the New York Public Library,* vol. 43, no. 11 (November 1939), p. 801.

The cage in which ten hungry Bostonians are shown being fed with fish had become a symbol of slavery and barbarity. Slaves convicted of capital offences in the Colonies were thus imprisoned and left to starve, or worse, as is so memorably described by Crèvecoeur in *Letters from an American Farmer.*

"Liberty Tree," at Boston, a rallying point for patriots, was cut down for fuel in the winter of 1775-76.

Literature: R. T. H. Halsey: *The Boston Port Bill as pictured by a contemporary London cartoonist,* Grolier Club, New York, 1904; M. D. George: *Catalogue of Political and Personal Satires . . . in the British Museum,* London, 1935, vol. v, pp. 174-175, no. 5241; R. T. Haines Halsey: "Impolitical Prints" in *Bulletin of the New York Public Library,* vol. 43 (November 1939), no. 11, pp. 803, 819.

Philip Dawe (attributed to)

230 *The Alternative of Williams-burg*
Mezzotint. 1775. 13⅞ x 10 inches (35.1 x 25.3 cm.). Inscription: *Plate IV. THE ALTERNATIVE OF WILLIAMS-BURG. London. Printed for R. Sayer & J. Bennett, No. 53 Fleet Street, as the Act directs, 16 Feb. 1775.* Boston, Boston Public Library, Courtesy of the Print Department.

The BOSTONIANS in DISTRESS.

THE ALTERNATIVE OF WILLIAMS-BURG.

Plate IV
London Printed for R. Sayer & J. Bennett, No. 53 Fleet Street, as the Act directs, 16 Feb. 1775.

This print is the fourth in the series to which [229] also belongs. It satirizes the reluctance of some Virginians to sign the Articles of Association. The Association was signed by all members of Congress on 20 October 1774, binding themselves and their constituents to cut off all trade with Great Britain: committees were named to secure signatures, and all who refused to sign or who infringed the articles were declared "enemies to liberty." The print appears to refer to an incident described in the *London Chronicle* of 26 January 1775: "Many Virginians being reluctant to sign a gibbet was erected in the capital, Williamsburg, from which was hung a barrel of tar and a barrel of feathers, each inscribed *A Cure for the Refractory*, which proved very effective in securing signatures."

The print also refers to the resolution drawn up by the Williamsburg Convention in August 1774. The inscription on the barrel alludes to Virginia and Maryland having subscribed tobacco towards the fund for Wilkes initiated by the Bill of Rights Society.

A statue to Lord Botetourt, the popular governor of Virginia between 1768 and 1770, was voted by the Virginia House of Burgesses on his death in 1770, and a statue by Richard Hayward was commissioned and shipped from London to Williamsburg, where it was erected in 1774. It still stands in Williamsburg.

Literature: M. D. George: *Catalogue of Political and Personal Satires . . . in the British Museum*, vol. v, pp. 196-197; R. T. Haines Halsey: "Impolitical Prints" in *Bulletin of the New York Public Library*, vol. 43 (November 1939), no. 11, pp. 803, 809.

Bunkers hill, or the blessed effects of Family quarrels.
17 June 1775.

231 *Bunkers Hill, or the Blessed Effects of Family Quarrels*
England. Engraving. ca. 1775. 5⅝ x 3⁹⁄₁₆ inches (14.3 x 9.1 cm.). London, the Trustees of the British Museum.

This anonymous print, probably from a magazine, is one of several reflecting the opinion held by many Englishmen that the American dispute was to be ascribed to the evil influence of the king's advisers, Lords North, Mansfield, and Bute.

> May Feathers and Tar be the next
>   Birth Day Suit
> And the Block be the fate of
>   N . . . , M . . . , and B . . . .

was, according to the *Kentish Gazette* on 2 February 1775, the "reigning toast" to "a certain triumvirate."

News of the battle of Bunker Hill did not reach London until 25 July 1775.

Literature: M. D. George: *Catalogue of Political and Personal Satires . . . in the British Museum*, vol. v, p. 200; R. T. Haines Halsey: "Impolitical Prints" in *Bulletin of the New York Public Library*, vol. 43 (November 1939), no. 11, pp. 804, 821.

232 *The Yankie Doodles*
Intrenchments near Boston 1776

England. Engraving. 1776. 8 x 9⅝
inches (20.3 x 24.4 cm.). Inscription:
Publish'd as the Act Directs and

> *Behold the Yankies in there ditch's*
> *Whose Conscience gives such*
>   *griping twitch's*
> *They'r ready to Be S—t their Brech's.*
>   *Yankee Doodle do.*
> *Next see the Hypocritic parson*
> *Who thay all wish to turn an A—s on*
> *Altho' the Devil keps the farce on.*
>   *Yankie &c.*
> *See Putnam that Commands in*
>   *Chief Sir*
> *Who looks & Labours like a thief sir*
> *To get them daily Bread & Beef sir.*
>   *Yankie &c.*
> *Their Congress now is quite*
>   *disjoint'd*
> *Since Gibbits sis for them appointed*
> *For fighting gainst ye Lords*
>   *Annointed. Yankie, doodle*

London, the Trustees of the British
Museum.

This is one of the very few anti-American prints issued in London during the
American Revolution—indeed only
two others are known. It contains an
attack on General Putnam—the cartoonist evidently being unaware that
Washington had been appointed Com-
mander-in-Chief in June 1775—and
this dislike was shared by others in
England. Boston was evacuated by
Howe on 17 March 1776.

Literature: M. D. George: *Catalogue of
Political and Personal Satires . . . in the
British Museum*, vol. v, pp. 218-219; R. T.
Haines Halsey: "Impolitical Prints" in
Bulletin of the New York Public Library,
vol. 43 (November 1939), no. 11, p. 808,
822.

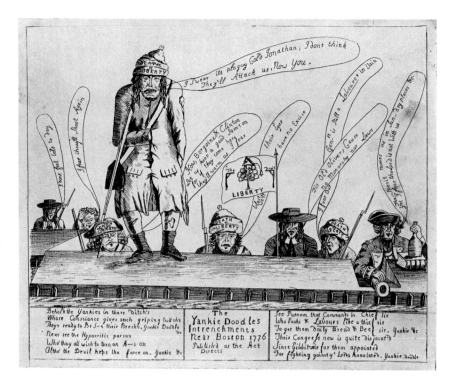

233 The Closet

England. Etching and aquatint. 1778. 8¹⁵⁄₁₆ x 14⁹⁄₁₆ inches (22.8 x 36.9 cm.). New York, The Metropolitan Museum of Art, Gift of William H. Huntington, 1883.

This is a satire ascribing tyranny, failure, and Indian atrocities to the influence of Bute, Mansfield, and Germain and to the obstinacy of the king. It shows, in the upper right corner, a scene in George III's private appartment. The king, Bute, Mansfield, Germain, and the devil are in close consultation. In the centre of the print the ships allude to the American war at sea and the success of American privateers against British merchantmen. Down the left side of the print are four episodes from the American war. At the top the famous murder of Jane McCrae is depicted. She was a loyalist and was being escorted by two Indians to her betrothed, who was serving with the British forces, but was killed by one of the escort. Below are further Indian atrocities. Further below is Burgoyne marching at the head of his men, who are without arms, their hands tied. Burgoyne is depicted as a theatrical mountebank (his play *Maid of the Oaks* was performed in 1774). In the bottom compartment Scottish soldiers and foreign mercenaries are shown in flight, dying, and dead.

Literature: M. D. George: *Catalogue of Political and Personal Satires ... in the British Museum*, vol. v, pp. 281-284.

west.m. Mag. Feb. 1778

A Picturesque View of the State of the Nation for February 1778.

234 A Picturesque View of the State of the Nation for February 1778

England. Engraving. 1778. 3⅞ x 6¾ inches (9.9 x 17.1 cm.). London, The Trustees of the British Museum.

This satire, in which a cow represents the commerce of Great Britain, indicates the advantages France, Spain, and Holland expected to derive from commerce with America during the war. It appeared in the *Westminster Magazine* for February 1778 (vol. vi, p. 66) with the explanation, as follows:

I. The commerce of Great Britain, represented in the figure of a Milch-Cow.

II. The American Congress sawing off her horns, which are her natural strength and defence: one being already gone, the other just a-going.

III. The jolly, plump Dutchman milking the poor tame Cow with great glee.

IV. and V. The Frenchman and Spaniard, each catching at their respective shares of the produce, and running away with bowls brimming full, laughing to one another at their success.

VI. The good ship *Eagle* laid up, and moved at some distance from Philadelphia, without sails or guns, ... all the rest of the fleet invisible, nobody knows where.

VII. The two Brothers [General and Admiral Howe] napping it, one against the other, in the City of Philadelphia, out of sight of fleet and army.

VIII. The British Lion lying on the ground fast asleep, so that a pug-dog tramples upon him, as on a lifeless log: he seems to see nothing, hear nothing, and feel nothing.

IX. A Free Englishman in mourning standing by him, wringing his hands, casting up his eyes in despondency and despair, but unable to rouse the Lion to correct all these invaders of his Royal Prerogative, and his subjects' property.

This print was frequently copied, in America and, in 1780, in Holland and France. It was also copied in America as *A Picturesque View of the State of Great Britain for 1780* (with *New York* substituted for *Philadelphia*) and attributed to Paul Revere.

Variants were published in England as *Poor Old England! or 1778. Or the Bl-s-d effects of a Wise Administration.*

Literature: M. D. George: *Catalogue of Political and Personal Satires . . . in the British Museum,* vol. v, pp. 285–286; R. T. Haines Halsey: "Impolitical Prints" in *Bulletin of the New York Public Library,* vol. 43 (November 1939), No. 11, pp. 811, 823.

235 *America to her Mistaken Mother*
England. Engraving. 1778. 13¾ x 9¾ inches (34.8 x 24.7 cm.). Inscription: See below.
London, The Trustees of the British Museum.

This "hieroglyphic letter" is one of a pair of engraved rebuses in which words are replaced by small engraved objects, dealing sarcastically with the Peace Commission sent to America by Lord North in 1778 after the French alliance. America is shown turning away from her "Mistaken Mother" and holds a *fleur-de-lys,* symbolising the French Alliance. The "pretty man" with "red heel shoes" is Lord Carlisle, who was said by the duke of Richmond to be unsuited to treat with the homely Americans.

The first rebus, entitled *Britannia to America,* to which this is the pair and sequel, begs acceptance of the Peace Commission, warns America against the double-faced French king, and entreats her return. Her answer, given in the print exhibited, is deciphered as follows:

(America) (toe) *her* (Miss)*taken* (Moth)*er.* (Yew) *s*(eye)*lly* (old woman) *t*(hat) (yew) *have sent a* (lure) (toe) *us is very* (plane) (toe) *draw our at*(ten)*t*(eye)*on from our re*(awl) (eye)*ntrests* (butt) *we are*

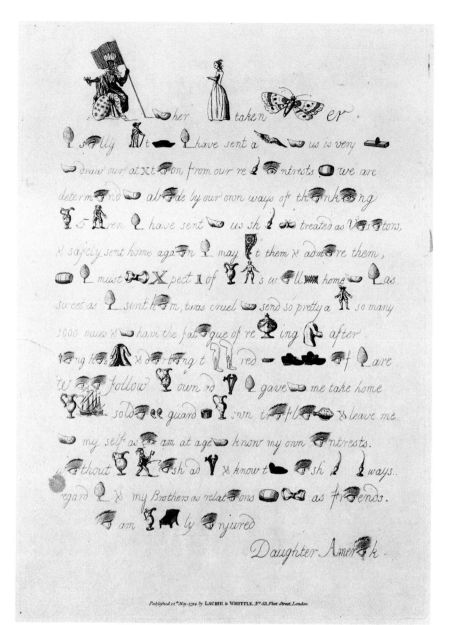

Published 12th May 1794 by LAURIE & WHITTLE, No 53, Fleet Street, London.

determ(eye)*n'd* (toe) *ab*(eye)*de by
our own ways of th*(eye)*nk*(eye)*ng*
(Ewer) [[your] 5 (child)*ren* (yew)
have sent (toe) *us sh*(awl) (bee)
treated as V(eye)ṣ(eye)*tors, & safely
sent home aga*(eye)*n* (yew) *may* [?
carved bracket]*t them & adm*(eye)*re
them,* (butt) (yew) *must* (knot)
(X)*pect 1 of* (ewer) (puppet)*s
w*(eye)*ll* (comb) [come] *home* (toe)
(yew) *as sweet as* (yew) *sent h*(eye)*m,
twas cruel toe send so pretty a* (man)
so many 1000 miles & (toe) *have the
fat*(eye)*gue of re*[t](urn)*ing back
after* (spike?)(eye)*ng h*(eye)*s* (coat)
& d(eye)*rt*(eye)*ng* [dirting] *t*[hose]
red (heel) (shoes) (eye)*f*(yew) *are
w*(eyes) *follow* (ewer) *own ad*(vice)
(yew) *gave* (toe) *me take home ewer*
(ships) *sold*(eye)(ears) [soldiers]
guard (well) (ewer) *own tr*(eye)*fl*(eye)
(ling?) [a fish]. *& leave me* (toe) *my
self as* (eye) *am at age* (toe) *know
my own* (eye)*ntrests. w*(eye)*thout*
(ewer) (fool)(eye)*sh ad*(vice) *& know
t*(hat) (eye) *sh*(awl) (awl)*ways regard*
(yew) *& my Brothers as relat*(eye)*ons*
(butt) (knot) *as fr* (eye)*nds.*
   (Eye) (am) (ewer) (grate)*ly*
(eye)*njured Daughter Amer*(eye)*k.*

Literature: M. D. George: *Catalogue of
Political and Personal Satires . . . in the
British Museum,* vol. v, p. 289.

236 *The Curious Zebra. Alive from America! Walk in Gem'men and Ladies, Walk in*

England. Engraving. 1778. 6¾ x 10¹⁄₁₆
inches (17.1 x 25.5 cm.). Inscription:
*London. Printed for G. Johnson as the
Act directs 3 Sep* *1778, and Sold at all
Printshops in London & Westminster.*
London, The Trustees of the British
Museum.

This satire on the past and present policy of the English government towards
America alludes to the Stamp Act,
Lord North, and the Commission sent
to treat with the Americans. A zebra,
on whose stripes are engraved the
names of the thirteen colonies, is being

treated in various ways by four men.
Standing behind and about to put a
saddle inscribed *Stamp Act* on its back
is George Grenville. On the left is Lord
North, holding the animal by a halter.
On the right two men hold it by its
tail: one, with the *fleur-de-lys*, represents France: the other, dressed as an
English military officer, is evidently
Washington and is so identified in a
contemporary hand. Behind Lord
North are the three commissioners sent
to treat with the Americans (the central
figure is probably Lord Carlisle, that
on the left is probably Eden, and that
on the right is probably Governor
Johnstone).

Literature: M. D. George: *Catalogue of
Political and Personal Satires . . . in the
British Museum,* vol. v, pp. 295-296.

237 *The Allies—Par Nobile Fratrum*

England. Engraving. 1780. 9 x 14⅛
inches (22.8 x 36.1 cm.). Inscription:
*Pubd. as the Act directs Febry. 3, 1780
by I. Almon, Piccadilly. Qui facit per
alium, facit per se.* and *Princ. Leg. Ang.*
and *Indignatio fecit.*
Boston, Boston Public Library, Courtesy of the Print Department.

George III is here shown sharing a
cannibal feast with an Indian chief,
tomahawk in hand. A bishop, with a
mitre, is hurrying towards the banquet,
followed by a sailor carrying a packing
case inscribed *Scalping knives, cruci-
fixes,* etc., a reference to the Bench of
Bishops in the House of Lords, all but
two of whom had voted in support of
the American war. In the *Declaration
of Independence* the king was accused

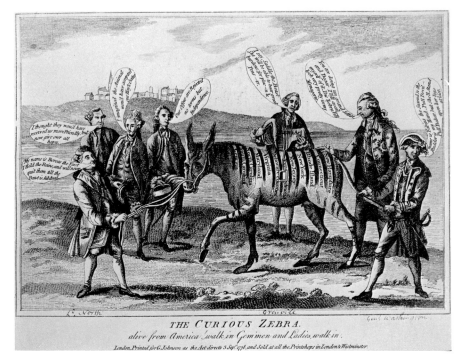

THE *CURIOUS ZEBRA.*
alive from America, walk in Gem'men and Ladies, walk in.
London, Printed for G. Johnson as the Act directs 3 Sep *1778, and Sold at all the Printshops in London & Westminster.*

of having "endeavoured to bring on
the inhabitants of our frontiers the
merciless Indian savages," and this
print was preceded by several others
on the same theme [233].

Literature: M. D. George: *Catalogue of
Political and Personal Satires . . . in the
British Museum*, vol. v, pp. 371-372; R. T.
Haines Halsey: "Impolitical Prints" in
Bulletin of the New York Public Library,
vol. 43 (November 1939), No. 11, pp.
809, 825.

238 *The Ballance of Power*
England. Hand-coloured engraving.
1781. Signed: *R.S.* (Monogram).
8⅞ x 13 inches (22.5 x 33 cm.). Inscription: *London. Published as ye
Act directs, Jany 17, 1781, by R. Wil-
kinson at No. 58 in Cornhill*, and

> America dup'd by a treacherous
>   train,
> Now finds she's a Tool both to
>   France and to Spain;
> Yet all three united can't weigh
>   down the Scale:
> So the Dutchman jumps in with
>   the hope to prevail.
> Yet Britain will boldly their efforts
>   withstand,
> And bravely defy them by Sea and
>   by Land:
> The Frenchman She'll Drub, and
>   the Spaniard She'll Beat
> While the Dutchman She'll Ruin
>   by Seizing his Fleet:
> The' Americans too will with Britons
>   Unite,
> And each to the other be Mutual
>   Delight.

Provenance: Purchased from the Old
Print Shop, New York, 1958.
Farmington, Connecticut, The Lewis
Walpole Library.

This satire alludes to the "ill got wealth" of Holland by contraband trade during the American war. It anticipates the capture of the Dutch colonies in the West Indies and on the South American coast (capture of St. Eustatius with its dependencies, St. Martin and Saba, on 3 February 1781, capitulation of Demarara and Essequibo to privateers on 14 March 1781). Britannia, on the left, weighs down the scales against her four enemies on the right, Holland, America, France, and Spain. Holland smokes a pipe and says, "I'll do anything for money," while coins inscribed *Ill got wealth* pour from his unbuttoned breeches pocket. America says, "My Ingratitude is Justly punished"; France, dressed as a fop, says, "Myneer assist or we are ruin'd"; and Spain, in a slashed doublet and cloak, says, "Rodney has ruined our fleet."

Literature: M. D. George: *Catalogue of Political and Personal Satires . . . in the British Museum,* vol. v., pp. 495-496; R. T. Haines Halsey: "Impolitical Prints" in *Bulletin of the New York Public Library,* vol. 43 (November 1939), No. 11, p. 828.

239 *The Reconciliation between Britania and her Daughter America*

Engraving. ca. May 1782. 7^{15}⁄$_{16}$ x 12¾ inches (20.2 x 32.3 cm.). Inscription: *Pub. by T. Colley N° 5. Acorn Court Rolls Buildings fetter Lane Old England* and below

1.
A curse upon all Artifice
May Britons never thrive
2.
While Roguish Minis—rs they keep
to Eat them up alive
3.
By Lots they sell oh Dam—em Well
Each place we put our trust in

4.
Cut them of [sic] *short twill make good sport*
Whilst honest men are thrust in.

Provenance: Edwin T. Truman (d. 1905) sale, 1906; Alfred Bowditch (d. 1918) by descent to Augustus P. Loring.

Farmington, Connecticut, The Lewis Walpole Library.

Britannia and America embrace—Britannia saying, "Be a good Girl and give me a Buss," America answering, "Dear Mama say no more about it"— while France and Spain try to pull America away and Holland watches them, with Fox pointing out the struggle to Keppel. France is saying to Spain, "Begar they will be friends again if you dont pull a little harder Cus . . .," and Spain replies, "Monsieur Toad stool me do all I can to keep them asunder pull her hair, but take care she Don't kick you." Holland,

leaning against a barrel of Dutch herrings, is saying, "I'll Delliberate a little, to see which is weakest, then I'll give you a direct answer Kate Rusia." Russia had offered to mediate in 1781, and as soon as Fox took office in March 1782, he tried to negotiate separately with Holland through Russia. He is saying to Keppel, "Da -n that Frenchman & his Cousin Don, how they strain to part them, make haste my boy Keppel & give them a Spank." The cards, dice, and dice-box inscribed *Forget* under Fox's feet allude to his having given up gaming at Brook's while in office. The print is by Thomas Colley, whose name is visible beneath an erasure on the British Museum specimen. Colley is known only from a number of satirical prints published at this period.

Literature: M. D. George: *Catalogue of Political and Personal Satires . . . in the British Museum,* vol. v, pp. 582-583½.

The RECONCILIATION *between* BRITANIA *and her daughter* AMERICA,
1 *A curse upon all Artifice*   2 *While Roguish Minis—rs they keep*   3 *By Lots they oh Dam—em Well*   4 *Cut them of a short twill make good sport*
May Britons never thrive   *to Eat them up alive*   *Each place we put our trust in*   *Whilst honest men are thrust in.*

XIII
A Fabulous
and Extravagant
Country

When French interest in North America was at its height in 1777, Jean-François Marmontel attracted new attention to the Centre and South with *Les Incas,* a very successful though now seldom read novel set in Mexico and Peru at the time of the *Conquista.* It could hardly have been better designed to appeal to the mood of the moment, combining sense with sensibility, enlightened ideas with exotic manners and costumes, attacks on colonialism and religious bigotry with praise of free love in a South Sea island and a passionate romance between a young Spaniard and a Peruvian, whom he abducts from the "convent of Virgins of the Sun" during an earthquake. "There are few works whose object is more essentially moral, more worthy of the philosopher and citizen," a contemporary wrote.[1] It thus provided the subject for Louis Hersent's strange painting of the "sublime loyalty" of a Cacique to the venerable Las Casas [240]. But in the early nineteenth century it seems to have owed its popularity less to its moral message than to its strong local colour, inspiring parts of Gasparo Spontini's frequently performed opera, *Ferdinand Cortez* [247, 248],[2] several other operas all entitled *The Virgin of the Sun,* and a set of scenic wallpapers printed by the Parisian firm of Dufour in 1826 [249]. By this time moral tales were associated with the United States and stories of sultry passion with the *tierra caliente* of Hispanic America.

In the years following the Revolution, the two images of America which had for so long been superimposed in the European mind were gradually separated, so that the North came to appear increasingly as an extension and often an idealisation of Europe, while the South remained an exotically alien land. The distinction was made more striking by travel books, which described either the "domestic manners of the Americans" in the United States or the primeval world of nature in the southern continent. Among European artists the latter seems to have exerted a far stronger appeal, attracting many to paint both its arid wastes and suffocatingly luxuriant jungles.

South America had been inaccessible to most Europeans from the time of the *Conquista.* Scientific expeditions were never encouraged and rarely permitted by the Spanish and Portuguese authorities. But in 1799 Alexander von Humboldt (1769-1859) succeeded in obtaining from the king of Spain a passport for himself and his botanist companion Aimé Bonpland (1773-1858). "Never before has a traveller been granted such unlimited permission, and never before has a foreigner been honoured by such marks of confidence from the Spanish government," Humboldt wrote.[3] He came from a noble family and, at the age of thirty, had already made a name for himself as a naturalist, mineralogist, and inspector of mines in his native Prussia. One of the last great universal geniuses, he was no dry scientist but a philosopher, anxious to draw general conclusions from minute observations, and a writer with the sensitivity of a poet. In many ways he recalls Goethe (with whom he was on friendly terms from 1795 onwards), though the importance of science and poetry in their lives was reversed.

From the moment of arrival at Cumaná in Venezuela, Humboldt appreciated the fact that the reality of this "fabulous and extravagant country" was far stranger than any fictitious fantasy. He and Bonpland studied every aspect of the surrounding country, then passed on to investigate the still unexplored upper reaches of the Orinoco. After a visit to Cuba they returned to the mainland in March 1801 and travelled from Cartagena to Lima through the Cordilleras, ascending en route to Chimborazo, then believed to be the highest mountain in the world. This eighteen-month trek was followed by a slightly less adventurous year in Mexico, where Humboldt interested himself in the relics of the Aztec civilization, as well as natural history and mineralogy. Before returning to Europe in 1804, he and Bonpland spent two months in the United States, mainly in order to visit Thomas Jefferson. To record the fruits of the five-year expedition Humboldt published between 1805 and 1834 no less than thirty volumes, ranging from highly specialised descriptions of flora and fauna [242, 243] to books which were intended for a wider public and which diffused his vision of the richness and strangeness of Central and South America throughout Europe [241].

Humboldt had been unable to take a qualified draughtsman on his expedition, and most of the natural history illustrations in his books were perforce made from dead specimens, while the landscapes were worked up either from his own drawings or from those he obtained in the course of his travels. But several later South American explorers were accompanied by artists. Johann Moritz Rugendas, for example, sailed to Brazil in 1821 to join an expedition to the interior. Later he went back to America on Humboldt's encouragement[4] and spent the next sixteen years painting landscapes and city-scapes in Mexico, Peru, Chile, Bolivia, Uraguay, the Argentine, and again Brazil [252-256]. In 1839 John Lloyd Stevens of New Jersey went to Yucatan with the English architect Frederick Catherwood, who made the most memorable and evocative of all drawings of Maya ruins [258-260].

The many books published in the nineteenth century did nothing to dispel the clouds of mystery hanging over Central and South America. Precisely recorded information about the Maya, the Aztecs, and the Incas, as about the wild-life of the swampy jungles of the Orinoco and Amazon, served only to make them seem stranger and more remote from Europe. It remained a world of inscrutable primeval natural forces—as in Leconte de Lisle's poems, where

Sous les noirs acajous, les lianes en fleur,
Dans l'air lourd, immobile et saturé de mouches,
Pendant, et, s'enroulant en bas parmi les souches,
Bercent le perroquet splendide et querelleur,
L'araignée au dos jaune et les singes farouches . . .
(Under the black mahogany trees, the flowering lianas hang in the heavy, motionless fly-infested air, and, twining down among the trunks cradle the brilliant quarrelsome parrot, the yellow-backed spider, and the savage monkeys.)

1. *Correspondence littéraire de Grimm et de Diderot* (March, 1777), Paris, 1830, vol. IX, p. 348. Horace Walpole thought otherwise, writing to William Mason, 18 April 1777: "I have *seen* but not read one syllable of Marmontel's *Yncas,* nor ever will. History is romance enough, without purposely perverting it. . . . I hope the Peruvians will have better masters to teach them liberty than French *philosophes.* . . ."
2. José Tudela: "Hernán Cortés en los Grabados Románticos Franceses" in *Revista de Indias,* IX (1948), pp. 383-391.
3. D. Botting: *Humboldt and the Cosmos,* London, 1973, p. 63.
4. Two other German artists went to South America at Humboldt's instigation and the expense of the king of Prussia—Ferdinand Bellermann (1814-1889) and Eduard Hildebrandt (1818-1869). Drawings by both of them are in the print-room of the Staatliche Museen zu Berlin (East). Other notable painters of the South American scene include Jean-Baptiste Debret (1768-1848), whose works are mainly in the Fundacao Raymundo Ottoni de Castro Maya, Rio de Janeiro, Thomas Ender (1793-1875), whose numerous Brazilian watercolours are in the Akademie der bildende Künste, Vienna, and Joseph Selleny, author of several drawings of Peru in the Graphische Sammlung Albertina, Vienna.

Louis Hersent

French, 1777-1860.
A pupil of the Neo-classical painter
Jean-Baptiste Regnault, Hersent won
the second Prix de Rome in 1797.
Later, after returning to Paris, he
painted contemporary subjects and
picturesque and sentimental anecdotes,
often with political undertones, which
made him very acceptable under the
Restauration. His popularity continued
under the July Monarchy, and his
work was widely diffused through
prints, especially lithographs.

Louis Hersent

240 *The Illness of Las Casas*
Oil on canvas. ca. 1808. 21¼ x 25½
inches (53.8 x 64.6 cm.).
New York, Collection of Robert
Rosenblum.

This strange scene from Jean François
Marmontel's *Les Incas ou la destruc-
tion de l'empire du Pérou* was illustrated by Jean-Michel Moreau the
Younger in the first edition of the book
(Paris, 1777) and again by Louis-
François Mariage, after a drawing by
Jean-Jacques-François Le Barbier of
1810 (Musée des Beaux Arts, Rouen).
Marmontel described how the great
Spanish Dominican and defender of
the American Indians, Bartolomé de
Las Casas, was so beloved by the
natives that when he fell ill and needed
mother's milk to restore his health, a
cacique named Henri proposed that
his wife, who had just lost an infant
and had been sprinkling the grave with
her milk [181], should feed him. Las
Casas at first demurred, but the Indian's wife persuaded him.
    Hersent exhibited his painting at
three Salons—in 1808 (not in the catalogue but recorded by C. P. Landon,
see Lit. below), in 1814 (no. 509), and
in 1824 (no. 1927). It was engraved by
Eléonore Lingée in 1808 and by Pierre
Adam in 1823.

    This was not Hersent's only paint-
ing of a New World subject. He had
exhibited in the 1806 Salon *Atala
s'empoisonne dans les bras de Chactas,
son amant,* and *Le tombeau aerien:
coutume américain.* In the 1830s he
painted *Debarquement de Christophe
Colomb à San Salvador* (Musée des
Beaux Arts, Beaune).

Literature: C. P. Landon: "Salon de 1808"
in *Annales du Musée et de l'Ecole des
Beaux-Arts,* Paris, 1808, vol. II, pp. 36-37;
Robert Rosenblum: "Caritas Romana
after 1760: Some Romantic Lactations" in
Thomas Hess and Linda Nochlin, eds.:
*Woman as Sex Object: Studies in Erotic
Art, 1730-1970 (Art News Annual
XXXVIII),* New York, 1972, pp. 57-59.

241 Alexander von Humboldt: *Vues des Cordillières et monuments des peuples indigènes de l'Amérique* France (Paris). Printed book with coloured engravings. 1810. Page size 22½ x 16 inches (57.2 x 40.6 cm.). New York, The American Museum of Natural History Library.

Humboldt called this book the "pictorial atlas" of the journey he and the botanist Aimé Bonpland made in South America from Cartagena in Columbia to Lima, ascending Chimborazo—then believed to be the highest mountain in the world—on the way. Providing the general context for his more detailed studies of geology, botany, and zoology, it also includes an account of the ancient civilizations of America and the earliest coloured illustrations of Aztec codices to be published. The text, which he wrote in French, is a commentary on the sixty plates drawn and engraved by a number of different artists from sketches made on the spot by Humboldt himself and his travelling companions. The volume is open at plate 41, a view of the gas volcanoes of Turbaco near Cartagena, which he and Bonpland visited in April 1801, carefully noting that the craters filled with mud and water five times every two minutes and analyzing the gas as nitrogen "purer than we can generally produce it in the laboratory." They were accompanied by an Indian and Louis de Rieux, the son of a Spanish colonial official, who made the sketch, which was re-drawn in Paris by Pierre-Antoine Marchais (1763-1859) and engraved by Michel Bouquet (1807-1890).

Literature: *Alexander von Humboldt und seine Welt,* exhibition catalogue, Schloss Charlottenburg, Berlin, 1969, no. 22.

Nicolas II Huet

French, 1770-after 1831.
The eldest son of Jean-Baptiste-Marie
Huet, by whom he was trained,
Nicolas II Huet began to exhibit still
lifes at the Exposition de la Jeunesse
in Paris in 1788 and showed animal
paintings at the official Salons from
1802. He was employed to paint the
animals in the menagerie of the
empress Josephine. In 1804 he was
appointed painter to the library of the
Muséum d'histoire naturelle in Paris,
for which he made 120 zoological illustrations on vellum. He provided illustrations for several zoological books
and also catalogues of collections of
shells.

Nicolas II Huet

242 *Simia ursina, illustration to
Alexander von Humboldt:*
Recueil d'observation de zoologie
et d'anatomie comparée, *vol.
I,
Paris, 1811*

Coloured engraving. Signed and dated:
Huet fils 1807. Page size: 13¼ x 9¾
inches (33.6 x 24.8 cm.).
Cleveland, Cleveland Museum of
Natural History.

This is an illustration to the work in
which Humboldt, assisted by Georges
Cuvier and others, published his observations on various aspects of South
American zoology. The second volume
did not appear until 1833. It is open at
the illustration of one of the alouattes,
or howling monkeys, which greatly
interested Humboldt. He described it
in his *Personal Narrative of Travels to
the Equinoctial Regions of America:*

> The araguato, which the Tamanac
> Indians call *aravata,* and the May-
> pures *marave,* resembles a young
> bear. It is three feet long, reckoning
> from the top of the head (which is
> small and very pyramidal) to the
> beginning of the prehensile tail. Its

fur is bushy, and of a reddish brown;
the breast and belly are covered with
fine hair, and not bare as in the
mono colorado or *alouate roux* of
Buffon . . . The face of the araguato
is of a blackish blue, and is covered
with a fine and wrinkled skin: its
beard is pretty long; and, notwith-
standing the direction of the facial
line, the angle of which is only thirty
degrees, the araguato has, in the
countenance, as much resemblance
to man as the marimonde . . . and
the capuchin of the Orinoco.

Noting the grave demeanour of these
monkeys, he remarked: "Monkeys are
more melancholy in proportion as they
have resemblance to man. Their
sprightliness diminishes, as their intellectual faculties appear to increase"
(translated T. Ross, London, 1852,
vol. I, p. 279).

Literature: C. Nissen: *Die zoologische
Buchillustration*, Stuttgart, 1966-69, no.
2048.2.

Simia ursina.

Pierre-Jean-François Turpin

French, 1775-1840.
Turpin was born at Vire (Calvados) and is said to have been self-trained as an artist. At the age of fourteen he joined the *bataillon du Calvados* and in 1794 was shipped to San Domingo, where he met a French botanist, Pierre-Antoine Poiteau, with whom he was to work for the rest of his life, collaborating after their return to France on several major illustrated botanical works, including several volumes for Humboldt. Turpin developed a very delicate style of draughtsmanship influenced by the most famous botanical illustrator of the day, Pierre-Joseph Redouté. Despite the minute accuracy of his work, he was immensely prolific and is said to have made some six thousand paintings on vellum. Goethe was among his many admirers.

Pierre-Jean-François Turpin

243 *Inga ornata, illustration to A. von Humboldt, A. Bonpland, and K. S. Kunth:* Mimoses et autres plantes légumineuses du Nouveau Continent, *Paris, 1819, pl. 14*

Coloured engraving. 1819. Page size: 21⅞ x 14⁹⁄₁₆ inches (55 x 37 cm.). Chicago, John Crerar Library.

The account of Mimoses and other leguminous plants of Central and South America fills the sixth of the thirty volumes of the *Voyage de Humboldt et Bonpland,* published in Paris from 1805 to 1834. It was completed after Bonpland had returned to South America, and the botanical descriptions were written mainly by Karl S. Kunth, who took over this part of the work in 1816. The volume is open at the illustration of one of the several showy plants which Humboldt and Bonpland found growing in the district of Popayan, Colombia. Turpin's drawing was probably made from a dried specimen.

Literature: C. Nissen: *Die botanische Buchillustration,* no. 954.4.

Inga ornata

François Gérard

French, 1770-1837.
Gérard was born in Rome, where his father, who had married an Italian, was in the household of the French ambassador, Cardinal de Bernis. When his father returned to Paris in 1780, he was admitted to the Pension du Roi, an establishment for the education of young artists. After studying under the sculptor Jean-Baptiste Pajou and the painters Nicolas-Guy Brenet and Jacques-Louis David, he spent two years at the French Academy in Rome, 1791-93. His painting of Belisarius in the Salon of 1795 won him general acclaim, and under the Consulate and

Empire he was much patronised by Napoleon, especially for portraits. After the Restauration he and Antoine-Jean Gros were generally regarded as the leading French painters. Louis XVIII made him a baron in 1819, and he was loaded with other honours. He was also an eminent social figure, and his house in Paris became a meeting place for the fashionable intelligentsia of Europe—writers, musicians, actors, scientists, as well as artists. Alexander von Humboldt took drawing lessons from him and was among his close friends.

François Gérard (after)

244 *Humanitas, Literae, Fruges*
Engraving. 1814. Signed: *F.Gérard Invt. Delt. B.Roger Sculpt.* 7⅞ x 6¹⁄₁₆ inches (20 x 15.3 cm.). Inscription: *Voy. de Humb. et Bonpl.*
New York, The Metropolitan Museum of Art, Gift of William H. Huntington, 1883.

This engraving is the frontispiece to Alexander von Humboldt's five-volume history of the discovery of America, *Examen critique de l'histoire de la géographie du Nouveau Continent et des progrès de l'astronomie nautique aux XVᵉ et XVIᵉ siècles* (Paris, 1814-34). It shows Pallas Athene, goddess of science, giving an olive branch of peace to a defeated and bowed Indian prince, while Mercury, patron of commerce, helps him to rise. The main aim of the book was to describe the history of mankind as that of progressive knowledge and mastery of the earth by means of self-knowledge and self-mastery—a process which would finally be achieved only through universal brotherly intercourse between the races of mankind. In another book Humboldt wrote that in neither of the Americas would permanent prosperity be established until the "humiliated races" (both Indian and African) participated in the advance of civilization. The title of the print, *Humanitas, Literae, Fruges* (humanity, letters, fruits of the earth) is taken from the younger Pliny.

In a letter to Gérard accompanying a set of proofs of the print, dated Paris 1815, Humboldt remarked, "I cannot express the various sentiments inspired by this frontispiece. I think I can read there the extraordinary events in the midst of which you have had the noble courage to work for a friend." Gérard seems to have derived the costume of the Indian prince, the Aztec carvings, the pyramid of Cholula, and also the distant view of Chimborazo, from Humboldt's *Vues des Cordillières* [241]. His drawing was engraved by Barthélemy-Joseph-Fuloran Roger (1767-1841).

Literature: H. Gerard, ed.: *Correspondence de François Gérard*, Paris, 1867, p. 237; *Alexander von Humboldt und seine Welt*, exhibition catalogue, Schloss Charlottenburg, Berlin, 1969, no. 72.

Voy. de Humb. et Bonpl.

245 Clock

France. Bronze, patinated and gilded, with rhinestones. ca. 1800. Height 22⅛ inches (56 cm.). Provenance: James Hazen Hyde.
New York, The Metropolitan Museum of Art, Gift of the Estate of James Hazen Hyde, 1959.

As recorded on the dial, the movement of the clock is by Ridel of Paris, known to have been working on the rue aux Ours in 1800. An almost identical clock, described as a "pendule au bon nègre" in the collection of Jean-Baptiste Diette, is illustrated in Tardy, *La Pendule française* (Paris, 1962), vol. II, p. 172, but its waterfall is missing. Others are known to exist, and their cases also follow this pattern closely. This clock and other clocks of the period having similar figures dressed in American Indian featherwork are implausibly associated with J.-H. Bernardin de Saint-Pierre's famous and very popular novel *Paul et Virginie* (1787), which was set in Mauritius.

The movement of this clock has a calendar, the thirty date divisions corresponding to the number of days in each month of the French Revolutionary calendar. This system was instituted in 1793 and officially discontinued in 1806.

Literature: Tardy, *La Pendule française*, Paris, 1962, vol. II; *idem., Dictionnaire des horlogers français*, Paris, 1972, p. 555.

246 Chocolate Pot

France, probably Paris. Porcelain with black transfer-printed decorations of two figures in fanciful American costume. ca. 1820-1830. Height 9¼ inches (23.5 cm.). Provenance: James Hazen Hyde.
New York, The Brooklyn Museum, Bequest of James Hazen Hyde.

The figures on this chocolate pot are singers in Gasparo Spontini's opera *Fernand Cortez,* which was in the repertoire of the Paris Opéra throughout the 1820s. Hector Berlioz heard it in these years and wrote: "In *Cortez* all is energetic, imperious, brilliant, passionate, and full of grace; its inspiration burns and overflows, yet is governed by reason." The libretto by Jouy was based partly on the seventeenth-century history of the conquest of Mexico by Antonio Solis and partly

on Marmontel's *Les Incas,* which provided the character of Amazili. The female figure on the chocolate pot is derived from a print inscribed: *Mlle. Grassari Artiste de l'Académie royale de Musique, Role d'Amazil dans Fernand Cortez* (specimen in New-York Historical Society).

Karl Friedrich Schinkel

Germany, 1781-1841.
The greatest German architect of the nineteenth century and the major exponent of Romantic-Classicism, Schinkel studied in Berlin, Italy, and Paris, returning to Berlin in 1805. At this unpropitious moment there was no opportunity for him to begin practicing as an architect. He worked as a furniture designer and painter until the end of the Napoleonic wars. In 1815 he was appointed Geheimer Oberbaurat in the newly formed Public Works Department. But while, in this capacity, he was designing his first buildings, he also designed stage-sets for forty-two plays and operas performed in Berlin between 1816 and 1830.

Karl Friedrich Schinkel (after)

247 *Peruvian Temple*
Lithograph. 1847. 17 x 22 inches (43.2 x 55.9 cm.). Inscription: *Potsdam 1847 Verlag von F. Riegel / Tempel der Peruaner / in dem ersten Act der Oper Cortez.*

248 *The Spanish Camp before Tenochtitlán*
Lithograph. 1847. 17 x 22 inches (43.2 x 55.9 cm.). Inscription: *Potsdam 1847 Verlag von R. Riegel / Decoration zu der Oper Fernand Cortez, Act II.*
Columbus, Ohio State University Libraries.

DECORATION ZU DER OPER FERNAND CORTEZ, ACT II.

These lithographs record the sets designed by Schinkel for the 1818 Berlin production of Gaspara Spontini's opera *Fernand Cortez*, first performed in Paris in 1809 but played in a version considerably revised by both composer and librettist, Jouy, from 1817. It was first performed in Berlin under Spontini's direction, and with Schinkel's sets, 28 June 1820. In 1836 a performance conducted by Spontini greatly impressed Richard Wagner, who later remarked that it was "the most important artistic experience" of this period: it astonished him more than anything he had heard before and guided his conception of *Rienzi*. Schinkel's sets were almost certainly re-used on this occasion.

Although much factual information about Aztec art had been made available by the early nineteenth century (notably by Alexander von Humboldt, who lived in Berlin) Schinkel derived his designs from the partly or largely imaginary views in seventeenth-century books (notably those by de Bry, [64, 65, 66, 67]), though he added an appealingly inappropriate Biedermeier framework to his distant prospect of Tenochtitlán. His original gouache designs for *Fernand Cortez* are in the Kupferstichkabinett, Staatliche Museen, East Berlin. The prints exhibited come from the 1874 reprint of his collected stage designs, first published in five parts from 1819 as *Dekorationen auf den beiden Königlichen Theatern in Berlin*.

Literature: P. Mahlberg: *Schinkels Theaterdekorationen*, Berlin, 1916, pp. 58-60.

249 *The Arrival of Pizarro in Peru*
France (Paris), Factory of Dufour et
Leroy. Wallpaper printed in distemper
colours from wood blocks. 1826. 90½
x 104¼ inches (230 x 265 cm.).
Kassel, Deutsches Tapetenmuseum.

This panel consists of five strips from a
panoramic or scenic wallpaper entitled
Les Incas. The subject is freely derived
from Jean-François Marmontel's
novel, *Les Incas ou la destruction de
l'empire du Pérou*, which was first published in 1777 and frequently reprinted
in the early nineteenth century. Other
parts of the paper show the Inca
"Ataliba" and his family by a tent, the
eruption of a volcano, and Bartolomé
de Las Casas pleading with a cacique
for the life of a Spaniard. Its strongly
theatrical character suggests that the
design may have been influenced by
one of the several operas based on
Marmontel's novel.

The factory of Dufour and Leroy,
which specialised in the production of
scenic wallpapers of this type, was
founded in Paris by Joseph Dufour
(1752-1827) in 1808; in 1821 his
daughter married Amable Leroy (d.
1880), who ran the concern until 1836.
They employed several artists (notably
Evariste Fragonard), but the designer
of *Les Incas* is unrecorded.

Literature: N. McClelland: *Historic Wallpapers*, Philadelphia, 1924, p. 322; H.
Clouzot: *Tableaux-Tentures de Dufour et
Leroy*, Paris, s.d. pl. 24, 25; H. Clouzot
and C. Follot: *Histoire de papier peint en
France*, Paris, 1935, pp. 175, 178; *Trois
siècles de papiers peints*, exhibition catalogue, Musée des Arts Décoratifs, Paris,
1967, no. 132.

Nicolas-Antoine Taunay
French, 1755-1830.
Son of an enamel painter at Sèvres,
Taunay was trained in Paris under
Lepicié, Brenet, and Casanova and was
encouraged by Fragonard, who is said
to have bought his first painting. He
illustrated *Les Plaideurs* in the great
Didot edition of Racine (1801). Under
the Empire he was much patronised as
a painter of battle scenes. In 1816 he
went to Rio de Janeiro with his
brother, the sculptor Auguste Taunay,
the architect Grandjean de Montigny,
the engraver Charles Pradier, and the
musician Neucom to found a Royal
Academy there at the invitation of the
Portuguese government. He returned
to France in 1821.

Nicolas-Antoine Taunay

250 *Coast Scene. Rio de Janeiro*
Oil on canvas. ca. 1817. Signed: *Tau-
nay*. 18 x 22¼ inches (45.7 x 56.5 cm.).
Provenance: C. H. Townshend, who
bequeathed it to the Victoria & Albert
Museum in 1868.
London, Victoria and Albert Museum.

According to A. d'Escragnolle Taunay,
this painting dates from 1817.

Literature: A. d'Escragnolle Taunay: "A
missão artistica 1816" in *Revista do Insti-
tuto Historico e Geografico Brazileiro*, 74,
pt. I, 1911, p. 112 (new ed. in *Publicaçoes
da diretoria de patrimonio historico é
artistico nacional*, no. 18, Rio de Janeiro,
1956); U. Thieme & F. Becker: *Allege-
meines Lexikon der bildenden Künstler*,
Leipzig, 1938, vol. XXXII, p. 474; C. M.
Kauffmann: *Victoria and Albert Museum.
Catalogue of Foreign Paintings*, 1800-1900,
London, 1973, p. 218.

William Havell

English, 1782-1857.
Born at Reading, Havell began under the influence of Turner, Varley, and Girtin and exhibited at the Royal Academy from 1804 onwards. In the following year he became one of the foundation members of the Royal Society of Painters in Watercolour. In 1816 he went to China with Lord Amherst's embassy but resigned and went to India in 1817, remaining there until 1825. He was back in England in 1827 and frequently exhibited during the following years.

William Havell

251 *Garden Scene on the Braganza Shore, Harbour of Rio de Janeiro*

Gouache. Signed and dated: *W. Havell 1827.* 13½ x 20¼ inches (34.2 x 51.6 cm.). Inscription on the back: *Garden Scene on the Braganza Shore, Harbour of Rio de Janeiro.* Provenance: S. C. Turner, who bequeathed it to the Museum, 1948.
London, Victoria and Albert Museum.

Literature: *Victoria and Albert Museum: Supplement to the Catalogue of Water Colour Paintings by British Artists and Foreigners working in Great Britain,* London, 1951, p. 40.

Johann Moritz Rugendas

German, 1802-1858.
Rugendas was born in Augsburg and trained first under his father, Johann Lorenz Rugendas (1775-1826), and then at the Munich academy. In 1821 he went to Brazil as draughtsman to the Russian consul general, Freiherr von Langsdorff, who was planning to explore the interior of the country. Rugendas returned to Europe in 1825 with some 500 drawings, of which 100 were published as lithographs in his *Voyage pittoresque dans le Brésil* (issued in four parts, Paris, 1827-35). This work brought him into contact with Alexander von Humboldt, who commissioned drawings of plants from him and urged him to return to South America to paint, especially "the world of palms, tree-ferns, cactus, snow-covered mountains and volcanoes." After a trip to Italy, still considered an essential part of a German painter's training, he crossed the Atlantic again in 1831. He was in Mexico from July 1831 until May 1834, travelled in Chile, Peru, and Bolivia between 1834 and 1845, then in Argentina, Uruguay, and again in Brazil before going back to Germany in 1847. While in South America he sent to Berlin from time to time consignments of his oil sketches, of which a large number were bought (on Humboldt's advice) by King Friedrich Wilhelm IV. But on his return to Germany he sold the many South American paintings and drawings he brought back with him to the king of Bavaria, Maximilian II, in return for an annuity. Thus his unique visual survey of Central and South America was divided between Berlin and Munich and was further split up in 1928, when all the Brazilian sketches in Munich were sold to the museum in São Paulo. His paintings faithfully reflected the ideas on the physiognomy of plants expressed in Humboldt's *Ansichten der Natur,* in the later edi-

tions of which his work was highly praised. But they also merit appreciation, which they have only recently begun to receive, for their artistic qualities. Working in a free, painterly style akin to that of Karl Blechen, he ranks among the more notable German late Romantic landscape painters.

Johann Moritz Rugendas

252 *The Plaza and Cathedral of Córdoba (Mexico)*

Oil on pasteboard. ca. 1831-1834. 9⅝ x 14³⁄₁₆ inches (24.5 x 36 cm.). Provenance: Acquired from the artist by Friedrich Wilhelm IV of Prussia, 1838. Berlin, Ibero-Amerikanische Institut Preussischer Kulturbesitz.

This is one of several views painted by Rugendas in Córdoba, probably soon after his arrival in Mexico in 1831. It reveals his unusual ability to evoke an impression of the atmosphere of the strangely spacious, dusty, sun-baked Hispano-American cities.

Literature: *Johann Moritz Rugendas 1802-1858 Reisenstudien aus Südamerika,* exhibition catalogue, Staatliche Graphischen Sammlung, Munich, 1960, no. 24.

Johann Moritz Rugendas

253 *View of the Volcano of Colima (Mexico)*

Oil on paper. ca. 1834. 8½ x 13 inches (21.6 x 33 cm.). Provenance: Acquired from the artist by Maximilian II of Bavaria in 1848.
Munich, Staatliche Graphische Sammlung.

This is one of many paintings and sketches by Rugendas which reflect Alexander von Humboldt's interest in both the flora and volcanoes of Central and South America. He made several sketches of Colima, one of which is dated 26 January 1834. He climbed the volcano to paint its crater.

Johann Moritz Rugendas

254 *View in a Gorge between Jalapa and Córdoba (Mexico)*

Oil on paper. ca. 1834. 9¹³⁄₁₆ x 14⅛ inches (24.8 x 35.8 cm.). Provenance: Acquired from the artist by Maximilian II of Bavaria in 1848.
Munich, Staatliche Graphische Sammlung.

In this and many other sketches, Rugendas answered Humboldt's call for an artist to study the various species of tropical American plants, not in hot-houses or from the descriptions of botanists, but in the "grand theatre of tropical nature." Here he shows various types of cactus and palm, faithfully recording the manner in which they grow.

Johann Moritz Rugendas

255 *Tropical Vegetation in Mexico*

Oil on pasteboard. ca. 1831-1834. 15 x 10½ inches (38 x 26.5 cm.). Provenance: Acquired from the artist by Friedrich Wilhelm IV of Prussia in 1838.
Berlin, Ibero-Amerikanisches Institut Preussischer Kulturbesitz.

The inhuman, oppressive scale and virulent vegetation of the tropical American jungle are vividly caught by Rugendas in this sketch.

Johann Moritz Rugendas

256 *Bivouac in the Chilean Andes*

Oil on paper. 1838. 13⅛ x 10⁹⁄₁₆ inches (33.3 x 26.7 cm.). Inscription: *Punta de las Vacas. 4 E°. 1838*. Provenance: Acquired from the artist by Maximilian II of Bavaria in 1848.
Munich, Staatliche Graphische Sammlung.

This is one of several sketches made by Rugendas as he travelled through the Chilean Andes with Robert Krause in January 1838.

Literature: *Johann Moritz Rugendas 1802-1858 Reisestudien aus Südamerika,* exhibition catalogue, Staatliche Graphischen Sammlung, Munich, 1960, no. 131; Bonifacio del Carril: Mauricio Rugendas. *Artistas extranjeros en la Argentina,* exhibition catalogue, Accademia Nacional de bellas Artes Republika Argentina, Buenos Aires, 1966, no. 11.

257 Karl Friedrich Philipp von Martius: *Flora Brasiliensis,* vol. 1, pt. 1, *Tabulae Physiognomicae*
Germany (Munich). Printed book with lithograph illustrations. 1840. Page size 12 x 20 inches (30.5 x 50.8 cm.). Columbus, Ohio State University Libraries.

The botanist Karl Friedrich Philipp von Martius (1794-1868) and the zoologist Johann Baptist von Spix (1781-1826) went to Brazil in 1817 at the expense of Maximilian Joseph I, king of Bavaria. They were accompanied by a painter of flowers and animals, a gardener, and a mineralogist. Probably influenced by Humboldt's example, they studied the natural history of the Amazon valley as carefully as he had the Orinoco. In 1820 they returned to Munich with specimens of some 3,300 animals and 6,500 plants. They published a general account of their travels, *Reise in Brasilien,* in 1823. Martius was appointed director of the Munich botanical garden in 1820 and professor at the university in 1826. The results of his botanising in Brazil were published over many years, beginning with a three-volume *Nova genera et species plantarum* (1824-32). The volume exhibited here is the first part of his major work on the flora of Brazil, of which he published forty-six instalments, though it was not to be completed until 1906, long after his death. It is open at the illustration of Spix and Martius in the jungle. The illustrations for Martius's books are by several different artists (those in the volume exhibited appear to be by Benjamin Mary, put on lithographic stone by C. A. Lebsché). Many of the original drawings are in the Staatsbibliothek, Munich (cf. *Bayern: Kunst und Kultur,* exhibition catalogue, Munchner Stadtmuseum, Munich, 1972, no. 1766).

Literature: A. Bettex: *The Discovery of the World,* London, 1960, p. 171; C. Nissen: *Die botanische Buchillustration,* no. 2248.

Frederick Catherwood

English, 1799-1854.

Catherwood began as an architect in London but in 1831 joined, as archaeological draughtsman, Robert Haig's expedition up the Nile valley, from where he explored Palestine and Arabia. In London in 1836 he met John Lloyd Stephens of New Jersey, who had been intrigued by accounts of the ruins of Central America, especially Juan Galindo's *The Ruins of Copan in Central America*, 1835. In 1839 Stephens set out, with Catherwood as artist and companion, to find and study them, and their expeditions resulted in the first generally available publication of accurate descriptions of the forty-four sites they visited, many of them being reported for the first time. Stephens was a friend of William H. Prescott, who began to write his *Conquest of Mexico* in 1840. Stephens and Catherwood produced several works on the remains of Maya culture which are classics of archaeology: *Incidents of travel in Central America, Chiapas and Yucatan*, New York-London, 1841 and *Incidents of travel in Yucatan*, New York, 1843, while Catherwood published a volume of his lithographs: *Views of ancient monuments in Central America, Chiapas and Yucatan*, London, 1844. Catherwood's drawings—and the lithographs and engravings made from them under his supervision—were the first to render faithfully the architectural and decorative style of the Maya monuments. As aids in achieving accuracy he employed a *camera lucida* and, on his second trip to Yucatan, an early daguerreotype camera. Even the hieroglyphic inscriptions, which were unintelligible to him, are so faithfully drawn that they are recognisable to modern students. But more important than their accuracy is the extraordinary dramatic power of Catherwood's Maya drawings.

Frederick Catherwood

258 *House of the Magician* or *House of the Dwarf* in the ruined city of Uxmal, Yucatan

Brush and brown ink and wash. ca. 1843. 36½ x 21½ inches (92.5 x 54.4 cm.). Provenance: Clarence King; W. H. Phillips, ca. 1890; Imogene Phillips, 1901.
Washington, D.C., Department of Anthropology, National Museum of Natural History, Smithsonian Institution.

Uxmal, a vast Maya site covering an area of two square miles, had been described by Lorenzo de Zavala *(Antiquités mexicaines*, Paris, 1834) and illustrated rather inaccurately by J. F. M. von Waldeck *(Voyage pittoresque*, Paris, 1838); it was thus one of the first objects of the expedition of Stephens and Catherwood. They went there again on their second journey, when Catherwood made the drawing, exhibited here, of the building they called the House of the Dwarf or House of the Magician, overlooking the site from a tall mound. "The front is much ruined," Stephens wrote, "but even in its decay presents the most elegant and tasteful arrangements of ornaments to be seen in Uxmal." He also recalled the rites which took place in front of it: "I cannot imagine a picture more horribly exciting than that of the Indian priest, with his white dress and long hair clotted with gore, performing his murderous sacrifices at this lofty height, in full view of the people throughout the whole extent of the city" *(Incidents of Travel in Yucatan*, New York, 1843, vol. I, p. 193). Catherwood made some fifty drawings on this visit to Uxmal but succumbed to malaria after six weeks and was carried away delirious by his companions.

Literature: V. W. von Hagen: *Frederick Catherwood Archt*. New York, 1950, pp. 76-78, Ill. No. 12.

Frederick Catherwood

259 *Well at Bolonchen*

Brush and brown ink and brown wash. 1843. Signed and dated: *F. Catherwood / 1843*. 18¼ x 13⅜ inches (46.3 x 34 cm.). Provenance: Henry Schnakenberg, 1947.
New Haven, Conn., Yale University Art Gallery, Gift of Henry Schnakenberg.

A lithograph after this drawing was published as plate xx in Catherwood's *Views of Ancient Monuments in Central America, Chiapas and Yucatan*, London, 1844. He wrote that Belonchon signified "nine wells" which "formed at this place the centre of a population, and these wells are now in the plaza of the village. The origin is as obscure and unknown as that of the ruined cities which strew the land, and as little thought of." He accompanied the plate with a description:

> From the brink on which we stood, an enormous ladder of the rudest possible construction led to the bottom of the hole. It was between seventy and eighty feet long, and about twelve feet wide, made of the rough trunks of saplings lashed together lengthwise, and supported all the way down by horizontal trunks braced against the face of the precipitous rock. The ladder was double having two sets, or flights, of rounds, divided by a middle partition, and the whole fabric was lashed together by withes. It was very steep, seemed precarious and insecure, and confirmed the worst accounts we had heard of the descent into this extraordinary well.

Literature: V. W. von Hagen: *Frederick Catherwood, Archt.*, New York, 1950, pp. 79-80, pl. 20; *Commemorative Exhibition Frederick Catherwood 1799-1854*, exhibition catalogue, Avery Memorial Library, New York, 1950, no. 29; *Art of Latin America since Independence*, exhibition catalogue, Yale University Art Gallery, New Haven, etc., 1966, no. 69; V. W. von Hagen: *F. Catherwood, Architect-Explorer of Two Worlds*, Barre, Mass., 1968, following p. 48; *Lost Cities as Sketched by Catherwood*, exhibition catalogue, The Newark Museum, Newark N.J., 1968, no number; E. Haverkamp Begemann & Logan: *European Drawings and Watercolours in the Yale University Art Gallery, 1500-1900*, New Haven and London, 1970, no. 232.

Frederick Catherwood

260 *The Mask of Isamal*
Lithograph, hand coloured. 1844.
14¾ x 11 inches (37.5 x 27.9 cm.).
Cambridge, Mass., Mr. A. Ledyard
Smith Collection.
This is plate no. xxv in Catherwood's
Views of Ancient Monuments in Central America, Chiapas and Yucatan,
London, 1844.

The colossal head was one of the
few remnants of the Maya buildings at
Izamal torn down by the Franciscans
when they established a friary there in
the sixteenth century. As late as the
nineteenth century Indians sometimes
burnt copal incense on the platform in
front of it. But it was destroyed after
Catherwood made his drawing. In the
foreground he showed Dr. Samuel
Cabot hunting a jaguar—an incident
which took place in another part of
Yucatan.

Literature: V. W. von Hagen: *Frederick
Catherwood, Arch^t,* New York, 1950, p.
137, pl. xxv.

Camille Pissarro

French, 1830-1903.
The son of a French businessman in
Saint Thomas in the Danish West Indies, Pissarro was educated in France
at Passy, 1841-47. In 1852 he returned
to Saint Thomas and, deciding to
abandon a business career and become
an artist, went to Caracas with the
Danish painter Fritz Melbye (1826-
1896). He returned to Saint Thomas in
1854 and finally settled in Paris in
1855. At this time he painted several
small pictures of his memories of the
Antilles, many of which were sold by
his friend P. Lecreux to collectors in
and around Lille. In the 1870s he became, with Monet and Sisley, one of
the three leading French Impressionist
landscape painters. Cézanne, who became a friend slightly later, revered
him as the "humble et colossal
Pissarro."

Camille Pissarro

261 *Paysage à Saint-Thomas*

Oil on canvas. 1856. Signed and dated:
C. Pizarro 1856. 18¼ x 15 inches
(46.2 x 38 cm.). Provenance: Sotheby's
1 December 1965, lot 147.
Collection of Mr. and Mrs. Paul
Mellon.

Camille Pissarro

262 *Deux Femmes Causant au Bord
de la Mer, St. Thomas*

Oil on canvas. 1856. Signed and dated:
C. Pizarro Paris 1856. 10½ x 15½
inches (26.7 x 39.3 cm.). Provenance:
Gunnar A. Sadolin, Dragor; Com-
mander G. L. Lowis; Sotheby's 1 De-
cember 1965, lot 146.
Collection of Mr. and Mrs. Paul
Mellon.

Literature: L.-R. Pissarro and L. Venturi:
Camille Pissarro, son art—son oeuvre,
Paris, 1939, p. 78, no. 5.

XIV
Atala

François René de Chateaubriand (1768-1848), the great French romantic writer and politician, sailed from Saint-Malo to the United States on 8 April 1791 and returned to France on 2 January 1792. Around the five months he spent on American soil he was later to weave a tissue of mystery. He declared that he went there in order to discover the Northwest Passage, though it is fairly clear that he was seeking a haven from recent events in revolutionary France. He claimed to have met and dined with George Washington and gave an account of his appearance and conversation. But Washington wrote to the mutual friend who had provided the introduction, regretting that he had been indisposed and unable to see Chateaubriand when he called.[1] He described his adventures among the Indians of Florida, though he went no further south than Maryland. He did, however, visit Niagara and make a foray into the American wilderness, probably on the Ohio River south-west of Pittsburgh. Brief as this may have been, it was an event of climactic importance in Chateaubriand's life. For the first time he came face to face with untouched nature—one of the three great themes which were to dominate all his subsequent work— and the amplitude and romantic sensibility of his descriptions refreshed the European vision of America by the addition of richer, deeper, and subtler tones. No European writer of comparable literary ability had previously visited the New World.

He first wrote of America briefly in his *Essai . . . sur les révolutions*, published in London in 1797. Then came *Atala*, the book that made him famous throughout France, printed and five times reprinted in 1801 and reissued the next year, together with its sequel, *René* (a fragment of fictionalised autobiography), as part of *Génie du Christianisme*. At about the same time he composed his long prose epic, *Les Natchez*, though this was not printed until 1826. The account of his travels, *Voyage en Amérique*, first appeared in 1827 [264]. He summarised its contents in his greatest work, and the sublime monument to his egotism; the posthumously published *Mémoires d'outre-tombe* (1849). So far as the visual arts are concerned, the most important of these works is *Atala*, which provided subjects for painters and sculptors throughout the nineteenth century.

Sub-titled "the loves of two savages in the wilderness," *Atala* is a strange melange of barbaric ferocity and soft but chaste amorous dalliance, erotic impulse and Christian piety. It is set among the vast rivers and forests of Florida, luxuriant with flowering plants of hot-house voluptuousness, yet its message is almost icily ascetic. The narrator is Chactas, a Natchez who has been fostered and educated by a Spanish settler named Lopez, but returns to the wilds. Falling into the hands of the fierce "Muscogulges," he is condemned to be burnt alive but is rescued by Atala, a half-Indian girl who is a Christian and daughter of Lopez, though her mother has been forced to marry the Muscogulge chief. They escape together and fall more deeply in love as they travel through the exotic landscape to the mission of Père Aubry. Here Atala reveals that in fulfillment of her mother's dying wish she took an oath of virginity. To escape temptation she poisons herself, Père Aubry administers the last sacraments, and he and Chactas bury her.

To an extraordinarily wide public in France, then just emerging from the austerities of the Revolutionary period and at the same time returning to Mother Church, it made an almost irresistible appeal. A Christian novel, set in the wilds of America, was something quite new, providing a Romantic equivalent to the *roman philosophe* of the Enlightenment, and the moment for its first appearance could hardly have been better timed. Significantly, most of the works of art inspired by it depict Atala's last communion, death, and burial. Chactas figures in them, however, as the prototype of the Romantic hero nursing a passion which can never be consummated—as in Anne-Louis Girodet's great painting [268].

Chateaubriand recalled in his memoirs the stir which the publication of *Atala* made. Crudely coloured engravings of Chactas, Père Aubry, and Atala were soon to be found in small wayside inns, he wrote. "On the quays, my characters modelled in wax were displayed like images of the Virgin and Saints at fairs." In a boulevard theatre he was bewildered to see Atala decked with chicken feathers and discoursing with a savage of the same type on "the soul of solitude."[2] He does not mention the pottery plates [271] and the handsome gilt bronze clocks [272] decorated with episodes from the novel. Nor does he refer to the several Salon paintings, in the first of which Pierre Gautherot (a pupil of Jacques-Louis David) in 1802 depicted life-size figures of Chactas carrying Atala to her grave.[3] Louis Hersent's picture of Chactas and Atala in the storm was in the Salon of 1806, Girodet's *Entombment of Atala* and Pierre-Jérome Lordon's *Communion of Atala* were in that of 1808. An amateur, the comte de Boulot [269, 270], and several professionals made drawings to illustrate the story. Nor did its popularity with artists cease at the Restauration. Delacroix took from its epilogue the subject for one of his most delicately poetic pictures [274]. Statues of Chactas were modelled in 1836 by Francisque-Joseph Duret [275] and in 1844 by Théodore-Charles Gruyère. The finest of the illustrated editions of *Atala* appeared in 1863, with plates by Gustave Doré which marvellously convey that sense of "rude, melancholy vastness" which appealed to Thomas Carlyle [276].[4] As late as 1882 yet another *Entombment of Atala*, by Gustave Courtois, was hung in the Paris Salon.

1. Washington's letter (Library of Congress, Department of Manuscripts) was published in the *Bicentennial Edition of the Writings of George Washington,* vol. XXI, 1939, and its significance was pointed out by Morris Bishop in *Modern Language Notes,* June, 1947; cf. P. Martino: "Le voyage de Chateaubriand en Amerique essai de mise au point 1952" in *Revue d'histoire littéraire de la France,* LII (1952), p. 50.
2. Chateaubriand: *Mémoirs d'outre-tombe* (1849), ed. M. Levaillant and G. Moulnier, Paris, 1957, vol. I, p. 445.
3. Reproduced in *Annales du Musée,* Paris, 1802, vol. III, p. 109.
4. C. R. Sanders and K. J. Fielding, ed.: *The Collected Letters of Thomas and Jane Welsh Carlyle,* Durham, North Carolina, 1970, vol. II, p. 115. Carlyle made the remark in reply to a letter from Jane in which she wrote: "I do not like Atala —What tempted you to send me such nonsense?"

Etienne Barthélemy Garnier

French, 1759-1849.

Garnier was born in Paris, studied under Louis-Jacques Durameau, Gabriel-François Doyen, and Joseph-Marie Vien, and, after winning the *grand prix* in 1788 (when Girodet was runner-up), at the French Academy in Rome until 1793. Under the Consulate and Empire he received several commissions for paintings, mainly of antique subjects but including also the vast *Wedding Procession of Napoleon and Marie-Louise*, now at Versailles. He also provided drawings for illustrated editions of Chateaubriand's *Atala* and *René* (see below) and the works of Racine. After the Restauration he specialised in religious paintings. In 1816 he was elected to the Institut.

Etienne Barthélemy Garnier

263 *Atala and Chactas*

Engraving. 1805. Signed: *Steph.Barth. Garnier del.* and *Aug. St.Aubin Sculp.* Page size 7 x 4¹⁄₁₆ inches (17.7 x 10.5 cm.). Inscription: *Je crus que c'était la Vierge des dernieres amours.* New Haven, The Beinecke Rare Book and Manuscript Library, Yale University.

This is one of the plates in the first illustrated edition of *Atala*, published by Le Normant in Paris in 1805. It illustrates the passage in which Chactas recalls how Atala first appeared to him when he was a captive of the Muscogulges. "I believed she was the 'Virgin of the last loves,' that virgin who is sent to the prisoner of war to charm his tomb. In this belief I said, stammering, and with a confusion which did not however derive from fear of the pyre, 'Virgin you are worthy of the first loves and were not made for the last' . . . ." Garnier maintained the old tradition for the representation of Indians with feather head-dresses, though he posed them in conformity with Neo-classical ideas and gave Atala a distinctly Grecian appearance. The illustration was engraved by Augustin de Saint-Aubin (1736-1807).

Literature: J.-R. Thomé: "Les illustrateurs de Chateaubriand" in *Le Courrier Graphique*, VII (1948), pp. 23-24; *Chateaubriand le voyageur et l'homme politique*, exhibition catalogue, Bibliothèque Nationale, Paris, 1969, no. 68.

... Je crus que c'était la Vierge des dernieres amours.

Pag. 28.

264 Francois Auguste René, vicomte de Chateaubriand: *Voyage en Amérique*, vol. XII of *Oeuvres complètes*

France (Paris). 1836. Page sixe 8⅞ x 5¼ inches (22.4 x 13.5 cm.). Washington, D.C., Library of Congress, General collection.

Chateaubriand's account of his travels in North America in 1791 was first published in 1827 as volumes VI and VII of the collected edition of his works issued by Ladvocat in Paris. It describes a journey from Baltimore to Philadelphia, New York, Boston, Albany, Niagara, Pittsburgh, then south to Florida and back to a vaguely indicated white settlement, where he learned of Louis XVI's flight from Paris and resolved to return to France. This account is geographically bewildering, especially in the later stages of the journey: it is improbable that Chateaubriand went far into the wilderness from Pittsburgh, and he certainly cannot have reached Florida. Although the book purports to be based partly on his travel diary, it seems to have been written in the 1820s—some thirty years after he returned to France—from memory, embellished by imagination and refreshed by reading eighteenth-century accounts of America. In some instances his descriptions were based on Jonathan Carver's *Travels through the Interior Parts of North America* (London, 1778), which was a mélange of accurate first-hand reports and wholly imaginative passages added by an English ghost-writer. But such was Chateaubriand's literary genius that he was able to evoke the natural world of America with far greater vividness than any previous writer, even—one might say especially—when he strayed farthest from what he had himself observed.

The volume exhibited is open at the engraving which illustrates Chateaubriand's account of the virgin forest—one of his most brilliant descriptive passages. "The sky is pure over my head, the water limpid under my canoe which flies before a light breeze," he begins, quoting from some "undated leaves" of his diary. "On my left there are peaked hills flanked by rocks where hang convolvulus with white and blue flowers, festoons of begonias, tall grasses and rock plants of all colours. . . ." A few pages later he describes the mysterious light and the sounds of the forest itself—one of those which are "as old as the world and can alone give an idea of Creation as it came from the hand of God."

Literature: G. Chinard: *L'exotisme américaine dans l'oeuvre de Chateaubriand*, Paris, 1918; P. Martino: *Le Voyage de Chateaubriand en Amerique, essai de mise au point 1952* in *Revue d'histoire littéraire de la France*, LII (1952), pp. 149-164; Chateaubriand: *Voyage en Amérique*, ed. R. Switzer, Paris, 1964.

FORÊT VIERGE
Amerique.   Natch.

Anne-Louis Girodet-Trioson

French, 1767-1824.
Girodet joined David's studio after his
father's death in 1784 (being adopted
by Dr. Trioson in 1806). In 1789 he
won the *Prix de Rome* and studied at
the French Academy there until 1795.
His *Sommeil d'Endymion* (1791) was
greatly admired both in Rome and at
the Paris Salon in 1793, but he did not
achieve preeminence until 1801, when
Napoleon commissioned him to paint
Ossian for Malmaison. This and his
Scène de Déluge (1806) established
him, the latter painting being preferred
by contemporaries to David's *Les Sa-
bines* at the decennial competition in
1810.

Anne-Louis Girodet-Trioson

265 *The Communion of Atala*
Pen and ink. ca. 1806-1807. 3¾ x 4½
inches (9.5 x 11.4 cm.).
Besançon, Musée des Beaux Arts.

This drawing is probably the earliest
connected with *The Entombment of
Atala* [268]. In the drawing Atala is
shown receiving communion from
Père Aubry on her deathbed. It faithfully follows Chateaubriand's text, in
which Chactas recalls how a super-
natural power made him fall to his
knees and bow his head at the foot of
Atala's bed as Père Aubry prepared to
administer the last sacraments. The
priest "took in his fingers a host as
white as snow and went towards Atala
pronouncing mysterious words. This
saint had her eyes raised to the sky in
ecstasy. All her sufferings seemed to
have ceased . . . ." This scene was also
illustrated by Pierre-Jérome Lordon
(1780-1838) in a large picture probably
begun in 1806-07 and exhibited at the
Paris Salon in 1808. (The painting is
now at Villa Carlotta, Lake Como.)
Whether or not Girodet was aware of
Lordon's painting before 1808 is not
known. But the drawing exhibited reveals that from a very early stage in the
conception of the painting Girodet envisaged both Atala and Père Aubry
much as he was finally to depict them.
He probably began to work out the
composition soon after completing his
Scène du Déluge, which was one of the
most highly admired paintings in the
Salon of 1806.

Literature: *Girodet 1767-1824*, exhibition
catalogue, Musée de Montargis, 1967, no.
78; G. Levitine: "Some Unexplored
Aspects of the Illustrations of *Atala*" in
R. Switzer, ed.: *Chateaubriand. Actes du
Congrès de Wisconsin pour le 200ᵉ anni-
versaire de la naissance de Chateaubriand*
(1968), Geneva, 1970, p. 140.

Anne-Louis Girodet-Trioson

266 *The Death of Atala*

Pen and brown ink. ca. 1806-1807.
12⅞ x 16⅝ inches (32.8 x 42.5 cm.).
Provenance: Gallerie du Fleuve, 1973.
Ottawa, The National Gallery of
Canada.

Here Girodet worked out the composition for another scene of the death of
Atala. It seems to represent the moment when Chactas promises the dying
Atala that he will become a Christian,
and Père Aubry, raising his arms towards the vault of the cave, exclaims:
"Il est temps d'appeller Dieu ici," an
incident which immediately precedes
that depicted in the drawing of *The
Communion of Atala* [265]. In the relationship of the figure of the priest to
Atala, the drawing is close to the final
composition [268]. The drawing probably dates from slightly after *The
Communion of Atala.*

Literature: *The Burlington Magazine,* cxv
(1973), p. 537.

Anne-Louis Girodet-Trioson

267 *The Entombment of Atala*

Black chalk heightened with white on
buff paper. ca. 1807-1808. 9¹³⁄₁₆ x
15¹³⁄₁₆ inches (24.9 x 40.3 cm.). Provenance: Mlle. Doria, who bequeathed
it to the Louvre, 1911.
Paris, Musée du Louvre, Cabinet des
Dessins.

By the time he made this drawing,
Girodet had finally decided which incident in Chateaubriand's novel was to
form the subject for his painting *The
Entombment of Atala* [268] and had
also determined its composition. In
another drawing for the oil, Chactas is
given an emphatically Indian scalp-
knot, but in this study, as in the final
painting, he looks quite European and
appears to have been drawn from a liv-

ing model. This deference to traditional academic anatomy reduces the
picture's exoticism but accords Atala
our undivided attention.

Literature: J. Guiffrey and P. Marcel:
*Inventaire général des dessins du Musée
du Louvre et du Musée de Versailles.
Ecole française,* vol. VI, (Paris, 1911), no.
4246; H. Lemonnier: "l'Atala' de Chateaubriand et l'Atala' de Girodet" in
Gazette des Beaux-Arts, 4ᵉ S., XI (1914),
pp. 363-371; *Gros, ses amis ses élèves,* exhibition catalogue, Petit Palais, Paris,
1936, no. 635; *Chateaubriand,* exhibition
catalogue, Bibliothèque Nationale, Paris,
1948, no. 94; *The Romantic Movement,*
exhibition catalogue, the Tate Gallery and
Arts Council Gallery, London, 1959, no.
718; *Girodet 1767-1824,* exhibition catalogue, Musée de Montargis, 1967, no. 79.

Anne-Louis Girodet-Trioson

268 *Les funérailles d'Atala (The
Entombment of Atala)*

Oil on canvas. 1808. 81½ x 105 inches
(207 x 267 cm.). Provenance: Bought
from the artist by Louis-François Bertin, from whom it was acquired by
Louis XVIII in 1819.
Paris, Musée du Louvre.

The most famous of all works of art inspired by *Atala,* this painting is an
evocation and conflation of two passages in Chateaubriand's text—the one
describing the night during which
Chactas and Père Aubry watch over
the dead Atala in the cave and the one

describing her burial the following
morning under the natural bridge of
rock. As described by Chateaubriand
in the first passage, she is wrapped in a
linen shroud which leaves her feet,
shoulders, and head uncovered, clasps
a crucifix in her hands, and resembles
a "statue of sleeping Virginity." The
words recited by Père Aubry in the
night, "J'ai passé comme une fleur, j'ai
séché comme l'herbe des champs"
(very freely adapted from the Book of
Job) are inscribed on the rock. The
second passage, describing the intern-
ment, is briefer. When the grave had
been dug, Chactas says, "we placed the
beauty in her bed of clay. Alas, I had

hoped to prepare another bed for her."

Girodet clearly read the text very closely, and his preparatory drawings reveal that he began by considering two other incidents before finally determining on the subject he was to paint. He mentions in a letter that he went to the Jardin des Plantes in Paris in search of suitably exotic vegetation for the picture. But he seems to have aimed at creating a work of art of wider significance than a straightforward depiction of a passage from *Atala* —a heightened and generalised interpretation of it rather than an illustration. Chactas, whom he had drawn with strongly Indian features and with his hair tied up in a scalp-lock, appears in the painting with only an earring and a few inconspicuous plaited strands in his mop of black hair to indicate his race. He seems, rather, to be a swarthy European, the visual prototype of many melancholy lovers who were soon to figure in Romantic stories of unconsummated passion.

In composition the painting strongly recalls depictions of the Lamentation over and Entombment of Christ. As Professor Levitine has pointed out, Père Aubry takes the place of St. Joseph of Arimathea and Chactas that of St. Mary Magdalene in Gothic and Renaissance paintings and carvings of these subjects. Chactas, with his magnificently muscular physique, is depicted by Girodet as the personification of manly strength subdued by frail virginity, of the lusts of the body overcome by the purity of the soul. But the picture is also an image of physical passion intensified by the unattainability of its object. Erotic impulse and religious sentiment are more closely identified than Chateaubriand had, perhaps, intended. Significantly enough, Chateaubriand made only one mention of the painting in all his voluminous published works, and its wording is a little ambiguous. In a footnote

to *Les Martyrs* (1809), he referred to Girodet's *Endymion*, adding: "It is only just that I should render this feeble homage to the author of the admirable picture of the entombment of Atala. Unfortunately I do not have the art of M. Girodet, and while he embellishes my pictures, I am much afraid of spoiling his."

The picture was first shown at the Paris Salon of 1808 and re-exhibited in that of 1814, receiving acclaim from most critics on both occasions. It was bought by Louis-François Bertin (later painted by Ingres in one of his finest and most famous portraits). Louis XVIII acquired a replica of it (now in the Musée d'Amiens) by Girodet's pupil Amable-Louis-Claude Pagnest in 1818 and acquired the painting itself in 1819 (as M. Pierre Angrand has recently demonstrated). It soon won a place among the accepted masterpieces of French early nineteenth-century painting. In 1846 Baudelaire cited it as an expression of "the essentially poetic side of Girodet's talent" and in 1855 he wrote: "As for Girodet's *Atala*, whatever aging wags may think of it, as drama it is far superior to a whole crowd of unmentionable modern insipidities." Numerous copies of it were painted shortly after its first exhibition and much later, including one of 1857 by Henri Fantin-Latour.

Literature: C. P. Landon: *Annales du Musée de l'école moderne des beaux-arts. Salon de 1808*, Paris, 1808, vol. II, pp. 17-19; Chateaubriand: *Les Martyrs* (Paris, 1809) in *Oeuvres complètes* (ed. Garnier), Paris, 1929, vol. IV, p. 347; *Equivoques*, exhibition catalogue, Musée des Arts Décoratifs, Paris, 1973 (unpaginated); *Lettre de M. Boher, peintre et statuaire et la réponse de M. Girodet . . .*, Perpignan, 1820, p. 1; M. Garnier and Raoul-Rochette: *Discours aux funérailles de M. Girodet-Trioson*, Paris, 1824, pp. 2, 6; E. Souesme de Montargis: *Girodet*, Paris, 1825, p. 2; P.-A. Coupin: "Notice nécrologique sur Girodet" in *Revue encyclopédique*, XXV (1825), p. 7; Constance de Salm: *Sur Girodet*, Paris, 1825, p. 7; Quatremère de Quincy: "Eloge historique de M. Girodet" (1825) in *Recueil de notices historiques*, Paris, 1834, pp. 322-323; P.-A. Coupin: *Oeuvres posthumes de Girodet-Trioson*, Paris, 1829, vol. I, pp. xvi, xxxiv, lii, lvii; M. Miel: "Notice sur Girodet-Trioson" in *Annales de la Société libre des Beaux-Arts*, XII (1842), p. 293; C. Baudelaire: *Le Musée classique du Bazar Bonne Nouvelle* (1846) and *Exposition Universelle* (1855) in *Curiosités esthétiques*, ed. H. Lemaitre, Paris, 1962, pp. 91, 224; E.-J. Delécluze: *Louis David, son Ecole et son temps*, Paris, 1855, pp. 267, 268, 270; P.-A. Leroy: *Girodet-Trioson, peintre d'histoire*, Orleans, 1892, p. 12; H. Jouin: "Lettres inédites d'artistes français du XIXᵉ siècle" in *Nouvelles Archives de l'art français*, 3 S., XVI (1900), p. 20; H. Lemonnier: "'L'Atala' de Chateaubriand et l'Atala' de Girodet" in *Gazette des Beaux Arts*, 4 S., XI (1914), pp. 363-371; J. Adhémar: "Notes sur Girodet" in *Bulletin de la Societe de l'histoire de l'art français* (1933), p. 272; J. Adhémar: "Girodet un fou" in *Arts*, 3 July 1936; F. Antal: "Reflections on Classicism and Romanticism" (1936) in *Classicism and Romanticism*, London, 1966, p. 24; W. Friedlander: *David to Delacroix* (1952), Cambridge, Mass., 1964, p. 43; *Girodet 1767-1824*, exhibition catalogue, Musée de Montargis, 1967, no. 38; G. Levitine: "Some Unexplored Aspects of the Illustrations of Atala" in R. Switzer, ed.: *Chateaubriand Actes du Congres de Wisconsin . . . 1968*, Geneva, 1970, pp. 139-145; P. Angrand: *Le Comte de Forbin et le Louvre en 1819*, Paris, 1972, pp. 97-103.

Comte de Boulet (or Boulot)

French, early nineteenth century.
The comte de Boulet was an amateur artist who is said to have lived in Dijon. His only known works are a series of illustrations to *Atala*, two of which are exhibited here.

Comte de Boulet (or Boulot)

269 *Chactas Led Captive by the Muscogulges*

Pen, ink, and charcoal. ca. 1810.
17¾ x 23 inches (44.9 x 58.3 cm.).

270 *Chactas and Atala*

Pen, ink, and charcoal. ca. 1810.
18 x 23½ inches (45.5 x 59.6 cm.).
Provenance: Marcel Duchemin; Librairie Vrin, Paris; Gilbert Chinard. Princeton, Princeton University Library.

The first of these drawings seems to represent the moment when Chactas is taken to be tied to the tree from which Atala will release him. The second shows the two lovers resting on their flight through the forest. Both are drawn in the linear style adopted in the late eighteenth and early nineteenth centuries for engravings of antique statues and, but for Chactas's feather head-dress, both might easily be mistaken for scenes from classical mythology. The drawings come from a set of nine which have belonged to two distinguished Chateaubriand scholars, Marcel Duchemin and Gilbert Chinard, who seem to have been responsible for attributing them to the otherwise unknown comte de Boulet.

Literature: *The French in America*, exhibition catalogue, Detroit Institute of Arts, 1951, nos. 327-328.

ATALA DÉLIVRE CHACTAS.
Par Brevet D'invention.

FUITE D'ATALA ET DE CHACTAS.
Par Brevet D'invention.

CHACTAS PLEURE SUR LE TOMBEAU
D'ATALA.
Par Brevet D'invention.

CHACTAS DEMANDE A RETOURNER
A LA MONTAGNE.
Par Brevet D'invention.

271 *Five Scenes from* Atala
France (Choisy-le-Roi). White earthenware with transfer printed decorations. ca. 1804-1815. Diameter 8½ inches (21.5 cm.).
Blérancourt, Musée National de la Coopération Franco-Américaine.

These plates, made to satisfy the demands of a largely middle-class market, are among the more popular expressions of the cult of *Atala*. They were made at the Choisy-le-Roi pottery (founded by the brothers Paillart in 1804) and come from a set of a dozen, each of which is decorated with a different scene from the story. The five exhibited show Atala freeing Chactas; flight of Atala and Chactas; Chactas carrying Atala to her grave; the burial of Atala; and Chactas asking to be returned to the mountain.

Literature: *Chateau de Blérancourt. Le Musée de la Coopération Franco-Américaine,* Paris, 1966, pl. 63; *Chateaubriand le voyageur et l'homme politique,* exhibition catalogue, Bibliothèque Nationale, Paris, 1969, no. 76.

272 *Clock*
France. Bronze, partly gilt. ca. 1805-1815. Height 14³⁄₁₆ inches (36.1 cm.). Paris, Collection of M. Maurice Chalvet.

Two of the most popular scenes from *Atala* are shown on this clock-case. The statuettes represent Atala freeing Chactas, while the Muscogulge guard dozes. The dial of the clock rests on the pyre of logs prepared for Chactas's immolation. In the relief at the base, Chactas carries the dead Atala to her grave, followed by Père Aubry. Clocks decorated with scenes from contemporary and earlier novels (e.g. *Robinson Crusoe* and *Paul et Virginie*) were popular in France under the Empire and Restauration, but they are rarely signed or dated and very little is known about the bronze sculptors who made their cases. A similar *Atala* clock is illustrated by H. Le Savoreux: *Chateaubriand* (Paris, 1930, pl. xi). Another without the Muscogulge guard and with different decorations on either side of the relief on the base is in the collection of M. Imbert, Paris.

Eugène Delacroix

French, 1798-1863.

A pupil of Baron Pierre Narcisse Guérin and a friend and admirer of Jean Louis Géricault, Delacroix first came to public notice at the 1822 Salon with *Dante and Virgil*. Two years later his *Massacre at Chios* caused both indignation and wild acclaim, and from then onwards he was acknowledged to be the guiding spirit of French Romantic painting. He dominated the Paris art world, Ingres being his only rival. His range was very wide, but a taste for the exotic, which drew him occasionally to American subjects, remained constant and found expression in several masterpieces painted after a journey to Morocco and Algeria in 1832. He combined a rare appreciation for Spanish painting, especially Velasquez and Goya, with deep sympathy for English literature and landscape painting. His large-scale decorative cycles in several public buildings in Paris are without parallel in the nineteenth century.

Ary Scheffer

Dutch, 1795-1858.

Scheffer was born at Dordrecht, the son of a German father and Dutch mother. On his father's death in 1809 he went with his mother and brothers to Paris. Here he studied from 1811 in the studio of P.-N. Guerin, began to work in the style of J.-L. David, but also came under the influence of Prud'hon and Géricault. Under the Restauration he soon emerged as one of the most highly regarded painters of the day. Politically he was a radical, but he became the drawing master and close friend of the Orléans family. His work included some outstanding portraits and many pictures inspired by contemporary literature, especially the work of Goethe, Schiller, Byron, and Scott.

Ary Scheffer

273 *The Death of Atala*

Oil on board. ca. 1820-1830. 12⅛ x 13⅜ inches (30.8 x 34 cm.). London, private collection.

Scheffer is not known to have made a finished painting of *The Death of Atala,* but there can be no doubt about the subject of the work exhibited, which corresponds very closely with his documented sketches of the 1820s, when he was associated with the young Romantics.

Eugène Delacroix

274 *Les Natchez*

Oil on canvas. 1824-1835. Signed: *Eug.Delacroix.* 35⁷⁄₁₆ x 45¹¹⁄₁₆ inches (90 x 116 cm.). Provenance: Paturle, 1838; Febvre, 1872; Sedelmeyer, 1877; Boussod Valadon et Cie, 1885; sold Goupil 25 May 1887 bought in; Edmond Guillot; Philippe Georges d'Ay, 1891; Durand-Ruel, 1900; Bessonneau, 1916; Frappié; Lefebvre Gallery. Royston, Hertfordshire, Lord and Lady Walston Collection.

Although not exhibited and presumably not finished until the 1835 Salon, this painting was begun many years before, in 1823, though it may have been even earlier, for Delacroix noted in his Journal on 5 October 1822: "Une

jeune Canadienne traversant le désert avec son époux est prise par les douleurs de l'enfantement et accouche; le père prend dans ses bras le nouveau-né." Despite the title, Delacroix did not take the subject from Chateaubriand's *Les Natchez* (1826) but from his *Atala* (1801). In the epilogue the narrator meets, near Niagara, two young Indians with their dying child. The mother recounts their tragedy. "We were the last survivors of the Natchez tribe. After the massacre of our people by the French," she goes on, "the few survivors found refuge with the Chickasaws, a neighbouring tribe. For some time we lived peacefully together. But seven moons ago white men from Virginia took possession of our land, saying it had been given them by a European king. We looked to the heavens and, taking with us the remains of our

ancestors, set off across the desert. I gave birth to my child during the journey, and since my milk was bad after all I had suffered, my child died."

The scene depicted by Delacroix— for which a preparatory drawing survives (Musée du Louvre, R.F. no. 219)— is that just before the child dies. But, of course, he goes far beyond a mere illustration to Chateaubriand. His painting is a poignant lament for a dying race.

Literature: *Journal de Eugène Delacroix,* ed. A. Joubin, Paris, 1960, vol. I, p. 15, vol. III, p. 375; *Correspondence générale de Eugène Delacroix,* ed. A. Joubin, Paris, 1936-38, vol. I, p. 409, vol. II, pp. 3, 4; A. T. (Alexandre Tardieu) in *Le Courrier français,* 30 March 1835; C. Lenormant in *Revue des Deux-Mondes,* 1 April 1835, 4th series, II, p. 197; E. S. in *La Tribune politique et littéraire,* 6 April 1835; Anon in *Le Moniteur Universel,* 15 April 1835; A in *Le Constitutionel,* 26 April 1835; L. P. . .e (Louis Peisse) in *Le Temps,* 30 August 1835; G. de F. (Guyot de Fére) in *Journal spécial des Lettres et des Beaux Arts,* 1835, vol. I, p. 204; Anon in *L'Artiste,* 1837, p. 212; A. Moreau: *E. Delacroix et son oeuvre,* Paris, 1873, pp. 89, 160, 175, 252; A. Robaut & E. Chesneau: *L'oeuvre complet de Eugène Delacroix . . .,* Paris, 1885, no. 108; M. Tourneux: *Eugène Delacroix devant ses contemporains, ses écrits, ses biographes, ses critiques,* Paris, 1886, pp. 61-63, 252; E. Moreau-Nélaton: *Delacroix raconté par lui-même,* Paris, 1916, vol. I, p. 154; L. Johnson in *The Burlington Magazine,* XCVIII (December 1956), p. 324; M. Serullaz: *Mémorial de l'exposition Eugène Delacroix . . .,* Paris, 1963, pp. 163-164; R. Huyghe: *Delacroix,* London, 1963, p. 182, 282, 302; *Chateaubriand: Le Voyageur et l'Homme Politique,* exhibition catalogue, Bibliothèque Nationale, Paris, 1969, no. 77; *Berlioz and the Romantic Imagination,* exhibition catalogue, Victoria and Albert Museum, London, 1969, no. 18.

Francisque-Joseph Duret

French, 1804-1865.
Duret was born in Paris and trained at
the Ecole des Beaux Arts, where, in
1823, he won the *grand prix* for sculpture, which enabled him to go to the
French Academy in Rome. After making his debut in the Paris Salon in 1831,
he won general acclaim in 1833 with
his bronze statue of a young fisherman
dancing a tarantella, *Souvenir de
Naples* (Musée du Louvre). Several of
his other statues are of similar subjects.
He received many official commissions,
including that for a marble statue of
Chateaubriand for Versailles (1854).
He was elected to the Institut in 1845.

Francisque-Joseph Duret

275 *Chactas Mourning Atala*
Bronze. ca. 1836. Height 17¾ inches
(45 cm.).
Paris, Mme. Lila Maurice Amour
Collection.

This is a reduced version of the bronze
statue which Duret exhibited at the
Paris Salon of 1836 and is now in the
garden of the Musée des Beaux Arts,
Lyon. It is inspired by a passage in the
epilogue of *Atala* describing how
Chactas returned to the Mescacebé to
gather the remains of his beloved and
also of Père Aubry, who had been
killed by the Cherokees. "He sat on
the rock of the Vigil of death where
he saw only feathers fallen from the
wing of a bird of passage. While he
wept there the missionary's tame
snake came out of the brushwood and
coiled itself at his feet. . . ." Another
example of the bronze is recorded in
a private collection in Paris.

Literature: S. Lami: *Dictionnaire des
sculpteurs de l'école française au dix-
huitième siècle,* Paris, 1914-21, vol. II, p.
262; *Chateaubriand le voyageur et
l'homme politique,* exhibition catalogue,
Bibliothèque Nationale, Paris, 1969,
no. 75.

Gustave Doré

French, 1832-1883.
One of the greatest book illustrators of
the nineteenth century, Doré was in-
ternationally famous and employed by
English and American as well as French
publishers. He was born in Strasbourg,
the son of an engineer, showed a precocious talent for drawing, and began
to make lithographs at the age of
thirteen. In 1847 he settled in Paris
and, though still a school boy, began
to contribute drawings to Philippon's
Journal pour rire. He became more
widely known with the comic *Histoire
de la Sainte Russie* (1864) and an illustrated monthly devoted to the Crimean
War, *Musée Franco-Anglaise*, published simultaneously in Paris and
London. At about the same time his
imaginative and very personal style
began to develop in illustrations to
Rabelais (1854) and Balzac's *Contes
drôlatiques* (1855). He achieved still
greater fame with illustrated editions
of Dante's *Inferno* (1861), *The Adventures of Baron Munchausen* (1862),
Don Quixote (1863), *Atala* (1863, see
below), the Bible (1866), Milton's
Paradise Lost (1866), and, perhaps
most notably of all, Blanchard Jer-
rold's *London. A Pilgrimage* (1872).
His other works include illustrations
to Gabriel Ferry's Red Indian story *Le
Coureur des Bois* (1860). He illustrated
some 120 books in all.

Gustave Doré

276 *The Great Storm, illustration to*
Atala

Woodcut. 1863. Signed: *G. Doré*. Page
size: 16 5⁄16 x 12 inches (41.5 x 30.5 cm.).
Cincinnati, Ohio, Public Library of
Cincinnati.

Doré's is incomparably the finest of the
illustrated editions of *Atala* and the
only one which successfully identifies

the passionate love of the two main characters with the wildness of American nature. On page after page he evoked with amazing skill the landscape of the southern United States— its immense mountain ranges, its rank creeper-hung and bat-infested forests, its fetid swamps and violent rushing rivers—which neither he nor Chateaubriand had ever seen! Presenting an interpretation of the story characteristic of his time, he emphasised its pantheism rather than its Catholicism, concentrating on Chateaubriand's vivid descriptions of nature, for which it was at that time mainly read. The human figures are, in Doré's illustrations, overwhelmed by and lost in the grandeur of this untamed landscape. The volume is open at the plate of one of the most dramatic scenes in the novel. On their flight Chactas and Atala are overtaken by a violent storm, in which lightning sets the forest on fire. Seeking refuge they

> advanced with great effort under an arch of similax, among the vines, the indigos, the haricots, and the creeping lianas, which caught our feet like nets. The spongy soil trembled beneath us, and countless insects and bats blinded us . . . Meanwhile the darkness increased, and the clouds moved into the shade of the trees. The sky ripped apart, and there the lightning sketched a lozenge of fire . . . An impetuous wind rolled clouds under each other. The trees bent, the sky opened up; and through its crevasses we could see the new heavens and their fiery campaign. What a magnificent spectacle! The thunderbolts set the woods afire in a head-dress of flame; columns of spark and smoke rose to the clouds, which vomited their flashes into the vast conflagration. Then the Great Spirit covered the mountain with thick shadows. From the midst of this vast chaos there arose a confused tumult of noise made by the roar of the wind, the groaning of the trees, the cries of the wild beasts, the crackling of the fire, and the repeated fall of thunderbolts hissing as they were quenched in the waters.

Clasping Atala to him, Chactas felt a tear fall onto his breast. "Is that a drop of rain from the storm in your heart?" he asks. She then reveals for the first time that her father was Lopez, and Chactas tells her how he had been adopted and educated by Lopez. In their mutual joy at this discovery, they embrace. "Eyes raised to the sky, in the flashes of lightning, I held my bride in my arms, in the presence of the Eternal Being," Chactas continues. "A wedding ceremony worthy of our sorrows and the grandeur of our love: magnificent forest waving your lianas and your domes like the curtains and ceiling of our bed, flaming pines which were our marriage torches, overflowing river, roaring mountains, terrible and sublime nature. . . ." Suddenly a tree falls at their feet; in the silence that follows they hear from afar the sound of a bell and the barking of a dog, and soon Père Aubry appears on the scene.

A number of artists were employed to engrave the wood blocks after Doré's drawings illustrating *Atala*. The plate exhibited is the work of Adolphe-François Pannemaker (1822-after 1885), a printmaker of Belgian origin who executed many woodcuts after Doré's drawings, assisted by another craftsman named Ligny, about whom nothing further is known.

Literature: *The Doré Gallery,* London, 1870; H. Leblanc: *Catalogue de l'oeuvre de Gustave Doré,* Paris, 1931.

XV
The Return of Christopher Columbus

"Columbus, my hero, royalest Sea-king of all! it is no friendly environment this of thine, in the waste deep waters; around thee mutinous discouraged souls, behind thee disgrace and ruin, before thee the unpenetrated veil of night." So wrote that great hero-worshipper Thomas Carlyle in *Past and Present* (1843). A few years earlier Richard Wagner had composed a *Columbus* overture. It began with "a forcible, pathetically yearning and aspiring theme" and ended with an "exquisite, gradually dawning and seductive" one, led by three pairs of trumpets in different keys. This, he later wrote, "was intended to represent the land of desire towards which the hero's eyes are turned, and whose shores seem continually to rise before him only to sink elusively beneath the waves, until at last they soar in very deed above the western horizon, the crown of all his toil and search, and stand clearly and unmistakably revealed to all the sailors, a vast continent of the future."[1]

Although Columbus was never forgotten or disregarded, full recognition of the magnitude of his achievement came late, and it was not until the nineteenth century that he reached his apotheosis as a Great Man and Romantic Hero in literature, music, and the visual arts. Before then his impact had been curiously limited. There was no full-length biography until 1571, when that by his son Hernando was published in Venice. He made no prominent appearance in Spanish literature until 1614—in Lope de Vega's play, *El Nuevo Mundo descubierto por Cristóbal Colón*. A few, mainly Italian, historians of the New World—Peter Martyr, G. B. Ramusio, and especially Gerolamo Benzoni—recounted anecdotes which gave life to a Columbus legend [62]. Eloquent tribute was paid to him by Tasso in *Gerusalemme Liberata* (1581), and several minor Italian poets of the same period made him the protagonist of now long-forgotten epics.[2] Yet very much the same might be said about other sixteenth-century figures of much less importance.

Benzoni remarked on the lack of any monument to Columbus. Had he lived in the time of the Greeks or Romans, he wrote, "they would have erected a statue." No such monument to him was to be set up for some three hundred years. But he appears in commemorative paintings from the mid-sixteenth century onwards—in the gallery of portraits of famous men assembled by Paolo Giovio at Como before 1552, and in the map-room at Caprarola in the early 1570s.[3] Prints of him were published after drawings by Stradanus and in de Bry's illustrated edition of Benzoni [91]. In the seventeenth century his achievements were celebrated by painters in his native Genoa, where he was usually depicted discovering the New World in the service not of the Spanish monarchy but of the Roman Catholic Church.[4] He has remained an Italian national hero ever since. It was, significantly, during the *Risorgimento* that a large sculptured monument was finally erected to his memory in Genoa. Outside Italy, too, he was represented as a lay hero of the Church—in Mme. du Boccage's epic *La Colombiade ou la foi portée au Nouveau Monde* of 1758 and in paintings of a century later.[5]

A few eighteenth-century plays and operas were devoted to Columbus, but it was not until the 1820s that he began to make frequent appearances on the stage.[6] At about the same time, paintings of him began to multiply.[7] To some extent this reflects new attitudes to America brought about by the increasing wealth and power of the United States, but it was also part of a more general nineteenth-century cult of the explorer and man of action, which of course included the Conquistadors [281] and such other New World discoverers as Jacques Cartier and René-Robert de La Salle as well [279,280]. But the story of Columbus was unique and, moreover, had a pathos and depth which very strongly appealed to Romantics.

Columbus could be interpreted as a prototype of the Romantic artist or poet. He was the explorer who had ventured into a totally new world, the visionary who had seen beyond the ken of ordinary men of common sense, the man of genius who was misunderstood by his contemporaries, but received from posterity the acclaim denied him in his life. Samuel Rogers described him as one

> Who among us a life of sorrow spent,
> And, dying, left a world his monument.

And as a melancholy dreamer he is usually depicted—musing in the convent of La Rábida [277], mocked by the learned of the Junta of Salamanca, gazing pensively into the distance from the bridge of the Santa Maria, returning humiliated and in chains from his third voyage, dying neglected in Valladolid [286]. Even when he is shown in happier circumstance, as he sometimes was, he wears an expression both sad and aloof [283]. Even his triumphal reception at Barcelona after his return from his first voyage is overlaid by Romantic artists with intimations of pathos.

1. T. Carlyle: *Past and Present* (1843) in *Collected Works*, London, 1870, vol. XIII, p. 248. R. Wagner: *My Life* (1870), London, 1911, p. 119. Wagner's overture was for a play by Theodor Apel first performed in Magdeburg in 1835.

2. *Gerusalemme Liberata*, Canto XV, stanzas 30 to 32. See also Leicester Bradner: "Columbus in Sixteenth Century Poetry" in *Essays Honoring Lawrence C. Wroth*, Portland, Maine, 1951, pp. 15-30.

3. No contemporary likeness of Columbus is known. The "portrait" painted for Giovio (now Museo Civico, Como) probably dates from the 1530s and is first mentioned in 1556. A portrait by Sebastiano del Piombo (Metropolitan Museum, New York) and another attributed to Ridolfo Ghirlandaio (Civico Museo Navale, Pegli, Genoa) appear to have had the name of Columbus attached to them some time after they were painted. For a medal said to have been modelled from the life, see R. Gaettens: "Christophoro Colombo His portrait from life sculptured by Guido Mazzoni" in *The Connoisseur*, CLVI (1964), pp. 174-181.

4. Drawings for three Columbus subjects painted by Lazzaro Tavarone in Palazzo Negrotto Cambiaso, Genoa, ca. 1615, are in the Galleria Estense, Modena (cf. L. C. Ragghianti: "Lazzaro Tavarone Disegnatore" in *Critica d'Arte*, I [1954], pp. 439-444). In 1655 Giovanni Battista Carlone painted frescoes of the discovery of America in the chapel of the Palazzo Ducale, Genoa. For Solimena's painting for the same building, see [128].

5. Pharamond Blanchard painted *The First Mass Celebrated in America* in 1850, now Préfecture de la Côte-d'Or, Dijon; cf. P. Guimard: *Dauzats et Blanchard*, Paris, 1967, p. 409 and pl. XLVII.

6. Eighteenth-century plays included Cardinal Pietro Ottoboni's *Colombo ovvero L'India scoperta* (three versions: 1691, 1710, 1730) and Pietro Chiari's *Colombo nell'America* (1754); there was also an opera by V. Fabrizi: *Colombo e la scoperta delle Indie* (1788). Rousseau began *La découverte du Nouveau Monde, Opéra-tragédie* but wrote only a part of the prologue; cf. *Annales de la Société J. J. Rousseau*, I, p. 229. In the nineteenth century there were Columbus operas by F. Morlacchi (1828), L. Ricci (1829), R. Carnicer (1831), G. Bottesini (1847), V. Mela (1857), F. Casella (1864-65), G. Marcora (1869), and A. Franchetti (1892), also a ballet by J. Monplaisir (1861-62).

7. A list of Columbus subjects painted between 1819 and 1848 is provided by Hamish Miles in "Wilkie's Columbus," *North Carolina Museum Bulletin*, VIII (1969), pp. 11-12. Some nineteenth-century paintings and prints of Columbus are reproduced in C. Giardini: *The Life and Times of Columbus* (Portraits of Greatness), Feltham, Middlesex, 1968.

Eugène Delacroix
French, 1798-1863.

277 *Columbus and his Son at*
La Rábida

Oil on canvas. Signed and dated:
Eug. Delacroix. 1838. 35⅝ x 46⅝
inches (90.5 x 118.5 cm.). Provenance:
Prince Demidoff; Edouard André; E.
Secrétan; P.A.B. Widener, 1890; Ferdinand Blumenthal (1912?); Count Cecil
Pecci-Blunt by 1930; Chester Dale,
1932.
Washington, D.C., National Gallery
of Art, Chester Dale Collection, 1962.
(Exhibited in Washington only.)

This painting and its pendant, *The*
Return of Christopher Columbus
[278], were commissioned by Prince
Anatole Demidoff in 1838 for his villa

at San Donato, Florence. In the Demidoff sale catalogue, 1870, *Columbus*
and his Son at La Rábida is titled
Christophe Colomb au couvent de
Sainte-Marie-de-Rabida, with the following comment: "Seven years before
the discovery of America, two strangers
travelling on foot, covered in dust and
bathed in sweat, came to the entrance
of the little monastery called Sainte-
Marie-de-Rabida not far from the port
of Palos in Andalusia. The two strangers were Christopher Columbus and
his son Diego. The prior of the monastery, don Juan Peres de Marchena,
came down to talk with them. The
prior, a man of feeling and of learning,
befriended Columbus and helped him
in his difficult enterprise." The incident
took place in 1484 and later became a
popular subject of Romantic writers

and artists in the nineteenth century.
The Franciscan monastery at La
Rábida survives, and relics associated
with Columbus are preserved there.

Literature: A. Moreau: *Eugène Delacroix*
et son oeuvre, Paris, 1873, p. 94, no. 259;
A. Robaut and E. Chesneau: *L'Oeuvre*
complet de Eugène Delacroix . . ., Paris,
1885, p. 178, no. 659; M. A. Wolff: *The*
Collection of Paintings . . . formed by Mr.
E. Secretan, New York-Paris, 1889, vol. I,
no. 16; E. Moreau-Nélaton: *Delacroix*
raconté par lui-même, Paris, 1916, vol. I,
pp. 192 ff.; *Exposition Eugène Delacroix*,
exhibition catalogue, Louvre, Paris, 1930,
no. 91; L. Hourticq: *Delacroix, L'Oeuvre*
du maître, Paris, ca. 1930, p. 69; E. Lambert: "Delacroix et l'Espagne" in *La Revue*
des Arts, September, 1951, pp. 159-171; M.
Serullaz: *Mémorial de l'Exposition Eugène*
Delacroix . . ., Paris, 1963, pp. 211-212; R.
Huyghe: *Delacroix*, London, 1963, pp.
294, 303-304; F. A. Trapp: *The Attainment of Delacroix*, Baltimore and London,
1971, p. 193.

Eugène Delacroix

278 *The Return of Christopher Columbus*

Oil on canvas. Signed and dated: *Eug. Delacroix 1839*. 33½ x 45½ inches (85 x 116 cm.). Provenance: Prince Demidoff; Hollender, 1873; Secrétan; Boussard-Valadon, 1889; Edouard André; Mrs. William A. Slater; Dr. Harold Tovell.
Toledo, Ohio, The Toledo Museum of Art, Gift of Thomas A. De Vilbiss.

This painting was commissioned by Prince Anatole Demidoff in 1838, together with its pendant [277], for his villa at San Donato, Florence. In the Demidoff sale catalogue, 1870, *The Return of Christopher Columbus* is titled *Christophe Colomb rapportant aux rois catholiques les richesses conquises dans sa première expédition au*

Nouveau Monde, with the following commentary: "Columbus made a solemn entry into Barcelona; the whole town turned out to see him; he was surrounded by Indians he had brought back with him, dressed in their native costumes. Gold, precious stones and other rarities were carried before him in baskets and panniers. Ferdinand and Isabella, seated on their thrones, waited for him and when he appeared, stood up."

Literature: A. Moreau: *Eugène Delacroix et son oeuvre,* Paris, 1873, pp. 94, 259; A. Robaut and E. Chesneau: *L'Oeuvre complet de Eugène Delacroix . . .,* Paris, 1885, no. 690; M. A. Wolff: *The Collection of Paintings . . . formed by Mr. E. Secrétan,* New York-Paris, 1889, vol. I, no. 16; E. Moreau-Nélaton: *Delacroix raconté par lui-même,* Paris, 1916, vol. I, p. 193; Blake-More Godwin: *European Paintings in the Toledo Museum,* Toledo, 1939, p. 170; L.

Rudrauf: *Eugène Delacroix et le problème du romantisme artistique,* Paris, 1942, pp. 249-250; *French Art from 1800 to 1860,* exhibition catalogue, Detroit Institute of Arts, Detroit, 1950, no. 33; E. Lambert: "Delacroix et l'Espagne" in *La Revue des Arts,* September, 1951, pp. 159-171; L. Rudrauf: "Delacroix et le Titien" in *Actes du XIX Congrès international d'Histoire de l'Art,* 1955, pp. 527-528; *Venice Biennale* XXVIII, *Eugène Delacroix,* exhibition catalogue, Venice, 1956, no. 21; L. Johnson: "Delacroix at the Biennale" in *The Burlington Magazine,* vol. 98 (1956), p. 327; O. Wittman: "L'Art Francaise au Musée de Toledo" in *Connaissance,* no. 125 (July 1962), pp. 40-47; M. Serullaz: *Mémorial de l'Exposition Eugène Delacroix . . .,* Paris, 1963, no. 282; R. Huyghe: *Delacroix,* London, 1963, pp. 294, 303-304; L. Johnson: *Eugène Delacroix,* London, 1963, p. 113; F. A. Trapp: *The Attainment of Delacroix,* Baltimore and London, 1971, pp. 194-196.

Théodore Gudin

French, 1802-1879.
Gudin was born in Paris, where he studied first under Girodet and then in the studio of Baron Gros. In 1822 he began exhibiting seascapes at the Paris Salon and soon became the most celebrated marine painter in Europe. He was much patronised by Louis-Philippe and painted sixty-three pictures for Versailles between 1838 and 1848. Nicholas I invited him to St. Petersburg, where he painted twelve large views of Russian ports in 1841. But his works met with increasingly hostile criticism from the mid-1840s. He married a daughter of Lord Hay and spent much of his old age in Scotland.

Théodore Gudin

279 *La Salle Discovering Louisiana*
Oil on canvas. 1844. 56⅝ x 88¾ inches (144 x 225 cm.). Provenance: Acquired by the Maison du Roi in 1844.
Versailles, Musée National du Château de Versailles.

René-Robert Cavelier de La Salle, with a party of twenty-three Frenchmen and a group of Mohican Indians, travelled from New France along the Illinois River and then down the Mississippi to the Gulf of Mexico in the winter of 1681-82. On reaching the delta of the Mississippi he set up a column inscribed: "Louis le Grand, Roy de France et de Navarre, Regne; Le Neuvième Avril, 1682" and claimed for Louis XIV and his successors "possession of this country of Louisiana" from the source of "the great river" to "its mouth at the sea." After going back to France to obtain royal support, La Salle returned to the Gulf of Mexico with four ships carrying soldiers and settlers to establish a French colony and landed in Matagorda Bay (on the coast of what is now Texas) in early January 1685. This is the event re-corded in Gudin's painting—though, in fact, no permanent French colony was to be established in the region until the le Moyne brothers founded Fort Biloxi in 1699.

The picture is one of numerous illustrations of French history painted for Versailles under Louis-Philippe. It was commissioned by 1842, when it was mentioned in a guide to the *Galeries historiques* at Versailles, but was not completed until 1844, when Gudin exhibited it in the Paris Salon together with six other paintings for the same series, including one commemorating the foundation of the French colonies on the islands of Saint-Christophe and Martinique.

Literature: *Galeries historiques du Palais de Versailles*, Paris, 1842, p. 308; E. Bellier de la Chavignerie and L. Auvray: *Dictionnaire des artistes de l'école française*, Paris, 1882, p. 707.

Joseph-Nicolas Robert-Fleury

French, 1797-1890.
He was born of French parents in Cologne and trained as an artist in Paris under Girodet, Gros, and Horace Vernet. After an extended visit to Italy he made his debut at the Paris Salon in 1824. In the following years he exhibited both portraits and numerous pictures of historical subjects, making something of a specialty of scenes from the lives of artists. His works had great popular success. Baudelaire admired them but remarked that he fell short of genius by "a millimetre or a milligram." Théophile Gautier also wrote of him favourably though complaining, in 1855, that his work showed no artistic development. He was made a member of the Legion of Honour in 1836 and commander in 1867, elected to the Institut in 1850 (seven years before Delacroix) and briefly served as director of the Ecole des Beaux Arts, Paris (1863-66) and the French Academy in Rome (1867). He seems to have retired in 1867.

Joseph-Nicolas Robert-Fleury

279A *The Reception of Columbus at Barcelona*
Oil on canvas. Signed and dated: *Robert-Fleury 1846*. 77 x 121 inches (195 x 306 cm.). Provenance: Comte Pillet-Will, who presented it to the Louvre, 1889.
Paris, Musée du Louvre.

Robert-Fleury was a friend of Delacroix, whose *Return of Christopher Columbus* [278] he may well have seen, but his picture more closely corresponds with the style of history painting popular with the general public in the mid-nineteenth century. Thus it is packed with story-telling detail. Great prominence is given to the Indians with their long black hair and to brilliantly coloured parrots. The facial features of Ferdinand and Isabella are derived from sixteenth-century portraits (like those in the English Royal Collection), though, strangely, Columbus himself differs from the usual types. The picture was exhibited at the Paris Salon in 1847 as *Réception de Christophe Colomb par la cour d'Espagne, à Barcelone (1493)*. In 1860 Eugène Devéria painted a still larger picture of the same scene (Musée des Beaux Arts, Clermont-Ferrand, sketch in Musée des Beaux Arts, Pau).

Literature: E. Bellier de la Chavignerie and L. Auvray: *Dictionnaire général des artistes de l'école française*, Paris, 1885, vol. II, p. 397; G. Brière: *Musée national du Louvre, catalogue des peintures exposées dans les galeries, l'école française*, Paris, 1924, no. 2984; C. Giardini: *The Life and Times of Columbus*, London, 1968, p. 47.

Théodore Gudin

280 *Jacques Cartier Discovering the St. Lawrence*

Oil on canvas. 1847. 56⅝ x 88¾ inches (144 x 225 cm.). Provenance: Acquired by the Maison du Roi in 1847. Versailles, Musée National du Château de Versailles.

Jacques Cartier, in the summer of 1534, sailed across the Gulf of St. Lawrence but, because of poor visibility, mistook the mouth of the river for a bay. When he returned the next year, he sailed up what he called the *Rivière du Canada*

as far as Saulte Ste. Marie and named a nearby hill *Mont Real* (he gave the name Saint-Laurent only to a tributary, but it was transferred to the great river and gulf by Ramusio). This voyage of exploration is the subject of Gudin's highly imaginative painting, commissioned for Versailles by 1842 (like [279]) and exhibited at the Paris Salon in 1847.

Literature: *Galeries historiques du palais de Versailles,* Paris, 1842, p. 308; E. Bellier de la Chavignerie and L. Auvray: *Dictionnaire des artistes de l'école française,* Paris, 1882, p. 707.

John Everett Millais

English, 1829-1896.
An infant prodigy, Millais was only nineteen when he, Holman Hunt, and Rossetti founded the Pre-Raphaelite Brotherhood in 1848. His first Pre-Raphaelite painting, *Isabella,* was exhibited the following year, and with *Ophelia* (1852), *The Blind Girl* (1856), and *Autumn Leaves* (1856), he established his reputation. But his most popular works date from much later, e.g. *The Boyhood of Raleigh* (1870) and *Bubbles* (1886).

John Everett Millais

281 *Pizarro Seizing the Inca of Peru*
Oil on canvas. Signed and dated:
J E M (monogram) *1846*. 50½ x 67⅝
inches (128.3 x 171.7 cm.). Provenance:
H. Hodgkinson, half-brother of the
artist, who presented it to the Museum,
1897.
London, The Victoria and Albert
Museum.

This was Millais's first exhibited picture. He was seventeen, and still a student at the Royal Academy. The subject is thus described in the Royal
Academy Catalogue, 1846: "Pizarro
himself advanced towards the Emperor, whom he took prisoner, while
his soldiers, incited by Vincent de Val-
verde, massacred all that surrounded
the Monarch—*vide Luffman's Chron-
ology*." What impelled his choice of
subject for this, his first large-scale
composition, is unknown. Prescott's
History of the Conquest of Peru was
not published until the following year.
But the incident was already famous.
Macaulay remarked in January 1840
that "every schoolboy knows who
imprisoned Montezume, and who
strangled Atahualpa." Holman Hunt
records that his and Millais's contemporary, Edward Goodall, "had
lately returned from a visit to South
America [he accompanied Schomberg's
expedition to British Guiana] bringing
back with him an artist's selection of
native ornaments and garments,"
which he lent to Millais as props for
his painting. Hunt also records seeing
Millais at work on the painting at his
home in Gower Street—a "large platform placed at an angle to serve for the
palanquin on which the doomed Inca
was being carried, so that the model

serving for the prince should lie correctly on the upset platform, and the position of Pizarro and the adjutant reaching forward from outside be characteristically posed." James Wallack, a celebrated comedian who later married Millais's sister, was the model for Pizarro. Millais's father posed for the priest and for other figures.

Literature: J. G. Millais: *The Life and Letters of Sir John Everett Millais,* P.R.A., London, 1899, vol. I, p. 18, vol. II, p. 466; W. Holman Hunt: *Pre-Raphaelitism and the Pre-Raphaelite Brotherhood,* London, 1905, vol. I, p. 58; M. Bennet: *PRB Millais PRA,* exhibition catalogue, Royal Academy, London, 1967, p. 22.

Aristodemo Costoli

Italian, 1803-1871.
A Florentine, trained at the Accademia under Lorenzo Bartolini, whom he later succeeded as professor of sculpture, Costoli was one of the best Italian artists of the mid-nineteenth century. He did the figure of Galileo in the Loggiato of the Uffizi in Florence, the Catalani monument in the Camposanto at Pisa, and the monument to Cavour at Ancona.

Aristodemo Costoli

282 *The Discovery of America*
Bronze. 1848. Height 33⅞ inches without base (86 cm.). Provenance: Leopold II, Grand Duke of Tuscany. Florence, Galleria d'Arte Moderna.

In 1846 Costoli unsuccessfully submitted a model for the monument to Columbus which was to be erected in Genoa. (The monument was commissioned from Bartolini, who did not live to finish it. It was completed by Pietro Freccia and others, including Costoli, who contributed the figure of Prudence at the base. It was completed in 1862 and stands in Piazza Acqua-

verde in Genoa.) However, Costoli's model was greatly admired by the Grand Duke of Tuscany, Leopoldo II, and he commissioned it to be cast in bronze by Clemente Papi. Costoli made some alterations to it before it was cast. His description of the programme is of some interest ideologically:

The hero is shown at the highest and most significant moment of his life, the moment in which he "discovers" America to her sister continents. In order to express this conception of my subject I have included personifications of the continents arranged according to their geographical position and characterised by various devices. Thus Asia, the cradle of the human race and of ancient wisdom and also the largest and most varied in natural riches, I have placed above the others. Africa, prostrate and morally weakened by centuries of slavery, hardly realises the significance of the great event which so changes the face of the world and which is also to bring new injuries and more painful sufferings to her people. I have placed her next to the lion which symbolises both her and Columbus himself. America is apprehensive and frightened, almost foreseeing the calamities which threaten and lie ahead of her. To Europe I have tried to give an expression more noble and dignified than that of the others, since she stands at the head of modern civilization on account of her religion and the superiority of her culture. To symbolize religion I have placed a book with a cross in her hand. She looks towards America firmly and confidently, as if at a new conquest, almost as if she were the ruler and queen of America.

Literature: *Cultura neoclassica e romantica nella Toscana Granducale,* exhibition catalogue, Palazzo Pitti, Florence, 1972, pp. 98-99, with bibliography.

Nicolas Eustache Maurin

French, 1799-1850.
Maurin was a member of a family of artists from Perpignan working in Paris, where he exhibited lithographs at the Salons from 1833 to 1835. Most of his lithographs were portraits of contemporaries, but he issued a series illustrating the discovery of America (see below) and another of scenes from the conquest of Mexico, apparently inspired by Spontini's opera (see [247, 248]).

Nicolas Eustache Maurin

283 *Columbus Builds a Fortress*
Lithograph. ca. 1835-1850. Signed: *N. Maurin.* 18⅝ x 22½ inches (47.2 x 57 cm.).
Paris, Bibliothèque Nationale, Cabinet des Estampes.

This comes from a set of lithographs by Maurin which includes the landing of Columbus, his reception in Barcelona, his "egg-trick," and his return in chains from his third voyage. They are among the best of many widely diffused popular prints of these subjects issued in the nineteenth century. The title *Colombe bâtit une fortresse* seems to refer to the rather substantial castle in the background.

Hermann Freihold Plüddemann

German, 1809-1868.
Plüddemann was born at Kolberg, studied under Carl Sieg and, from 1828, in Berlin under Karl Begas. From 1831 to 1848 he worked in Düsseldorf. In his time he was one of the most famous German painters, specialising in large, sometimes enormous, wall-paintings and canvases of historical subjects. Most of his themes were derived from German history, but from

COLOMB BÂTIT UNE FORTERESSE.   COLON FABRICA UNA FORTALEZA.

1836 he also painted a series of pictures of the life and death of Columbus (now lost). Like other German artists of the day, he took great pains to depict costumes and furnishings accurately. He is, in fact, a prime exemplar of nineteenth-century historicism.

Hermann Freihold Plüddemann

284 *Columbus Disputing with the Junta of Salamanca*

Pencil and wash. Signed and dated: *H. Plüddeman 1851.* 10⁷⁄₁₆ x 15¾ inches (26.4 x 40 cm.). Essen, Museum Folkwang.

The story of Columbus's vain attempt to convince the learned scholars assembled by Queen Isabella at Salamanca in 1486 of the feasibility of reaching the Indies by sailing westward made strong appeal to nineteenth-century artists. This drawing is presumably a preliminary design for Plüddemann's lost painting of the same subject exhibited at the Cologne academy in 1861 (cf. F. von Boetticher: *Malerwerke des Neunzehnten Jahrhunderts*, vol. II, Leipzig, 1898, p. 1). Plüddemann's other Columbus pictures represented his arrival at La Rábida, his first sight of the New World, his reception by the Catholic monarchs in Barcelona, his return to Spain in chains after his third voyage, and his death.

Literature: A. Schulz in U. Thieme and F. Becker: *Allgemeines Lexikon der bildenden Künstler,* vol. XXVII (1933), p. 160; J. Schultze: *Museum Folkwang Essen. Handzeichnungen des 19. Jahrhunderts,* Essen, 1966, no. 109.

H. Plüddemann 1851.

Claudius Jacquand

French, 1803-1878.
Jacquand was born in Lyon and trained at the Ecole de Beaux-Arts there under Fleury-François Richard. After moving to Paris he made his debut in the Salon in 1824, winning a second class medal. He received a first class medal in 1836 and was made a chevalier of the Légion d'honneur in 1839. From 1824 until 1876 he was a regular Salon exhibitor, showing both genre scenes and history pieces of mediaeval, Renaissance, and seventeenth-century subjects, all in the slightly severe style of the Lyonnais school, to which he remained faithful. His works were bought by the Crown and by several notable collectors, including Prince Demidoff, who acquired a picture from him and two from Delacroix in the same year [277, 278]. They also seem to have enjoyed success with the general public, though not with the critics: Baudelaire dismissed him as a "twentieth rate" imitator of Delaroche.

Claudius Jacquand

286 *The Last Moments of Christopher Columbus*

Oil on canvas. 1870. 48⅞ x 64⁹⁄₁₆ inches (124 x 164 cm.).
Le Havre, Musée des Beaux Arts.

The full title of this picture is: *Christopher Columbus, feeling the approach of death, shows his son the chains with which he had once been bound and asks to be buried with them in his coffin.* In this way it combines two of the pathetic episodes in Columbus's life which strongly appealed to nineteenth-century sentiment—his humiliating return in chains from his third voyage in 1500 and his obscure death in Valladolid six years later. The picture was exhibited at the Paris Salon in 1870 and is a characteristic example of the type of "story-telling" work which enjoyed popular success throughout the century. The same scene was also the subject of paintings by Hermann Freihold Plüddemann (1840), Pierre Nolasque Bergeret (1851), Joseph Nicolas Robert-Fleury (1860), and Luigi Sciallero (ca. 1870-1890).

Literature: E. Bellier de la Chavignerie and L. Auvray: *Dictionnaire générale des artistes de l'école française,* Paris, 1882, vol. I, p. 811.

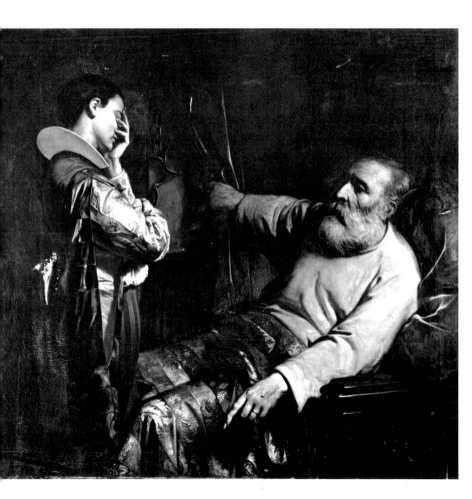

XVI
Indians in
the Nineteenth
Century

American Indians were taken to Europe, either singly or in small groups, almost continuously from 1493, when Columbus returned from his first voyage with some of them on board. For Europeans they never seem to have lost their fascination. Indeed, European interest in them increased and reached a new peak in the nineteenth century. A party of Osages who landed at Le Havre in July 1827 was mobbed in Rouen (where Brazilians had made a sensation nearly three centuries earlier) and fêted in Paris [292]. In the 1840s George Catlin owed much of his success to the Indians he employed to perform their tribal dances at his exhibition of paintings [298]. And later in the century, of course, Buffalo Bill's Wild West show was still more spectacularly popular everywhere it went—in England, France, Italy, Austria, Germany, and Belgium.[1]

The extraordinary appeal these various troupes of Indians held for town-bred Europeans can be partly attributed to the popularity of novels about life among the Indians, and vice versa. Chateaubriand's *Atala* appeared in the first year of the century and soon became a French classic. From the later 1820s James Fenimore Cooper's *Leatherstocking Tales* seem to have been as eagerly read in France and Germany as in England and America. (French translations appeared almost simultaneously with publication in the U.S.A.) The most famous of American poetic accounts of the Indians, Longfellow's "Song of Hiawatha," first published in 1855, had an immediate success in England and also in France, where Baudelaire wrote "Le Calumet de Paix, imité de Longfellow" in 1860.[2] By this time, however, the Indians had also begun to figure in an ever increasing number of adventure stories written by Europeans for Europeans—a new genre anticipating the Spaghetti Westerns of the mid-twentieth century. Gabriel Ferry's *Coureur des Bois* (1853), quickly translated into German, Spanish, Danish, and English, was followed by the numerous novels of Gustave Aimard, with such enticing titles as *Les Trappeurs de l'Arkansas* (1858), *Le Chercheur de pistes* (1858), *L'Aigle Noir des Dakotahs* (1878). In England, Mayne Reid spun similar yarns—*The Rifle Rangers* (1850), *The Scalp Hunters* (1851), and so on. The German public was regaled with stirring tales of life on the American frontier by Karl Postl (who changed his name to Sealsfield) and Friedrich Gerstäcker, both of whom had travelled widely in North America. They were completely superseded, however, in the last decades of the century by the still more popular stories of Karl May, who had never been out of the fatherland when he wrote them, and whose vision of the Wild West remained essentially Teutonic. His several volumes recounting the exploits of Old Shatterhand and the pure-bred Apache, Winnetou, made and continue to make an irresistible appeal to the youth of Germany.

The widening of the cult of the fictional Indian was negatively reflected in the visual arts. Popular as they were with the reading public, the *Leatherstocking Tales* seem to have begotten fewer paintings and sculptures than *Atala*. There were, of course, illustrated editions, most notably that with plates by Alfred and Tony Johannot [293]. And that eccentric genius Rodolphe Bresdin was inspired to make a drawing and an etching by *The Last of the Mohicans*, from which he took his nickname, "Chien-Caillou" or "Chingachook" [300]. This novel and *The Prairie* also provided subjects for Salon painters, most of whose works are lost and whose names are all but forgotten—H.-F.-E. Philippoteaux (1833), Auguste Jugelet (1834), E.-A. Vanden Berghe (1835), and P.-J.-E. Castan (1845).[3] An equally obscure sculptor, Jean Schey, exhibited a statue of Uncas, *Le Cerf agile*, in 1839. Gustave Doré seems to have been the only notable artist to have turned his attention to these popular books, illustrating Gabriel Ferry's *Coureur des bois* in 1839 and re-using the same illustrations without any alteration for a novel by Gustave Aimard and later for two novels by Mayne Reid!

On the other hand, more artists than ever before painted the Indians from life. Some were amateurs or only semi-professionals, working in the tradition of eighteenth-century travellers, though with greater attention to detail [287, 294, 295]. But Karl Bodmer set a new standard for ethnographical illustration with the watercolours he made on a tour of the West in 1832-33. Indians taken to France were drawn by Louis-Léopold Boilly in 1827 [292] and by Delacroix in 1845 [298]. From the mid-century several artists visiting America painted them in their natural surroundings, sometimes sending their pictures back for exhibition to Europe, where there seems to have been a steady demand for authentic Indian subjects.[4]

To nineteenth-century Europeans, the true Indian appeared both stranger and more fascinating than fiction (significantly, the more successful novels, including those of Karl May, purported to describe the genuine experiences of palefaces among the redskins). Without losing any of the virtues associated with the "noble savage," he won admiration for what had previously been regarded as his vices. The atrocities committed by Indian auxiliaries of the British army during the Revolution and the War of 1812 horrified most Europeans. In about 1810 Goya painted scenes of cannibalism, apparently as demonstrations of the monsters produced when reason sleeps [290, 291]. But to the Romantics the cruelty of the Indians was simply an expression of unbridled passion. George Sand was thrilled by Catlin's "terrifyingly dramatic scenes of savage life" and transported by the performance of a scalp-dance [298]. That they were also a dying race—being swept away, as one writer remarked, "by whisky, smallpox and the aggression of the whites"—simply gave them a still more romantic aura. They represented, and to some extent still represent, the natural man valiantly but vainly fighting for survival against a mechanised, dehumanized modern world.

1. For Buffalo Bill's various Wild West shows, see C. T. Forman: *Indians Abroad 1493-1938*, Norman, Oklahoma, 1943, pp. 190-209.

2. Baudelaire's poem was to have formed part of a *Hiawatha* oratorio composed by Robert Stoepel, who asked Baudelaire to translate passages from Longfellow in 1860. It was first published in *Revue Contemporaine*, 28 February 1861 and included in subsequent editions of *Les Fleurs du Mal*.

3. These works are listed in the index of French Salon paintings compiled by Dr. Jon Whiteley (to whom I am indebted for permission to consult it) in the Department of the History of Art, Oxford.

4. Several sculptures of Indians were also made, notably a series of statues and reliefs by Ferdinand Pettrich, modelled between 1835 and 1843, now in the Vatican Museo Missionario Etnologico. A marble statue of an Indian girl by François-Joseph Bosio exhibited at the Paris Salon of 1845 is now in the Musée Calvet, Avignon (cf. *Baudelaire*, exhibition catalogue, Petit Palais, Paris, 1968-69, no. 123). Professor H. W. Janson kindly drew my attention to a bust of an Indian by Antoine-Augustin Préault, formerly in the Museum of Saint-Lô but destroyed in World War II.

George Heriot

Scottish, 1766-1844.

As a cadet at the Royal Military Academy at Woolwich, Heriot had instruction from Paul Sandby in topographical drawing. He went to Canada in 1792 in the civil service and in 1800 became deputy post-master general of British North America. He exhibited two Canadian views at the Royal Academy in London in 1797, and sketches and paintings of Canada survive from the following years, many of them made during his journeys of inspection from Halifax to Niagara. He also began a *History of Canada,* of which only the first volume was published (in 1804), and *Travels through the Canadas* (1807), illustrated with aquatints after his watercolours. He resigned in 1816, returned to England, and during the next few years travelled in France, Spain, Italy, and Austria, sketching and painting. The first of several projected volumes of *A Picturesque Tour* appeared in 1824.

George Heriot

287 *Calumet Dance*

Watercolour on paper laid down on card. ca. 1804-1805. Signed: *G H.* 8⅜ x 13 inches (21.2 x 32.9 cm.).

288 *Ceremonial Scalp Dance*

Watercolour on paper laid down on card. ca. 1804-1805. Signed: *G H.* 8¼ x 12¾ inches (20.9 x 32.3 cm.). Provenance: Joseph Pariseau; Henry Pariseau; Mrs. E. K. Burnett; Kennedy Galleries, Inc.
Windsor, Ontario, The Art Gallery of Windsor.

These two drawings belong to a group of nine now in the Art Gallery of Windsor, two of which are dated 1804 and 1805. They form a coherent series of studies of Indian life, all but one depicting dances. They may have been intended by Heriot as illustrations to a projected publication on the life and customs of the Indians, perhaps forming a supplement to his *History of Canada.*

Literature: J. Russell Harper: *Painting in Canada: A History,* Toronto, 1966, pp. 42, 44-46; Gerard Morisset: *L'Encyclopédie du Canada Francais,* Ottawa, 1960, vol. II, pp. 74-75; *Nine Watercolour Paintings by George Heriot (1766-1844) in the Collection of the Art Gallery of Windsor,* exhibition catalogue, Windsor, Ontario, 1967; D. Reid: *A Concise History of Canadian Painting,* Toronto, 1973, pp. 27-29.

Charles-Balthazar-Julien Févret de Saint-Mémin

French, 1770-1852.
Born at Dijon of a cultivated family belonging to the *petite noblesse,* Saint-Mémin went to America as a refugee from the French Revolution and in the hope of regaining possession of family property in Santo Domingo threatened by Toussaint L'Ouverture. Stranded in New York, he earned a living by drawing landscape views and portraits. He introduced the *physionotrace,* a recent French invention by which small profile portrait heads could faithfully and quickly be made and subsequently repeated. He became well known for his small medallion portrait heads, of which some eight hundred are in the Corcoran Gallery in Washington. They provide an unequalled panorama of Americans at this period. He also did larger, life-size or nearly life-size portrait heads in crayon on pink-tinted paper. He remained in America until 1814, when he returned to Dijon, where he was appointed director of the Museum. (See Pierre Quarré: *Charles-Balthazar-Julien Févret de Saint-Mémin,* exhibition catalogue, Dijon, 1965.)

Charles-Balthazar-Julien Févret de Saint-Mémin

289 *Shahaka* or *Le Grand Blanc*
Crayon on pink paper.1807. 19 x 13½ inches (48.2 x 34.3 cm.). Inscription: *Mandan / nommé Le Grand Blanc / venu Philad 1807 / accompagné Par M. Cheste, Lewis and Clark.* Provenance: Lewis and Clark papers, acquired by American Philosophical Society in 1817.
Philadelphia, American Philosophical Society.

The great east-west transatlantic expedition of Meriwether Lewis and William Clark, sent out by Jefferson in 1804 to reach the Pacific across the Rockies, returned in 1806, after successfully finding the mouth of the Columbia River. They brought back with them Shahaka, with his wife and child, and he was received by Jefferson in Washington in December 1806 and was a guest of honor at a dinner given to Lewis in 1807. This drawing was presumably made while Shahaka was in Philadelphia that year.

Francisco José de Goya y Lucientes

Spanish, 1746-1828.
Born at Fuente de Todos and trained
in Saragossa, Madrid, and Rome, Goya
very quickly established himself as the
leading painter in Spain. He became
Painter to the King in 1786 and Prin-
cipal Painter to the King in 1789. But
the powerful and increasingly bitter
and ferocious works for which he is
best known were made some years
later—*The Disasters of War* between
1808 and 1814, *The 3rd May* in 1814,
and the Black Paintings after 1819. In
1824 he went into voluntary exile at
Bordeaux.

Francisco José de Goya y Lucientes

290 *Cannibals Dismembering a Victim*

Oil on panel. ca. 1812. 12¹⁵⁄₁₆ x 18⁷⁄₁₆
inches (32.8 x 46.8 cm.). Provenance:
Jean Gigoux (by 1867), who be-
queathed it to the Musée des Beaux-
Arts, Besançon.
Besançon, Musée des Beaux-Arts.

Francisco José de Goya y Lucientes

291 *Cannibals*

Oil on panel. ca. 1812. 13 x 18⁹⁄₁₆
inches (32.7 x 47 cm.). Provenance:
Jean Gigoux (by 1867), who be-
queathed it to the Musée des Beaux-
Arts, Besançon (1896).
Besançon, Musée des Beaux-Arts.

This painting and its companion [290]
have been variously dated and titled,
but they have always been associated
with Canada. Goya's source of inspiration is unknown. When first recorded,
in 1867, they were titled *Archevèque de
Quebec* and *J'en ai mangé*. However,
the first archbishop of Quebec, Mgr.
de Plessis, died a natural death in 1819.
Later they were thought to depict
Gabriel Lallement and Jean de Brébeuf
of the Jesuit Mission in Canada, who
were tortured and killed (but not

eaten) by the Iroquois in 1649. A print of these Jesuit Mission martyrdoms by the Indians was issued in Paris in 1664 [108], but it bears no pictorial relationship to Goya's paintings, which, indeed, have no specifically Indian details—the cannibals even have hair on their faces and bodies, unlike Indians. However, a drawing by Goya of *American Indians Capturing a Monk* (Brod Gallery, London), which formed part of an album dated ca. 1812, has clear affinities with these paintings, and in the drawing the figures are identified as Indians by feather head-dresses. Two paintings in the Villagonzalo collection in Madrid, entitled *Killing of One of the Victims* and *Orgy by the Bonfire* are of the same dimensions and appear to have formed part of a group with [290] and [291].

Literature: C. Yriarte: *Goya*, Paris, 1867, p. 151; A. Estignard: *Jean Gigoux, sa vie, ses oeuvres, ses collections*, 1895, p. 110; V. von Loga: *Francisco de Goya*, Berlin, 1903, nos. 581, 582; A. F. Calvert: *Goya*, London, 1908, nos. 46, 47; A. L. Mayer: *Francisco de Goya*, London, 1924, nos. 706, 707; X. Desparmet Fitzgerald: *L'Oeuvre Peint de Goya*, Paris, 1928-50, vol. I, nos. 249, 250, vol. II, p. 307; F. J. Sánchez Cantón: *Vida y Obras de Goya*, Madrid, 1951, p. 115; A. Malraux: *Saturn. An Essay on Goya*, London, 1957, p. 106; J. A. Gaya Nuño: *La Pintura Española fuera de España*, Madrid, 1958, nos. 1083, 1084; *Goya and his Times*, exhibition catalogue, Royal Academy, London, 1963-64, nos. 103, 104; P. Gassier and J. Wilson: *Ouevre et Vie de Francisco Goya*, Paris-London-New York, 1970, nos. 922, 923; J. Gudiol Richart: *Catalogo analitico de las pinturas de Goya*, Barcelona, 1970, nos. 475, 476; *Goya*, exhibition catalogue, Mauritshuis, The Hague, 1970, nos. 23, 24.

Louis-Léopold Boilly

French, 1761-1845.
After working in Douai and Arras, Boilly settled in Paris in 1785 and from 1791 onwards exhibited at the Salon. He survived the Revolution but went into eclipse after 1830. Primarily a portrait and anecdotal *genre* painter, he is now admired for his crisp and elegantly painted scenes from Parisian bourgeois life.

Louis-Léopold Boilly (after)

292 *Osages*

Lithograph coloured by hand. Signed and dated: *L. Boilly 1827* and *S. Lith*

de Delpech. 14¹⁵⁄₁₆ x 10⅝ inches (38 x 27 cm.). Inscription: *Peuplade sauvage de L'Amérique Septentrionale, dans l'Etat du Missouri / arrivés a Paria* [sic] *le 13 Aout 1827.*
Paris, Bibliothèque Nationale, Cabinet des Estampes.

An Osage Indian had visited France in 1725, and of course many others of other tribes had been there by the early nineteenth century, but the group of six Osages who arrived in 1827 aroused greater interest than any before. This may have been partly because the first French translation of *The Last of the Mohicans* appeared a few months before their arrival, but it must also have been because of their "promotion" by David Delauney and Paul Loise, who brought them from America. They were fêted at Le Havre, where they landed in July, and in Rouen, while in Paris they became the rage. Crowds gathered outside their hotel in the rue de Rivoli, they were entertained by the *noblesse,* applauded at the opera, received by the minister of foreign affairs, and presented to Charles X at Saint Cloud. Crowds assembled to watch their ascent in a balloon. Several prints of them were issued, and a booklet entitled *Six Indiens Rouges de la Tribu des Grands Osages ! Arrivés du Missouri au Havre, le 27 Juillet, 1827, sur le Navaire Américan "New England," Cap. Hunt* ran into several editions. However, public interest waned by the end of the summer, and, after being toured through the Netherlands, Germany, and Italy, they were almost abandoned by their promotors, and a public subscription had to be raised for their repatriation. The party consisted of Kihegashugah or Little Chief, a prince of the blood and probably a descendant of the Osage who had visited France a century earlier; Washingsahba or Black Spirit; Minkchatahook or Young Soldier; Marcharkitahtoonhah or Big Soldier, also called The Orator; and two women, Myhanghah and Gretomih. Kihegashugah, Minkchatahook, and Gretomih are portrayed in the print exhibited. (See C. T. Foreman: *Indians Abroad 1493-1938,* Norman, 1943, pp. 132-146.)

The print exhibited was plate 89 in Boilly's *Recueil des grimaces,* in which all but this plate and plate 90 (also of Osages) are caricatures. The lithographer, Delpech, was presumably a relation of the lithographer François-Séraphin Delpech (1778-1825).

Literature: H. Harrisse: *L.-L. Boilly peintre dessinateur et lithographe sa vie et son oeuvre 1761-1845,* Paris, 1898, pp. 212-213.

Tony Johannot

German-French, 1803-1852. Johannot and his brother Alfred (1800-1837) were among the most popular book illustrators of their time in France. Of French origin, they were born at Offenbach-am-Main, where their father, François, established a silk factory, but were taken by him to Paris in 1806. They often worked in collaboration, illustrating the complete works of Walter Scott (1826), James Fenimore Cooper (1827), Chateaubriand (1832), Rousseau (1832), and Byron (1833), as well as single novels by Balzac and Victor Hugo and volumes of poetry by Lamartine and others. They also supplied illustrations for periodicals, including *Annales romantiques.* Oil paintings, watercolours, and drawings by them were exhibited in the Salon. They were both much admired by the Romantic writers. Tony was very prolific, drawing more than three thousand vignettes for 150 books.

Tony Johannot

293 *Illustration to James Fenimore Cooper:* The Last of the Mohicans

Engraving. 1827. Signed: *Dessiné et gravé à l'eau forte par Tony Johannot.* 4¾ x 3¼ inches (12.1 x 8.4 cm.). Paris, Bibliothèque Nationale.

The Last of the Mohicans was the novel which made Fenimore Cooper's name in France, where a translation was published in 1826, only a few months after it had come out in America. Such was its success that in the following year the Parisian publishers Furne, Gosselin, et Cie. began to issue a *de luxe* edition of his complete works, illustrated by the Johannot brothers. It was no less admired by writers than by the general public. George Sand much preferred it to

Chateaubriand's *Atala,* seeing in it an epic quality and particularly relishing the "Homeric virtues," the "terrible heroism," and the "sublime barbarity" of the Indian characters. Balzac alluded to it in *La Cousine Bette*—"she became the Mohican whose snares are inescapable, whose thoughts are impenetrably dissembled, whose swift decisions are reached on the evidence brought by senses developed to perfect keenness."

The print exhibited is one of the two illustrations which Tony Johannot drew and engraved for the 1827 edition and showed in the Paris Salon in the same year. It depicts the death of Cora in the penultimate chapter.

Literature: A. Marie: *Alfred et Tony Johannot,* Paris, 1925, pp. 19, 87; M. M. Gibb: *Le roman de Bas-de-Cuir en France,* Paris, 1927, p. 128.

Peter Rindisbacher

Swiss-American, 1806-1834.

Rindisbacher was born at Eggiwil in Switzerland (Canton of Berne) and received some instruction in draughtsmanship from a local artist. In 1821 he emigrated with the rest of his family to Canada and made a number of drawings on the journey to Lord Selkirk's colony on the Red River. Here he was employed as a clerk in the fur trading office, but mixed with the Indians and soon acquired a reputation for his drawings of them, some of which were sent to England. After bad floods destroyed the work of the settlers at Red River in 1826, the Rindisbachers and twenty-three other Swiss families moved south into the United States, settling in southern Wisconsin. In 1829 he appears to have joined Caleb Atwater on his mission to make treaties with the Winnebago and other Indian tribes at Prairie du Chien. Later that year he settled in St. Louis and began

to sell drawings for reproduction in *The American Turf Register and Sporting Magazine*. In 1831 he advertised in the *St. Louis Times* that he was available to execute "Miniature and landscape paintings &c. on the most reasonable terms." His drawings and watercolours—of which 124 are recorded—are of considerable ethnographical interest. He seems to have been the first artist to have lived among the North American Indians, preceding Catlin, who copied his work on one occasion [295]. He died of cholera on 13 August 1834.

Peter Rindisbacher

294 *Interior of a Tipi*
Watercolours. ca. 1829-1834. Signed: *P. Rindisbacher*. 12 x 16 inches (30.4 x 40.5 cm.) approximately.
West Point, West Point Museum Collections, United States Military Academy.

Rindisbacher is the first artist who is known to have painted the interiors of Plains Indian tipis. A drawing by him in the Peabody Museum, Cambridge, Mass., shows a group of Indians with a white youth (presumably a self-portrait) and seems to have been made ca. 1824-25 near Red River. The drawing exhibited here is technically more skillful and rather later in date, probably worked up from an earlier sketch, but it is none the less accurate in the depiction of details. The Indians shown in it still wear traditional costume, although they have begun to trade with the whites. But the rifle carried by the man who holds a scalp in his other hand, the knife on the floor, the metal pot on the fire, and the tomahawk hanging on one of the tent poles are all of European origin.

Literature: G. L. Nute: "Peter Rindisbacher Artist" in *Minnesota History*, XIV
(1933), pp. 283-287; J. F. McDermott:
"Peter Rindisbacher Frontier Reporter"
in *The Art Quarterly*, XII (1949), pp. 134-
137; Karl Meuli: "Scythica Vergiliana" in
Schweizerisches Archiv für Volkskunde,
LVI (1960), pp. 173, 196; A. M. Josephy Jr.:
The Artist was a Young Man, Fort Worth,
1970, p. 38.

Peter Rindisbacher

295 *Blackfeet Hunting on Snowshoes*
Watercolours. Signed and dated: *P.
Rindisbacher. 1833.* 9¾ x 16⅛ inches
(24.8 x 41 cm.). Provenance: J. William Middendorf III, New York; Kennedy Galleries Inc., New York, from
whom it was acquired in 1966.
Fort Worth, Texas, Amon Carter
Museum.

This drawing shows Indians hunting
buffalo in early spring, when the snow
is still hard enough to bear men wearing snowshoes, but the animals if
driven into a drift break through and
cannot run. The scene was described
in a letter about Rindisbacher's work
published in the *American Turf Register*, July, 1830 (cf. J. F. McDermott:
"Peter Rindisbacher Frontier Reporter" in *The Art Quarterly*, XII
[1949], p. 140). Two other drawings
by Rindisbacher of this subject are
known, in the Peabody Museum, Cambridge, Mass., and the West Point Museum. They are all scrupulously accurate in their depiction of the method of
hunting and details of costume, including the snowshoes. George Catlin, who
never spent a winter with the Indians,
seems to have derived his better known
painting (Smithsonian Institution,
Washington, D.C.) and lithographs of
the subject (in *North American Indian
Portfolio*, London, 1844) from Rindisbacher—but Catlin inaccurately
showed the Indians wearing ceremonial costume (cf. Karl Meuli: "Scythica
Vergiliana" in *Schweizerisches Archiv
für Volkskunde*, LVI [1960], pp. 140,
192-193).

Literature: *The Kennedy Quarterly*, VI
(1966), p. 68; A. M. Josephy, Jr.: *The Artist was a Young Man*, Fort Worth, 1970,
p. 64.

P. Lormier

French, fl. 1837.

Nothing is known about P. Lormier, apart from his designs for *Les Mohicans,* 1837, of which the watercolour exhibited is one.

P. Lormier

296 *Indian with Pipe of Peace*

Watercolours. Signed and dated: *P. Lormier 1837.* 11⁵⁄₁₆ x 8⅜ inches (28.6 x 21.2 cm.).

Paris, Bibliothèque de l'Opéra.

This is one of the costume designs for the ballet-pantomime *Les Mohicans,* arranged by Guerra and performed on 5 July 1837 at the Académie Royale de Musique in Paris. James Fenimore Cooper's *Leatherstocking Tales* were very popular in Europe, and French translations appeared very soon after publication. However, in Europe it was the Indians and not Leatherstocking or Natty Bumppo who appealed. In *Les Mohicans* the Indians held the centre of the stage, although the frontiersmen were augmented by an English colonel, his daughter and her lover, and a dancing master named Jonathas. The Indians captured them and were preparing to eat them when Jonathas charmed them with his fiddle and kept them dancing until English troops arrived. (See Margaret Murray Gibb: *Le Roman de Bas-de-cuir en France,* Paris, 1927, pp. 192-193.)

Karl Bodmer

Swiss-French, 1809-1893.

Born at Riesbach in Switzerland, Bodmer was trained as an artist under his maternal uncle, Johann Jakob Meyer a watercolourist and etcher, then briefly in Paris. He began his career by drawing views of the Rhine and Moselle engraved by his elder brother Rudolf. In 1832 he went to North America as draughtsman to Prince Maximilian zu Wied (1782-1867), a naturalist who had visited Brazil in 1815-1817 and published an account of his travels in 1820. Prince Maximilian, accompanied by a personal attendant named Dreidoppel and Bodmer, landed at Boston in July 1832. During the following weeks Bodmer visited Providence, New York, Philadelphia, the interior of Pennsylvania, and the Allegheny mountains. While Prince Maximilian spent the winter at New Harmony, Indiana, Bodmer made a visit to New Orleans. In the spring of 1833 the three travellers went by steamer down the Ohio and Mississippi rivers pausing near St. Louis where Bodmer inspected the collection of paintings by George Catlin at the home of Benjamin O'Fallon (nephew of General Clark). They then travelled up-river to Fort Osage, Belle Vue (an American Fur Company trading post), Fort Lookout, Fort Pierre, Fort Clark, Fort Union, and Fort McKenzie where they witnessed a battle between two Indian tribes. The return journey began in September, and they spent the winter at Fort Clark. In May 1834 they returned to St. Louis where Bodmer again saw Catlin's paintings. By way of the Mississippi and Ohio they then travelled to New York whence they sailed back to Europe. While in North America, Bodmer made numerous water-colour sketches of Indians and landscapes (a large collection of them, belonging to the Northern National Gas Company, is in the Joslyn Mu-

seum, Omaha) on which he based the finished drawings to be engraved and published in an atlas illustrating Prince Maximilian's two-volume book *Reise in das Innere Nord-Amerika in den Jahren 1832 bis 1834* (Coblenz, 1839-41). In drawing these illustrations he seems also to have made use of the several North American Indian artifacts taken to Europe by Prince Maximilian (acquired by the King of Prussia in 1844 and now in the Museum für Völkerkunde, Berlin; cf. Horst Hartmann: *Die Plains-und Prärieindianer Nordamerikas,* Berlin, 1973). After completing this work Bodmer seems to have lost interest in the Indians; when asked by an American publisher in 1850 to provide a series of illustrations of frontier life, he turned the commission over to Jean-François Millet [301]. The rest of his long career was devoted mainly to painting scenes in the Forest of Fontainebleau, several of which were exhibited at the Paris Salon from 1850. Having settled in France soon after returning from America, he bought a house at Barbizon in 1856, became a naturalized French subject, and was made a chavalier of the Legion of Honour in 1876.

THE TRAVELLERS MEETING WITH MINATARRE INDIANS

297A *The Travellers Meeting with Minatarre Indians Near Fort Clark*

Aquatint and etching. 1840. Signed: *K. Bodmer pinx. ad nat.* and *Alex Manceau sculp.* 17⅝ x 24⅛ inches (44.7 x 61.3 cm.).

297B *The Interior of the Hut of a Mandan Chief*

Aquatint and etching with stipple. 1840. Signed: *Carl Bodmer pinx. ad nat.* and *Desmandryl sculp.* 17¾ x 24¼ inches (45 x 61.5 cm.).

297C *Pehriska-Ruhpa. Moennitarri Warrior in the Costume of the Dog Danse*

Aquatint and etching coloured by hand. 1840. Signed: *Ch. Bodmer pinx. ad nat.* and *René Rollet sc.* 24⁹⁄₁₆ x 17⁹⁄₁₆ inches (61.7 x 44.6 cm.).

These prints come from the atlas of eighty-two engravings published to illustrate Prince Maximilian zu Wied's account of his travels in North America. They are among the most revealing images ever made of the Plains Indians —the fruit of a unique collaboration between a well informed ethnologist and a highly talented painter. Although Bodmer spent much less time among the Indians than Rindisbacher [294, 295] and George Catlin, whose early works he had seen, he was able to illustrate their appearance, surroundings, and customs with greater fidelity and artistic accomplishment. The first of the prints exhibited (A) shows Maximilian and two Europeans (presumably his attendant Dreidoppel and Bodmer) encountering outside the palisade of Fort Clark a group of Hidatsa (or Minitari as Maximilian called them), one of whom has ac-

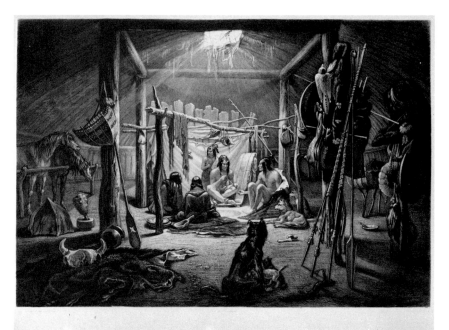

THE INTERIOR OF THE HUT OF A MANDAN CHIEF

quired a top-hat which he has decked
with feathers. The next (B) shows the
interior of a Mandan lodge with a
group of Indians seated around the
central hearth, their dogs and horses,
their hunting and war equipment all
carefully delineated. Pehriska-Ruhpa
(C) was a member of a Hidatsa league
of warriors known as "The Dogs."
Wearing a magnificently elaborate
feather head-dress, strings of glass
beads, the tail of a prairie wolf (symbol
of courage in battle) attached to his
ankle, he carries his bow and arrows in
one hand and a rattle in the other. Bodmer persuaded him to pose for several
days while he painted his portrait. His
depiction of the Mandan dance to attract buffalo (D) was worked up in
Europe from sketches made on the
spot though it vividly conveys a sense
of the frantic rhythm of the dance accompanied by the wailing of pipes, the

PEHRISKA-RUHPA.

297D *Bison-Dance of the Mandan Indians in Front of their Medicine Lodge*

Aquatint and etching. 1840. Signed: *K. Bodmer pinx. ad nat.* and *Alex Manceau sculp.* 17⅜ x 24 inches (43.7 x 60.9 cm.).

297E *Offering of the Mandan Indians*

Aquatint. 1840. Signed: *Dessiné d'après nature par Ch. Bodmer.* and *Gravé par Himely.* 17¾ x 24⁷⁄₁₆ inches (45 x 62 cm.). Inscriptions: each print is inscribed with the following—its title in German, French, and English (the English titles are given above); *Coblenz, bei J. Hölscher;* the plate number (XXVI, 19, 28, 18, and XIV respectively); the names of the printers (A, B, C, and E being *Imp. de Bougeard* and D being *Imp. de Chardon aine et Aze*) and of the English and French publishers: *London, published by Ackermann & Co. 96 Strand* and *Paris, Arthus Bertrand, editeur.*
Fort Worth, Amon Carter Museum of Western Art.

beating of drums, firing guns, and raucous whooping. But Bodmer was no less successful in giving an impression of the vast extent and immemorial silence of the Great Plains, as in his eerie depiction of the "offerings of the Mandan Indians" (E). The Mandan were seriously depleted by smallpox after the middle of the nineteenth century.

Literature: Bernard De Voto: *Across the Wide Missouri,* Boston, 1947, pp. 401-6; J. T. Flexner: *That Wilder Image* (1962), New York, 1970, pp. 74-7; Marshall B. Davidson: "Carl Bodmer's Unspoiled West" in *American Heritage,* XIV, no. 3 (April 1963), pp. 43-65; John C. Ewers: *Artists of the Old West* (1965), New York, 1973, pp. 86-97.

Eugène Delacroix
French, 1798-1863.

298 *A Study of Indians*

Pen and india ink. 1845. 7¾ x 12¼ inches (19.5 x 31 cm.). Stamped *E.D.* (Lugt 838a). Provenance: Presumably Delacroix Sale 1864, part of lot 652; Berheim-Jeune; Moreau-Nélaton. Geneva, Jean-Pierre Durand Collection.

Delacroix greatly admired the Indian tribal dances performed in Catlin's "Indian Gallery" at the Salle Valentino in Paris in 1845. He saw them with George Sand, who wrote a vivid account of both Catlin's pictures and the Indians, whom she also met off-stage ("Les Sauvages de Paris" in *Le Diable à Paris*, Paris, 1846). It was a spectacle "to impassion our artists," George Sand wrote. As the warriors in war paint burst into the room, her imagination transported her into the most lurid scenes of *The Last of the Mohicans*. Then to the sounds of strange instruments the dance began; one of the warriors, who seemed gigantic in his terrible garb, rushed forward, shaking his bow and tomahawk.

Others followed him; some throwing off their cloaks and showing their panting breasts and their arms as supple as snakes were still more terrifying. A kind of delirious rage seemed to transport them; raucous cries, barks, roars, shrill whistles and the war-cry which the Indian makes by putting his fingers on his lips and which uttered far off in the deserts freezes the strayed traveller with fear, interrupted the song creating an infernal concert. A cold sweat came over me; I believed I was witnessing the real scalping of some vanquished enemy or some still more horrible torture. Of all that was in front of me I saw nothing but the redoubtable actors and my imagination placed them in their true setting, under ancient trees by the light of a fire burning the flesh of victims, far from all human help: for these were not men that I saw but demons of the desert, more dangerous and implacable than wolves or bears among whom I would gladly have sought refuge.

Delacroix's reactions were rather less emotional, and in a letter to Louis Planet he compared the Indians to ancient Greeks. "The chief brandishing his lance is Ajax defying the Gods," he wrote. "In the scalp-dance, the women leaping on their toes with such noble and mysterious poise, and holding the lance with the scalp on top, recall the Panathenaic Virgins of Phidias." Later he made several drawings of the Ob-

jiwas who performed in Catlin's show after the original Iowas had returned to America. (Cf. Robert N. Beetem: "George Catlin in France, His Relationship to Delacroix and Baudelaire" in *The Art Quarterly*, XXIV (1961), pp. 129-145.) The drawing exhibited seems to represent an incident in a scalp-dance: another of Indians in relaxed poses is in the Cabinet des Dessins of the Louvre (RF 9 311). Both probably formed part of a group of drawings of Indians included in the Delacroix sale in 1864.

Literature: M. Sérullaz: *Mémorial de l'Exposition Eugène Delacroix organisée à l'occasion du centenaire de la mort de l'artiste*, Paris, 1963, p. 260, no. 351.

Alfred Boisseau

French-American, 1823-1901.
Boisseau studied at the Ecole des
Beaux-Arts in Paris from 1838 and was
also a pupil of Paul Delaroche. He exhibited at every Salon from 1842 until
1848, sending paintings from New Orleans to the 1848 Salon, for by then he
had left France for America. Between
1849 and 1852 he lived in New York,
exhibiting at The National Academy
of Design and at the American Art
Union. Towards the end of 1852 he
settled in Cleveland, where he advertised his talents as a portrait and landscape painter and as an art teacher and
dealer. He left Cleveland in about 1859
and settled in Montreal as a portrait
painter. He died in Buffalo, New York.

Alfred Boisseau

299 *Louisiana Indians Walking Along
a Bayou*

Oil on canvas. 1847. Signed and dated:
Al Boisseau 1847. 24 x 40 inches
(60.8 x 101.4 cm.). Provenance: Dr.
Isaac M. Cline, New Orleans; William
E. Groves, New Orleans, 1956.
New Orleans, New Orleans Museum
of Art, Gift of Mr. and Mrs. William
E. Groves.

This painting was exhibited at the
1848 Salon in Paris as *Marche d'Indiens de la Louisiane*, together with
other paintings Boisseau had sent back
from New Orleans: *La Créole, Le
Barbier nègre*, and a number of New
Orleans portraits. The scene is somewhat reminiscent of that described by

Harriet Martineau in *Society in America* (1837):

> The squaws went by, walking one
> behind the other, with their hair,
> growing low on the forehead, loose,
> or tied back on the head . . . These
> squaws carried large Indian baskets
> on their backs, and shuffled along,
> barefooted, while their lords paced
> before them, well mounted; or, if
> walking, gay, with blue and red
> clothing and embroidered leggings,
> with tufts of hair at the knees, while
> pouches and white fringes dangled
> about them. They looked like grave
> merry-andrews; or, more still, like
> solemn fanatical harvest men going
> out for largess. By eight o'clock they
> had all disappeared; but the streets
> were full of them again the next
> morning.

Literature: E. Bellier de la Chavignerie
and L. Auvray: *Dictionnaire Général des
Artistes de l'Ecole Française*, Paris, 1882,
vol. I, p. 112; *Mississippi Panorama*, ex-
hibition catalogue, City Art Museum of
St. Louis, St. Louis, 1949, p. 67; *Louisiana
Indians 12,000 Years*, exhibition catalogue,
Louisiana State Museum, New Orleans,
1966, p. 28; *The Painter and the New
World*, Montreal Museum of Fine Arts,
Montreal, 1967, no. 298; *The Louisiana
Landscape 1800-1969*, Anglo-American
Art Museum, Louisiana State University,
Baton Rouge, 1969, no. 10; Martin and
Margaret Wiesendanger: *Louisiana Paint-
ers and Paintings from the Collection of
W. E. Groves*, New Orleans, 1971, p. 15;
J. Burt and R. Ferguson: *Indians of the
Southeast: Then and Now*, Nashville,
1973, p. 129; T. H. Watkins: *Mark
Twain's Mississippi*, Palo Alto, 1974, p.
39; W. H. Gerdts: *Revealed Masters 19th
Century American Art*, New York, 1974.
pp. 25, 56, 135.

Rodolphe Bresdin

French, 1822-1885.

The son of a tanner and copper-smith,
Rodolphe Bresdin was born at In-
grande (between Angers and Nantes).
At the age of 17 he went to Paris where
he soon became a member of the "Bo-
hemian" world of writers and artists.
Much impressed by James Fenimore
Cooper's *Last of the Mohicans* he took
to calling himself Chingachook or
Chien-Caillou, a French corruption of
this name—and thus provided both the
central character and title for Champ-
fleury's novel of 1847. As an artist he
was self-trained but had made a very
close study of the great North European printmakers of the past, especially Dürer and Rembrandt. His earliest print is dated 1839 though it was
not until the late 1840s that his highly
personal style was developed in drawings, etchings, and lithographs of an extraordinary nightmarish fantasy and
complexity executed with miniscule
delicacy. His life was that of a vagrant
and he travelled about France on foot.

In 1861 illustrations by him were published in the *Revue Fantaisiste*. Some
years later he won a competition for a
Canadian bank-note design and went
to Canada but in 1876 returned to
France. He is said to have spent his last
years as a Paris street-sweeper by the
Arc de Triomphe. His work was much
admired by Victor Hugo who helped
him financially, and also by J. K. Huy-
mans who vividly described it in *A Re-
bours* (1884) and by Odilon Redon. It
was re-discovered by C. R. Roger-
Marx in the later 1920s.

Rodolphe Bresdin

300 La Torture

Pen and brown ink with brown and
black washes. ca. 1850-1870. Signed
with an oval blind stamp: *RB ft.*
4 x 6³⁄₁₆ inches (10.1 x 15.7 cm.).
Provenance: Paul Bresdin (son of the
artist); P. A. Regnault; L. Baskin.
Boston, Mass., R. M. Light & Co.

In 1850 Bresdin made an etching of
The Death of Uncas inspired by James
Fenimore Cooper's *The Last of the
Mohicans*. No precise source has been
found for the drawing exhibited
though the naked figures are clearly
intended to represent Red Indians.

Literature: D. van Gelder: *Rodolphe
Bresdin* (forthcoming).

Jean François Millet

French, 1814-1875.

Millet was the son of a peasant and is famous for his paintings of peasant life. Trained in Cherbourg and later in Paris under Delaroche, he attracted little attention until 1848, when he exhibited *The Winnower,* which was a great success in that year of revolution and was bought by Alexandre Ledru-Rollin, a minister in the revolutionary government. It was given a Socialist interpretation, as were several later paintings, though Millet always protested that he was entirely unpolitical. In 1849 he settled at Barbizon and remained there for the rest of his life. His two most famous paintings, *The Gleaners* and *The Angelus,* were painted in 1857 and 1858-59 and were among the best known and best loved paintings of the nineteenth century.

Jean François Millet

301 *The American Mazeppa*

Lithograph. 1852. 14⁵⁄₁₆ x 20¾ inches (36.4 x 52.8 cm.). Inscription: *Composed & Drawn on stone by K. Bodmer. Printed by L'emercier Paris.* New York, The Metropolitan Museum of Art, Gift of the Museum of the American Indian, The Heye Foundation.

This print represents an incident in the Revolutionary War. Simon Butler, one of the first settlers of Kentucky, was taken prisoner by the Indians, who lashed him to an unbridled and unbroken horse and turned it loose — as had been done to Mazeppa. (Ivan Stepanovitch Mazeppa was a Polish nobleman, born about 1645. The story of his being lashed to a wild horse when a page to Casimir V, king of Poland, was first told by Voltaire, and became famous as the subject of a very popular and frequently illustrated poem by Byron.) Simon Butler survived his ordeal. The horse was unable to shake him off and eventually returned. Butler escaped a few days later.

This was one of the subjects included in a commission given by an American publisher to Karl Bodmer in 1850. A considerable number of prints were envisaged, perhaps as many as a hundred, to illustrate a work on the colonial wars or the works of James Fenimore Cooper and Washington. Bodmer later wrote: "As I could not undertake such a task, requiring so many figures, I asked Millet if he would make them provided I furnished the sketches and all the needed materials. He gladly consented." However, the American publisher "was not pleased at the substitution" when he found Millet at work on the drawings and withdrew the commission. Four of the drawings were later published as lithographs by Goupil in 1852, entitled *Annals of the United States Illustrated*

— The Pioneers. They depicted *The Rescue of the Daughter of Daniel Boone and Richard Callaway, The Capture of the Daughters of Daniel Boone and Richard Callaway, The Leap of Major McCullough,* and the print exhibited here.

Although these prints are stated in the inscriptions to have been "Composed and Drawn on stone by K. Bodmer" and certainly began as a collaboration in which Millet was to draw the figures and Bodmer the landscapes and horses, there can be little doubt that Millet alone worked on the print exhibited and made the drawing for it, since Bodmer explicitly confirmed this in a letter to Etienne Arago of 1889, quoted by Delteil.

Literature: L. Delteil: *Le peintre-graveur (19e et 20e siècles),* (1906), nos. 26, 99; De Cost Smith: "Jean François Millet's Drawings of American Indians" in *Century Magazine,* 80, no. 2, May, 1910; J. Laran and J. Adhémar: *Bibliothèque Nationale, Département des Estampes, Inventaire au fonds français après 1800,* III (Paris, 1942), pp. 17, 20; B. P. Draper: "American Indians — Barbizon Style" in *Antiques,* 44, no. 3, September, 1943, pp. 108-110; [Anonymous]: "From Fontainebleau to the Dark and Bloody Ground" in *The Month at Goodspeed's Book Shop,* 16, nos. 6-7, March-April 1945, pp. 151-155.

Jules-Emile Saintin

French, 1829-1894.
Saintin was a pupil of Michel-Martin
Drölling and François-Edouard Picot
in Paris and began exhibiting at the
Salon in 1848. In 1853 he went to
America and became an associate of
the National Academy of Design in
New York in 1861. In 1865 he returned
to Paris, where he was patronised by
Princess Mathilde. He continued to exhibit at the Salon while in America,
mainly portraits but also scenes of contemporary life (*Rag Pickers* or *Chif-
fonière de New York*, 1859, and *Pony
Express, Transport de la malle de
Placerville, Californie, à Saint-Joseph,
Missouri*, 1863) and also Indian subjects (*Femme de colon enlevée par des
indiens peaux rouges pendant l'au-
tomme de 1863*, 1864, and *La Piste de
Guerre, scène de la vie indienne*, 1865).

Jules-Emile Saintin

302 *Indian on Horseback*

Red chalk. ca. 1860. 11 x 14⁹⁄₁₆ inches
(28 x 37 cm.).
Blérancourt, Musée National de la
Coopération Franco-Américaine.

This is one of a group of drawings of
American subjects by Saintin now in
the museum at Blérancourt.

Literature: R. Lacour-Gayet: *Musée de
Blérancourt*, Paris, 1966, pl. 83.

Frank Buchser

Swiss, 1828-1890.

Buchser was born at Feldbrunnen near Solothurn and, after leaving school, worked first for an organ builder in Solothurn and then in a pianoforte factory in Bern. In Florence in 1847, while on his way to Rome to join the Papal Swiss Guard, he began to draw and determined to become a professional artist. While serving with the Swiss Guard he studied at the Accademia di San Luca in Rome. In 1849 he fought in Garibaldi's army. He then went to study under Jean-Victor Schnetz in Paris and Gustaaf Wappers in Antwerp. In the following years he visited Spain, England, and Paris (where he came under the influence of Gustave Courbet), travelled through Morocco 1857-58, and was in England again in 1861-63. The next few years he spent in Switzerland, where he took part in founding the Gesellschaft schweizerische Maler und Bildhauer.

In 1865 a group of Swiss radicals planned to commission a painting for the parliament house in Bern to celebrate the end of the American Civil War as a tribute from the only European republic to the United States, and also as an expression of their desire to democratize the Swiss constitution according to the American pattern. As the most eminent Swiss artist of the day, and also as a political radical, Buchser was the obvious choice. And, although he received no official commission, he set off for America. He arrived in New York in May 1866 and then went to Washington, where he very soon met all the leading personalities, including President Johnson and the secretary of state, William H. Seward. His first American paintings were a portrait of his fellow-countryman Johann August Sutter (owner of the land on which gold had been found in California in 1848) and a group of black shoeshine boys, which was praised in the Washington newspapers. In August he joined an expedition led by General William Sherman and his brother, Senator John Sherman, to explore the Far West, travelling through the as yet undeveloped prairies as far as Fort Laramie. On this journey he made numerous sketches, some of which he worked up into finished pictures after his return to Washington in October. He also made further paintings of the black population. In the summer of 1867 he went to Woodstock, Virginia, but here his artistic interest in the former slaves aroused suspicion, and he was denounced in the local press and obliged to leave the town. Next spring he went to New York, made a tour of the Great Lakes in search of Indian subjects, spent the fall in Detroit, then went on to Chicago and St. Louis, stayed with General Sherman, and painted his portrait (Kunstmuseum, Bern). In April 1869 he stayed with William H. Seward, whose portrait he painted at Auburn [335]. That October he went to Lexington, where he painted General Robert E. Lee—the most notable of his American portraits [336].

By this time Buchser seems to have abandoned his plan to paint a large commemorative picture for Bern. To continue his study of the black people in the South, he settled in Charlottesville, where he painted, among other works [320], *The Ballad of Mary Blane*, which he regarded as the masterpiece of his American period (Museum der Stadt Solothurn). In October he appears to have gone to New York, where several of his pictures were exhibited at the Union League Club in April 1871, but he failed to find many buyers for them. From New York he recrossed the Atlantic in May. After his return to Switzerland he continued to make visits to various parts of Europe and North Africa until 1885.

Frank Buchser

303 *Indian Encampment on the Laramie River*

Oil on canvas. 1866. Signed and dated: *At Laramie 31. Aug 66 F.B.* $13\frac{13}{16}$ x $19\frac{3}{4}$ inches (35 x 50 cm.). Provenance: Inherited from the artist by his brother Dr. Josef Buchser, who gave it to the Museum, 1896.
Basel, Öffentliche Kunstmuseum.
Colorplate 7.

This is one of the several sketches made by Buchser on a tour of the West with the brothers General William Sherman and Senator John Sherman in the late summer of 1866. A writer in the Washington *National Intelligencer,* 10 November 1866, reported:

> Mr. Buchser . . . has just returned from a journey into the far West and re-opened his studio in Metzerotti's Building. He is very enthusiastic in his descriptions of the wild grandeur of the country over which he has travelled and has brought home with him a valuable collection of sketches illustrative of the country and the people. His sketches of the Indians and the backwoodsmen are particularly picturesque and lifelike, displaying a fine appreciation of their habits and character.

Buchser was also praised for his Western scenes in the Baltimore *Catholic Mirror,* 6 April 1867:

> How little idea have most of us of the magnificence and beauty of our land! We read in the dailies of the Plains, Forts Kearney, Laramie &c., names inappropriate it is true and much better replaced by poetic Indian ones, and we associate them with such dreary dismal scenes; yet with what a charm to the eye of a foreigner have these glimpses of true nature. A spirit of enterprise too will soon work changes. "There is to be a railroad there," says the artist at our side, recalling us from our reverie, "and that will spoil all."

(Quotations from the artist's collection

303 Frank Buchser, *Indian Encampment on the Laramie River*. Kunstmuseum Basel.

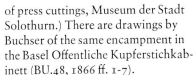

of press cuttings, Museum der Stadt Solothurn.) There are drawings by Buchser of the same encampment in the Basel Offentliche Kupferstichkabinett (BU.48, 1866 ff. 1-7).

Literature: H. Lüdeke: *Frank Buchsers amerikanische Sendung,* Basel, 1941, p. 31 and pl. 13.

Frank Buchser

304 *Chippewas on the Warpath*
Oil on canvas. ca. 1868. Signed: *F.B.*
13 x 27³⁄₁₆ inches (33 x 69 cm.).
Provenance: Inherited from the artist by his brother Dr. Josef Buchser, who gave it to the Museum in 1899. Solothurn, Museum der Stadt Solothurn, Besitz des Kunstvereins.

Buchser visited the Great Lakes in the summer of 1868, in search of subject matter for a large painting. He went first to Lake Superior but noted in a sketchbook: "all the storys of Indians in these quarters are when seen close, nothing at all. The full blood if found is utterly spoiled by the imitation of the whites, there costumes are more like the tasteless makserada of a beggar than an Indian, they can only be used as a stafage in a Landskip therefore let us make for the south" (Offentliche Kupferstichkabinett, Basel, BU.56.1867 /8 f. 50). He seems to have been rather more favourably impressed by Chippewas, whom he encountered in a reservation near Sault Ste. Marie and of whom he made drawings and oil sketches, though they appear only as staffage figures in his large, finished picture *The Rapids of Ste. Marie* (Museum der Stadt Solothurn), which he painted in Detroit in the fall of 1868. He probably painted *Chippewas on the Warpath* at the same time.

Literature: Peter Vignau-Wilberg: *Museum der Stadt Solothurn. Gemälde und Skulpturen,* Solothurn, 1973, p. 222.

INDIENS PEAUX-ROUGES

PELLERIN & Cie. imp.–edit.　IMAGERIE D'ÉPINAL. N° 781

Chef Crow (Corbeau) — Le Scalpe — Chefs Chayennes — Chef Sioux

Indien Naya — Chef Yute — Acteurs de la danse des Bisons — Chef Paunie — Indiens Mandans

Danse des Esprits — Sur le sentier de la guerre — Danse de guerre des Sioux

Guerrier Apache — Le Calumet —— Comanches au Conseil — Guerrier Apache

305 *Indiens Peaux Rouges*
France. Chromolithograph. 1891.
15 5/16 x 12 3/16 inches (38.9 x 28.3 cm.).
Inscription: *Pellerin & Cie imp. edit.*
and *Imagerie d'Epinal no. 781.*
Paris, Bibliothèque Nationale, Cabinet
des Estampes.

Pellerin was one of the best known
publishers of popular colour lithographs at Epinal, the town in central
France which gave its name to this
type of print, often made for *pantins*—
i.e. to be cut out and applied to pup-
pets. Prints of Indians were issued at
Epinal throughout the nineteenth century, usually in the traditional manner,
with feather head-dresses and skirts.
By the 1890s more accurate representations were demanded, as in the
exhibited print, where several tribes
are shown. The pair to this print
(Imagerie d'Epinal no. 782) is titled
*Les Derniers Peaux-Rouges (Insurrec-
tion des tribus cantonnés dans leurs
réserves de l'Ouest 1891)* and depicts
General Miles and United States soldiers as well as Indians.

XVII
Men and Brothers

"The Indians will perish in the same isolated condition in which they lived, but the destiny of the Negroes is in some measure interwoven with that of the Europeans," Alexis de Tocqueville prophecied in 1835. "These two races are fastened to each other without intermingling; and they are alike unable to separate entirely or to combine."[1] He was one of the few Europeans who advocated the abolition of slavery, while recognizing that it would create new and equally formidable problems. He foresaw how fateful the consequences would be for the two races in whose hands the future of American democracy rested. His remarks also serve as a reminder of the way in which the black people had, since the late eighteenth century, gradually emerged from the background and begun to play a significant part in the European vision of America.

Africans had reached the New World very soon after Europeans. It seems probable that personal slaves were taken to the West Indies by the Spaniards some years before 1505, when King Ferdinand had seventeen sent to the royal mines on Hispaniola. They were found capable of work which Spaniards were unwilling and Indians unable to do. In 1518 Charles V licenced the transporation of 4,000 more to the Indies, and from that date onwards the numbers steadily increased, reaching eventually many millions.[2] By 1830 the blacks formed about one-fifth of the entire population of the United States, far outnumbering the Indians. But of all this there was very little reflection in the visual arts. Not only were the black people rarely depicted by Europeans, but, on the few occasions they were, it was merely to add a touch of exoticism to the scene. Thus they appear gaily dressed as attendants to white masters, carousing merrily among themselves, or even happily cutting sugar canes [306]. And similar idyllic scenes of happy, contented slaves continued to be depicted in the nineteenth century [314].

A very different picture of their lot was presented by the Society for the Abolition of the Slave Trade, founded in 1787. Its emblem was a kneeling manacled slave, with the inscription: *Am I not a Man and a Brother*. Modelled in black and white jasper-ware at the Wedgwood factory, this was delicate enough to serve as the decoration for a hat or snuff-box [309]. But the abolitionists also issued the more disturbing engraved plan of a ship showing the inhuman conditions in which Africans were stowed on a transatlantic crossing. And the slave-ship was to haunt the European imagination, inspiring one of Joseph Turner's greatest paintings [315] and a savagely ironical late poem by Heinrich Heine—"Das Sklavenschiff." What would probably have been the great masterpiece of this theme—Jean Géricault's *Traite des Négres*—was unfortunately abandoned. However, there were numerous illustrations and prints, often accompanying written descriptions, of the atrocities committed on slaves in America, though none more horrific than those engraved by William Blake to illustrate J. G. Stedman's narrative of the suppression of the slave revolt in Surinam [310].

The British abolitionists were initially concerned mainly with the activities of their own compatriots in the West Indies. But opposition to slavery was often allied with, and sometimes an expression of, hostility to the United States. "How is it that we hear the loudest *yelps* for liberty among the drivers of negroes?" asked Dr. Johnson in his anti-American pamphlet, *Taxation no Tyranny* (1775). A French writer acidly commented in 1788: "The friends of justice and humanity will perhaps be astonished to learn that in the United States, in that asylum of peace, happiness and liberty, which has so often re-echoed to those sacred words 'all men are created equal' there are still today nearly seven hundred thousand slaves."[3] In the nineteenth century, as one country after another renounced slavery, its persistence in the United States seemed ever more anomalous, a subject on which every travel-writer felt bound to comment. Yet is was an American book, Harriet Beecher Stowe's *Uncle Tom's Cabin*, translated into twenty-three languages, that probably played the largest part in creating the image of America as a land of slavery.

Mrs. Beecher Stowe's illustrators—in both Europe and America—presented Uncle Tom as a gentle, docile, rather child-like creature, reminiscent of the Wedgwood medallion, very much the "humble friend" of little Eva [318, 319]. Like the book itself, they reveal a humanely patronising attitude, which helped to achieve abolition, yet militated against the establishment of a sound relationship between the black and white races afterwards. But these were the images of black people which appealed to the public on both sides of the Atlantic. Johann Heinrich Fuseli's slave calling down the wrath of heaven had few if any sequels [311]. Frank Buchser found few purchasers for his coolly realistic pictures of the conditions in which the black people of Virginia were living immediately after emancipation [320]. The life-size bronze statue of a proud and muscular liberated slave by an otherwise unknown Austrian sculptor named "Pezzicari," shown at the first centennial exhibition in Philadelphia in 1876, has mysteriously vanished without trace.[4]

1. A. de Tocqueville: *Democracy in America,* tr. H. Reeve (1835), ed. P. Bradley, New York, 1945, vol. I, p. 370.

2. The number of Africans taken to Brazil between 1559 and 1850 has been estimated variously between three and eighteen million; R. Konetzke: *America centrale e meridionale; I. La colonizzazione ispano-portoghese* (1965), Milan, 1968, pp. 71-81.

3. *Mercure de France,* 6 October, 1787, quoted by D. Echeverria: *Mirage in the West,* Princeton, 1968, p. 129.

4. E. Parry: *The Image of the Indian and the Black Man in American Art 1590-1900,* New York, 1974, p. 133.

306 *Slave Cutting Sugar Canes*
France. Watercolours. ca. 1770.
14⅕/16 x 9⅝ inches (38 x 24.5 cm.).
Inscription: *Negre domestique aux
Isles de l'Amerique coupant des
Cannes à Sucre.*
Paris, Bibliothèque Nationale, Cabinet
des Estampes.

Sugar cane was first introduced into
the West Indies by Columbus in 1493
from the Canaries, and sugar gradually
became the main West Indian export.
By the eighteenth century the islands
were supplying a constantly increasing
European demand for sugar. The plantations were worked with slave labour.

As a result many abolitionists in the
late eighteenth and early nineteenth
centuries renounced sugar for tea and
coffee. The watercolour exhibited
presents a somewhat rosy view of the
life of a slave on a West Indian plantation.

Le Masurier
French, fl. 1772-1774.
This artist is known only by a painting
of the freeing of St. Peter, signed and
dated 1772, in the church of St. Ger-
main-des-Près, Paris, and three recently discovered scenes of life on
Martinique, dated 1775 (see below).

Negre domestique aux Isles de l'Amerique coupant des cannes à sucre.

Le Masurier

307 *Black Slaves in Martinique*

Oil on canvas. Signed and dated: *Le Masurier pingebat in Martinicâ 1775.* 49¼ x 41¾ inches (125 x 106 cm.). Paris, Secrétariat d'Etat aux Départements et Territoires d'Outre-mer.

This idealised view of the life of slaves among the natural riches of Martinique is one of three paintings of the same year by Le Masurier—the others showing a white family with their black nurse in a very elegant interior and a white lady and girl visiting black people in their hut. They provide a vivid glimpse of French colonial life and had an additional interest, as they were painted during the childhood on Martinique of the future empress Josephine (born there in 1763). The French began to colonize Martinique in 1635 and, with their other islands in the West Indies, it provided their man source of sugar, coffee, and cotton throughout the later seventeenth and eighteenth centuries. It was captured by the British in 1762 but returned to France by the Treaty of Paris the next year.

Christian August Lorentzen

Danish, 1749-1828.

Lorentzen studied at the Copenhagen academy and then travelled in the Netherlands and France, 1779-82. After returning to Copenhagen he was elected to the academy (1784), of which he later became professor (1803) and eventually director (1809/10). He was very productive, painting portraits, *genre* and history paintings.

Christian August Lorentzen

308 *Homage to Benjamin Franklin*

Oil on canvas. ca. 1780. 23⅞ x 25⅝ inches (60.5 x 65 cm.).

Copenhagen, Royal Museum of Fine Arts.

Benjamin Franklin was one of the most stalwart opponents of slavery of his time in America and president of the Pennsylvania Abolition Society. Yet this painting by Lorentzen is one of the very few European images of him in this role. (An anonymous wax conversation piece shows him with Rousseau, Voltaire, and two children, one black, the other white; cf. C. C. Sellers: *Benjamin Franklin in Portraiture*, New Haven and London, 1962, p. 388.) Supporters of the American Revolution played down the prevalence of slavery and the need for a society to abolish it, at a time when many European abolitionists (e.g. Samuel Johnson and William Cowper) were anti-American. Josiah Wedgwood was a notable exception. On both sides of the Atlantic the Quakers, who played a major part in the Abolitionist movement, tended to adopt an attitude of pacifist neutrality to the war. But Franklin's opposition to slavery was determined both by his Quaker upbringing and his reading of the *philosophes.*

Lorentzen's picture, which shows the strong influence of Greuze in both colour and handling of paint—as well as in the portrayal of Franklin—was probably painted in Paris ca. 1780-82 or very shortly after Lorentzen returned to Denmark. Greuze's well-known portrait of Franklin was painted in 1777.

Literature: K. Madsen in *Kunstmuseets Aarskrift*, VI (1920), pp. 129-131; *C.A. Lorentzen*, exhibition catalogue, Thorvaldsens Museum, Copenhagen, 1971, no. 50.

William Hackwood

English, d. 1839.

As an "ingenious boy" who "has never had the least instruction," Hackwood was employed by Josiah Wedgwood from 1769 and soon became the chief modeller at the Etruria factory. His works included imitations of the antique, portrait cameos of Shakespeare, Garrick, George III and Queen Charlotte, Josiah Wedgwood and, probably, Benjamin Franklin. He also provided the models for the reliefs of allegorical and mythological subjects which were the largest made in jasperware.

William Hackwood

309 *Anti-Slavery Medallion*

Stoneware (Jasper-ware). 1787-1788. Marked with the impressioned inscription: *Wedgwood* O. Oval: 2⅛ x 2¹⁄₁₆ inches (5.4 x 5.2 cm.).
Inscription: *Am I Not a Man and a Brother?*
Merion, Pennsylvania, Buten Museum of Wedgwood.

The English Society for the Suppression of the Slave Trade, which was founded in 1787, adopted as its emblem the figure of a kneeling slave with the inscription: *Am I Not a Man and a Brother?* Josiah Wedgwood (1730-1795), founder of the famous Staffordshire pottery named after him, was a member of the committee, and he (or one of the artists he employed) may have been responsible for its design. Very shortly afterwards he employed William Hackwood to make a model of it for production as a black-and-white jasper-ware cameo. The first of these cameos was made before 29 February 1788, when Wedgwood wrote to Benjamin Franklin,

> I embrace the opportunity of a packet making up by my friend Philip to inclose for the use of yourself and friends a few Cameos on a subject which I am happy to acquaint you is daily more and more taking possession of men's minds on this side of the Atlantic as well as with you. It gives me great pleasure to be embarked on this occasion in the same great and good cause with you, and I ardently hope for the final completion of our wishes. This will be an epoch before unknown to the World, and while relief is given to millions of our fellow Creatures immediately the object of it, the subject of freedom will be more canvassed and better understood in the enlightened nations.

In his very appreciative reply, Franklin wrote that this image had an effect "equal to that of the best written pamphlet in procuring favour to those oppressed people."

Thomas Clarkson (1760-1846) later recorded the widespread diffusion of the cameos: "Some had them inlaid in gold on the lid of their snuff-boxes. Of the ladies, several wore them in bracelets, and others had them fitted up in an ornamental manner as pins for their hair. At length the taste for wearing them became general, and thus fashion . . . was seen for once in the honourable office of promoting the cause of justice, humanity and freedom."

Literature: T. Clarkson: *The History of the Rise, Progress, and Accomplishment of the Abolition of the Slave Trade by the British Parliament*, London, 1808, vol. II, pp. 191-192; A. Finer and G. Savage: *The Selected Letters of Josiah Wedgwood*, London, 1965, p. 311; R. C. Smith: "Liberty Displaying the Arts and Sciences; A Philadelphia Allegory by Samuel Jennings" in *Winterthur Portfolio*, II (1965), pp. 89-90; *The Black Presence in the Era of the American Revolution*, exhibition catalogue, National Portrait Gallery, Washington, D.C., 1973, no. 95; Elwood Parry: *The Image of the Indian and the Black Man in American Art*, New York, 1974, p. 48.

William Blake
English, 1757-1827.

310 *Illustration to John Gabriel
Stedman:* Narrative of a five
year's expedition against the
Revolted Negroes of Surinam . . .,
London, 1796, p. 110
Engraving. 1792. Signed: *Blake Sculpt.*
10 1/16 x 8 inches (25.5 x 20.2 cm.).
Inscription: *A Negro hung alive by the
Ribs to a Gallows* and *London, Pub-
lished Decr. 1st 1792. by J. Johnson,*

St. Paul's Church Yard.
Cleveland, Cleveland Public Library,
History Department.

John Gabriel Stedman (1744-1797)
was born in Holland, became a soldier,
served in the Scots brigade of the
Dutch army, and in 1772 went to
Surinam (Dutch Guiana), where, as a
captain, he played a part in putting
down a slave rebellion. The volume
exhibited is the first of two in which
he narrated his experiences in Surinam
and described in horrifying detail the
atrocious ways in which the slaves
were tortured to death. His sympathy
towards them was greatly sharpened
by his own love affair with a fifteen-
year-old slave girl, whose freedom he
was unable to purchase. He also provided an account of the flora and
fauna of the region. The text of the
book was completed by 1791 and consigned to the London publisher Joseph
Johnson, who commissioned several
different artists to engrave illustrations
after Stedman's drawings. Johnson
was at this time on friendly terms with
William Blake, who engraved some
sixteen plates for this book, delivering
them in two main batches, in December 1792 and December 1793 and a
single plate in 1794. The whole work

A Negro hung alive by the Ribs to a Gallows.

was not published until 1796. As none
of Stedman's drawings survives, it is
impossible to determine how closely
Blake's engravings corresponded with
them. The plates by Blake are, however, more forceful than the other
illustrations in the book. They have
the fluidity of line and something of
the hallucinatory quality of his original
work. The book made a profound
impression on him, and he incorporated several images from it in his
poem "Visions of the Daughters of
Albion," written and illuminated while
he was making the engravings and
published in 1793.

The volume is open at the illustration of the "Negro hung alive by the
ribs" who lived for three days without
murmuring and upbraided a flogged
fellow rebel for complaining. It is one
of the several plates in the book which
probably helped the abolitionists'
cause, though Stedman attacked the
abuses of slavery rather than the institution itself and included an illustration of a "contented" slave branded
with his initials.

Literature: A. G. B. Russell: *The Engravings of William Blake,* Boston, 1912, p.
162; D. V. Erdman: "Blake's Vision of
Slavery" in *Journal of the Warburg and
Courtauld Institutes,* XV (1952), pp. 242-
252; D. V. Erdman: *Blake: Prophet
Against Empire,* Princeton, 1954.

Johann Heinrich Fuseli

Swiss-English, 1741-1825.
Fuseli was born in Zurich but settled
in England in 1779, where he was
known as John Henry Fuseli. In 1761
he became a Zwinglian minister but
quickly abandoned the ministry for
literature and, later, for painting. He
made his name in London in 1782 with
The Nightmare and was elected an
Associate of the Royal Academy in
1788 and a full member in 1790. He
then began a series of huge paintings
illustrating Milton, with which he
hoped to achieve immortality. In 1803-
04 he illustrated Joel Barlow's patriotic
epic *The Columbiad*. He became
keeper of the Royal Academy in 1804.

Johann Heinrich Fuseli

311 *The Negro's Complaint*

Oil on canvas. 1806-1807. 35¾ x 28
inches (91 x 71 cm.). Provenance:
Professor Paul Ganz.
Zollikon, Switzerland, Collection of
Dr. Martin Hürliman.

Fuseli was commissioned to provide
eight illustrations for an edition of the
collected works of William Cowper—
a poet he greatly admired—issued in
two volumes in 1807 by the London
publisher Joseph Johnson [310]. In the
work exhibited he illustrated the
fourth and fifth stanzas of the anti-
slavery poem "The Negro's Complaint," which Cowper wrote in 1788:

> Is there, as ye sometimes tell us,
> Is there One who reigns on high?
> Has he bid you buy and sell us,
> Speaking from his throne, the sky?
> Ask him, if your knotted scourges,
> Matches blood-extorting screws,
> Are the means that duty urges,
> Agents of his will to use?
> Hark! he answers—Wild tornadoes,
> Strewing yonder seas with wrecks;
> Wasting towns, plantations,
>   meadows,

Are the voice with which he speaks.
He, forseeing what vexations
Afric's sons should undergo,
Fix'd their tyrants' habitations
Where his whirlwinds answer—No.

Fuseli had declared his opposition to slavery many years earlier in *Remarks on the Writing and Conduct of J. J. Rousseau* (1767). At about the same time he engraved an illustration to Aphra Behn's story *Oroonoko* (or Thomas Southern's dramatization of it), though he took objection to its suggestion that the institution could be justified and only the abuses were to be censured. The claim that slavery was an economic necessity was, he wrote, contrary to "the laws of nature, conscience and the truth." On a visit to Liverpool, built partly on the profits of slavery, he later remarked: "methinks I everywhere smell the blood of slaves." Passing beyond Cowper's gentle, religious humanitarianism, he claimed liberty as a natural right of all mankind. And in illustrating "The Negro's Complaint" he rejected the usual abolitionist image of the slave as a pathetic, weak creature, representing him as a figure of great human dignity, calling down the wrath of heaven on the ship which founders beneath his imperious gesture.

Literature: *Johann Heinrich Fussli—Henry Fuseli*, exhibition catalogue, Kunsthaus, Zurich, 1926, no. 43; A. Federmann: *Johann Heinrich Füssli: Dichter und Maler*, Zurich-Leipzig, 1927, p. 64; *Johann Heinrich Füssli*, exhibition catalogue, Kunsthaus, Zurich, 1941, no. 58; *Liotard-Füssli*, exhibition catalogue, Paris, 1948, no. 118; F. Antal: *Fuseli Studies*, London, 1956, pp. 124, 130; *Johann Heinrich Füssli*, exhibition catalogue, Bremen and Dusseldorf, 1957, no. 39; *Johann Heinrich Füssli*, exhibition catalogue, Kunsthaus, Zurich, 1969, no. 91; P. Tomory: *The Life and Art of Henry Fuseli*, New York and London, 1972, p. 20; G. Schiff: *Johann Heinrich Füssli*, Zurich and Munich, 1973, pp. 329, 567 (no. 1253).

Pavel Petrovich Svinin

Russian, 1787-1839.
After attending the School for the Nobility in Moscow and the Academy of Fine Arts in St. Petersburg, Svinin entered the diplomatic service and in late 1811 went to Philadelphia as secretary to the Russian consul general. During the following twenty months he travelled widely, from Virginia to Maine, and gathered copious notes and some fifty watercolour drawings of American scenes and subjects. He left America in June 1813 and in 1815 published in St. Petersburg his *A Picturesque Voyage in North America*, which was later translated into German and Dutch. In 1818 he established a review, *Otechestvemmiya Zapiski*, and was elected a member of the Imperial Academy of Arts.

Pavel Petrovich Svinin

312 *Negro Methodists Holding a Meeting in a Philadelphia Alley*

Watercolours on paper. 1811-1813.
6⁹/₁₆ x 9¹³/₁₆ inches (16.4 x 25.2 cm.).
Provenance: R. T. H. Halsey, New York.
New York, The Metropolitan Museum of Art, Rogers Fund.

Svinin, like most European travellers in America, was particularly interested in the variety of sects and races in the United States and admired the way in which Quakers and Methodists, Indians and black people all lived peacefully within the republic. He predicted the complete emancipation of the slaves.

Literature: A. Yarmolinsky: *Picturesque United States of America, 1811, 1812, 1813, being a Memoir on Paul Svinyn, Russian Diplomatic Officer, Artist, and Author*, New York, 1930, pl. 8.

Pavel Petrovich Svinin

313 *Negroes in Front of the Bank of Pennsylvania, Philadelphia*

Watercolours on paper. 1811-1813. 9³⁄₁₆ x 6¹¹⁄₁₆ inches (23.4 x 15.2 cm.).
Provenance: R. T. H. Halsey, New York.
New York, The Metropolitan Museum of Art, Rogers Fund.

Benjamin Latrobe's Bank of Pennsylvania of 1798 was an epoch-making building, for it initiated the Greek Revival in America. Svinin did not have much to say about America architecture, however. "Briefly," he wrote, "English architecture prevails here throughout. In New York State, settled originally by the Dutch, and in the interior of Pennsylvania, inhabited mostly by the Germans, there are still some old houses built according to the national taste of those peoples; but

they are fast disappearing. . . ." As regards country houses, he wrote: "the Americans have for some time adopted the Italian style, and I have found here many such homes, of the most modern and very pleasant style of architecture."

Literature: A. Yarmolinsky: *Picturesque United States of America, 1811, 1812, 1813, being a Memoir on Paul Svinyn, Russian Diplomatic Officer, Artist, and Author,* New York, 1930, pl. XVI; M. Jeffery: "As Russia Saw Us in 1812" in *The Metropolitan Museum of Art Bulletin,* November, 1942, vol. I, nos. 3, 139.

David Wilkie
Scottish, 1785-1841.

314 *A Negro with a Tray of Glasses*
Watercolours. Signed and dated:
D Wilkie f 1836. 17 x 13½ inches (43.1
x 34.2 cm.). Provenance: Wilkie Sale,
Christie's 1860, lot 364, bt. Colnaghi.
The Duke of Buccleuch and Queens-
berry Collection.

This is a study for the painting *The
Empress Josephine and the Fortune
Teller* (Edinburgh, National Gallery
of Scotland), which illustrates an event
in Martinique, Josephine's native land,
where a negress reading her palm predicted that she would one day be
crowned, and would be greater than a
queen. This head is not unlike that of
a negro in Rubens' *Feast of Herod*
(National Gallery of Scotland), which
Wilkie could have seen at Langton
House, Duns, in the early 1830s.

Literature: John Woodward: *Paintings
and Drawings by Sir David Wilkie R.A.
1785-1841,* exhibition catalogue, Royal
Academy, London, 1958, no. 104.

Joseph Mallord William Turner
English, 1775-1851.
The greatest English Romantic
painter, Turner was the son of a
London barber. He was trained under
Thomas Malton, at the Royal Academy schools, and under Girtin. He
began as a watercolour painter in the
English topographical tradition and
exhibited from 1790 onwards. He became an Associate of the Royal Academy in 1799 and a full member in
1802. After 1800 his work began to be
increasingly criticised and sometimes
ridiculed, and it was not until 1843,
with the publication of Ruskin's
Modern Painters, that his reputation
broadened.

Joseph Mallord William Turner

315 *The Slave Ship*
Oil on canvas. 1840. 35¾ x 48 inches
(90.8 x 122 cm.). Provenance: Pur-
chased from the artist by John Ruskin,
Sr., and given to his son, 1844; sold
Christie's 15 April 1869, lot 50 bought
in; John Taylor Johnston, New York;
sold New York, Chickering Hall, 19-
22 December 1876, lot 76; Miss Alice
Hooper, Boston; W. H. S. Lothrop,
Boston; bought Museum of Fine Arts,
Boston, 1899.
Boston, Museum of Fine Arts, Henry
Lillie Pierce Fund.

The Slave Ship was exhibited at the
Royal Academy, London, in 1840 as
*Slavers throwing overboard the dead
and dying—Typhon coming on,* with
the following extract from Turner's
poem "Fallacies of Hope":

Aloft all hands, strike the top-masts
and belay;
Yon angry setting sun and fierce-
edged clouds
Declare the Typhon's coming.
Before it sweep your decks, throw
overboard

The dead and dying—ne'er heed
their chains.
Hope, Hope, fallacious Hope!
Where is thy market now?

Though rich and complex in its conception and meaning, this horrifying
masterpiece's immediate inspiration
was the increasing anti-slavery agita-
tion of 1839-40 in England. T. F.
Buxton founded his *Society for the
Extinction of the Slave Trade and for
the Civilisation of Africa* in that year,
which also saw the publication of the
Life of Wilberforce by his sons and a
new edition of T. Clarkson's *History
of the Abolition of the African Slave-
Trade.* The latter contains a spine-
chilling account of the slave ship *Zong*
in 1783, when the captain had a large
cargo of slaves thrown overboard during an epidemic, so that insurance,
payable for those lost "at sea" but not
from disease, could be claimed.

Further inspiration probably came
from James Thomson's "Seasons,"
which was one of Turner's favourite
poems, and which contains accounts
both of a typhoon and of a slave ship
in shark-infested waters:

Increasing still the terror of these
storms,
His jaws horrific arm'd with
threefold fate,
Here dwells the direful shark. Lur'd
by the scent
Of steaming crowds, or rank
disease, and death,
Behold! he rushing cuts the briny
flood,
Swift as the gale can bear the ship
along;
And from the partners of that cruel
trade
Which spoils unhappy Guinea of
her sons,
Demands his share of prey—
demands themselves.

T. F. Buxton probably had this
passage from Thomson in mind when,
at the anniversary meeting of the
Society for the Extinction of the Slave
Trade in June 1840, he alluded to the

slave ship as "a pestilence . . . upon the waters . . . the very shark knew the slave ship to be a bark of blood, and expected from it his daily sustenance."

Another possible source is an anonymous French lithograph entitled *Les Noirs, avant, pendant et après l'Emancipation*, in which the central and largest scene depicts a slave ship throwing slaves overboard in order to increase speed and escape from a British man-of-war. It is undated but appears to be connected with the emancipation of slaves in the British colonies in 1833 and the riots in Jamaica and suspension of the constitution in 1839. The print is anti-abolitionist, but Turner may well have been familiar with it.

This was the most advanced of Turner's pictures to be exhibited up to this time, and the critics were startled and bewildered by its colour and handling. Thackeray asked, when it was first exhibited in 1840: "Is the picture sublime or ridiculous? Indeed I don't know which." He went on to describe the "flakes of white laid on with a trowel; bladders of vermilion madly spirted here and there. . . . gasping dolphins redder than the reddest herrings; horrid spreading polypi, like huge, slimy, poached eggs, in which hapless niggers, plunge and disappear." Ruskin, however, thought it "beyond dispute, the noblest sea that Turner has painted, and, if so, the noblest certainly ever painted by man" and wrote one of his finest descriptive passages about it in *Modern Painters:*

Purple and blue, the lurid shadows of the hollow breakers are cast upon the mist of night, which gathers cold and low, advancing like the shadow of death upon the guilty ship as it labours amidst the lightning of the sea, its thin masts written upon the sky in lines of blood, girded with condemnation in that fearful hue which signs the sky with horror, and mixes its flaming flood with the sun-

light, and, cast far along the desolate heave of the sepulchral waves, incarnadines the multitudinous sea. I believe, if I were reduced to rest Turner's immortality upon any single work, I should choose this. Its daring conception, ideal in the highest sense of the word, is based on the purest truth, and thought out with the concentrated knowledge of life; . . . and the whole picture dedicated to the most sublime of subjects and impressions (completing thus the perfect system of all truth, which we have shown to be formed by Turner's works)—the power, majesty, and deathfulness of the open, deep, illimitable sea!

Ruskin's father gave it to him as a New Year's present in 1844. Ruskin later sold it, because the subject, "the throwing overboard of the dead and dying, who are seen struggling in the water surrounded by sharks and gulls—had, he used to say, become too painful to live with."

Literature: W. M. Thackeray in *Fraser's Magazine,* June 1840, reprinted in *Critical Papers in Art,* London, 1904, p. 124; W. Thornbury: *Life of J. M. W. Turner,* London, 1877, pp. 532-533; C. F. Bell: *The Exhibited Works of J. M. W. Turner, R.A.,* London, 1901, pp. 140-141; W. Armstrong: *Turner,* London, 1902, pp. 121, 147, 150-153, 231; J. Ruskin: *Works,* ed. E. T. Cook and A. Wedderburn, London, 1903-12, *passim;* C. B. Tinker: *Painter and Poet,* Cambridge, Mass., 1938, pp. 149-152; A. J. Finberg: *The Life of J. M. W. Turner* (1939) rev. H. F. Finberg, Oxford, 1961, pp. 378-9, 408, 505; K. Clark: *Landscape into Art,* London, 1949, p. 108; J. Evans and J. H. Whitehouse, ed.: *The Diaries of John Ruskin,* vol. I, Oxford, 1956, pp. 250, 253, 255, 257, 259, 263, 270, 363; A. Livermore: "J. M. W. Turner's unknown verse-book" in *The Connoisseur Year Book,* 1957, p. 80; *The Romantic Movement,* exhibition catalogue, The Tate Gallery, London, 1959, no. 357; T. S. R. Boase: *English Art 1800-1870,* Oxford, 1959, pp. 122-123; L. Gowing: *Turner: Imagination and Reality,* exhibition catalogue, Museum of Modern Art, New York, 1966, p. 38; *Turner 1775-1851,* exhibition catalogue, Royal Academy, London, 1974-75, nos. 518 and B107-109.

Auguste-François Biard

French, 1798-1882.
Biard was born at Lyon and educated for the priesthood but decided to become a painter and studied under Pierre-Henri Révoil. In 1824 he went to Paris and began to exhibit in the annual Salons. His works included *genre* and historical scenes and portraits, especially of Louis-Philippe and his family, but he was probably best known for paintings of exotic subjects. He travelled in the eastern Mediterranean in 1827-28 and visited Lapland and Spitzbergen in the 1830s. He later became known for his paintings of slaves and the slave trade, ranging in date from 1835 to 1861, which imply a close connection with the Abolitionist movement. A journey to the United States and Brazil provided him with material for a travel book, *Deux années au Brésil* (Paris, 1862), and several paintings, which were shown in the Salon of 1861, including *Railroad Travel in North America, The Sale of Slaves in the Southern States, The Pursuit of Fugitive Slaves,* and *Travel in South America.* Edgar Degas, describing New Orleans in 1872, remarked that the colourful scene would "appear in a different light to Biard."

Auguste-François Biard

316 *The Slave Trade*
Oil on canvas. 1835. Signed: *A. F. Biard*. 64 x 90 inches (162.5 x 228.6 cm.).
Kingston upon Hull Museum and Art Galleries, Wilberforce House.

The cruelties and humiliations inflicted on African slaves—flogging, branding, manacling, inspection of teeth to judge age and value—and the cold indifference of both black and white traders to their sufferings—form the subject of this picture. A contemporary remarked that Biard "made the 'slave trade' by a single picture, more infamous than it had been depicted by a score of advocates for its suppression" (*Art Union*, 1847, p. 208; I am grateful to Professor Francis Haskell for this reference). The picture exhibited is probably identical with that shown as *La traite des nègres* in the Paris Salon of 1835. Biard also showed a painting entitled *The Slave Trade* (probably the same work) at the Royal Academy in London in 1840 (no. 441).

A smaller version of it was formerly in the Albert Lieutaud Collection, New Orleans, but cannot now be traced (cf. *American Processional 1492-1900*, exhibition catalogue, Corcoran Gallery of Art, Washington, D.C., 1950, no. 132).

Slave traders on the coast of Africa had previously been depicted by George Morland in a painting exhibited at the Royal Academy, London, in 1788, now lost and known only from copies and prints published in London in 1791 and 1814 and Paris, ca. 1794 (cf. H. Honour: *The New Golden Land*, New York, 1975, pl. 150. I am grateful to Dr. David Winter for information about this work). Théodore Géricault projected a monumental painting of the African slave trade and shortly before his death in 1824 made drawings for it (Ecole des Beaux Arts, Paris and Musée Bonnat, Bayonne).

Literature: E. Bellier de la Chavignerie and L. Auvray: *Dictionnaire général des artistes de l'école française*, Paris, 1882, vol. I, p. 87; Algernon Graves: *The Royal Academy of Arts*, vol. I, London, 1905, p. 190; J. B. Fay: *Wilberforce House, Hull, History and Collections*, Kingston upon Hull, 1955.

Auguste-François Biard

317 *Proclamation of the Abolition of Slavery in the French Colonies*

Oil on canvas. 1849. Signed: *Biard*. 102⅜ x 154⅜ inches (260 x 392 cm.). Versailles, Musée Nationale du Château de Versailles.

Although slavery was abolished in all French territory by the first Republic in 1794, it was re-established in 1802. After the Restauration in 1815, Louis XVIII agreed to ban the slave trade between Africa and the French colonies in the West Indies (Guadeloupe and Martinique), but the law could not be implemented until 1831, when Louis-Philippe permitted the search of French ships suspected of carrying slaves. The French navy played a part in suppressing the trade, and Biard painted *The liberation of slaves on board a slaver captured by a French ship of war* (exhibited Royal Academy, London, 1847, no. 456, but now lost).

Opposition to slavery mounted in France under the July Monarchy, owing mainly to the efforts of Victor Schoelcher, Comte Agénor-Victor de Gasparin, Pierre-Paul Castelli, and Alphonse de Lamartine. Abolition was finally achieved by the 1848 Revolution. As one of its first measures the Provisional Government abolished slavery in all French territory on 27 April 1848, thus freeing some half million slaves. Biard's painting, which evokes the reception of the decree of emancipation in the French colonies, was exhibited in the Paris Salon in 1849. It was bought by the state and hung at Versailles, though it was later transferred to the Musée Bargoin at Clermont-Ferrand.

Literature: E. Bellier de la Chavignerie and L. Auvray: *Dictionnaire général des artistes de l'école française,* Paris, 1882, vol. i, p. 88; *La Révolution de 1848,* exhibition catalogue, Bibliothèque Nationale, Paris, 1848, no. 400.

Louisa Corbaux

English, born 1808.
Like her elder and better known sister Fanny Corbaux (1812-1883), she was self-taught. They exhibited for the first time in 1828 and went on exhibiting in London until the 1880s, usually *genre* and animal paintings. Louisa Corbaux was well known as a lithographer, publishing *Sculpture from the Exhibition of 1851*, a series of twenty lithographs, in 1852. She also published *Amateur's Painting Guide* in 1852.

Louisa Corbaux

318 *Eva and Topsy*

Lithograph. 1852. 8⁵⁄₁₆ x 11⁷⁄₁₆ inches (21 x 28 cm.). Inscription: *Louisa Corbaux delᵗ et lith. London, Printed and Pubᵈ, Novʳ 1st 1852, by Stannard and Dixon 7 Poland Sᵗ Stannard & Dixon Imp.*
Washington, D.C., Library of Congress, Prints and Photographs Division.

Topsy, in Mrs. Beecher Stowe's famous anti-slavery novel *Uncle Tom's Cabin,* was the little slave girl who said she had neither father nor mother, and being asked who made her, replied, "I spect I grow'd." *Uncle Tom's Cabin* first appeared in the *National Era* in 1851-52 and in book form in 1852.

319 *Five scenes from* Uncle Tom's Cabin

France (Montereau-Creil). White earthenware with transfer-printed decorations. ca. 1852-1865. Diameter 7⅞ inches (20 cm.).
Blérancourt, Musée National de la Coopération Franco-Américaine.

These five plates come from a set of at least sixteen, each of which is decorated with a different scene from Harriet Beecher Stowe's novel, which was translated into French as *Le case de l'Oncle Tom* soon after its first appearance in America (an illustrated edition with lithographs after J. Bettanier was published in Paris in 1855). Slavery had already been abolished in French territory before they were made, but such images probably helped to win support for the Union in the American Civil War. Like the novel itself, they also played a part in diffusing a patronising attitude to the black races. The plates were among many decorated with transfer-printed scenes from contemporary fiction made at the Montereau-Creil pottery, which had been founded in 1794 and continued to operate until 1895.

Louise Corbaux delᵗ et lith   Stannard & Dixon Imp

EVA AND TOPSY.

"I love you because you haven't had any Father, or Mother, or Friends.— because you've been a poor abused child!

Frank Buchser
Swiss, 1828-1890.

320 *Negro Home in Virginia*
Oil on canvas. Signed and dated
(verso): *Frank Buchser, Charlottesville
Va Sept 25 1869.* 39⅜ x 29³⁄₁₆ inches
(100 x 74 cm.). Provenance: Inherited
from the artist by his brother Dr.
Josef Buchser, who gave it to the
Museum, 1896.
Basel, Offentliche Kunstmuseum.

Immediately after his arrival in America, Buchser began to paint black
people, in whom he showed increasing
interest and sympathy. In order to
pursue his study of them, he went to
Charlottesville, where he stayed in the
new hotel, Farish House, from 3 August 1869. The picture exhibited is one
of the first he painted there. Its stark
realism makes a striking contrast with
such an American view of a similar
subject as Eastman Johnson's sentimental vision of *Negro Life in the
South* (later re-titled *Old Kentucky
Home*, New-York Historical Society)
of 1859. The latter may indeed have
inspired Buchser to present a more
truthful and more discomforting view.
His aims were well understood by
some contemporary critics, one of
whom, writing in the *New York Daily
Tribune* of 29 January 1870, highly
praised his paintings of black people:

> There is not the slightest effort to
> invest his subjects with a dignity
> borrowed from extrinsic embellish-
> ment. What he paints is the negro in
> his average condition, and with such
> common surroundings as those amid
> which he may ordinarily be found
> ... In the face of such obstacles to
> popularity, it required no small
> amount of courage and faith to
> undertake this class of paintings. It
> must be said to Buchser's credit, too,
> that he has not had the courage
> alone, but also the honesty to pursue
> with conscientious fidelity the task
> he has accepted, for while he has
> painted no ideal negro born of
> political sympathy, he has on the
> other hand conceded nothing to
> prejudice, but has faithfully recorded
> all the gentleness of nature, the exal-
> tation of purpose, the real manliness
> and dignity of character whereby
> nature herself has stamped on the
> face of the negro his true patent of
> nobility, and his just title to be
> regarded in truth as "a man and a
> brother."

Literature: H. Lüdeke: *Frank Buchsers
amerikanische Sendung*, Basel, 1941, pp.
95, 125-127; *Frank Buchser 1828-1890*,
exhibition catalogue, Kunstsammlung der
Stadt Thun, Thunerhof, 1967, no. 89.

XVIII
Democracy
in America

In the hundred years after the Declaration of Independence, Europeans sailed to the United States in steadily increasing numbers. The vast majority were poor emigrants, who sought and usually found a better life there. But there was also a constant trickle of political refugees, which became a flood as soon as the first rumbles of the French Revolution were heard. Aristocrats and priests were followed by Constitutionalists, Conventionalists, Thermidorians, Fructidorians. By about 1800 Philadelphia seemed a "veritable Noah's ark" of refugees to the comte de Moré, who wrote that "when the vessel of the French monarchy blew up as a consequence of their follies and foolish systems, the explosion hurled a good number of them as far as the United States."[1] A little later opponents of Napoleon were to find asylum in America: and after 1815 they were followed by Bonapartists—among them the deluded colonists at Champ d'Asile in Texas [323]—then by the liberals fleeing from the authoritarian regimes of Metternich's Europe and later from that of Napoleon III in France. From so heterogeneous a population very diverse and often contradictory interpretations of American democracy were only to be expected.

A royalist *emigrée*, Mme. de la Tour du Pin, scoffed at an English admirer of the United States as one who had "created for himself an imaginary America, and was unwilling to give it up."[2] The same could be said of many travellers who barely gave themselves time to unpack, let alone discard, their preconceived ideas before returning to Europe and hastening to print accounts of their transatlantic experiences. The sheer quantity of nineteenth-century American travel literature—ranging from the adulatory by way of the coolly dispassionate to the almost hysterically hostile—is daunting, and few general deductions can be drawn from it.[3] But almost invariably America was seen simply as a better or worse alternative to Europe—usually the latter, as in Mrs. Trollope's *Domestic Manners of the Americans* [326] and Dickens's *American Notes for General Circulation* [328]. Seldom, if ever, was the United States described as a foreign country with its own individual conditions, customs, and institutions. Even the sage Alexis de Tocqueville, author of the most penetrating assessment of it published in the nineteenth century *(Democracy in America),* wrote with one eye, and sometimes both, focussed on France. In the following years several enthusiastic accounts of America—including Laboulaye's entertaining novel *Paris en Amérique*—were published, often as concealed attacks on the French government of the day, whether of the July Monarchy or the Second Empire. Similarly in the visual arts, a medal struck to commemorate Lincoln might also serve as a manifesto of French Republicanism [332], and portraits of Civil War generals might have, or at any rate be intended to have, a political significance for the artist's compatriots in Europe [336].

The most hostile of the travel writers in the first half of the nineteenth century were the English, who felt quite certain of the superior merits of their own political system. They were both astonished and appalled to find Americans just as self-assured. "A single word indicative of doubt, that anything, or everything, in that country is not the best in the world, produces an effect which must be seen and felt to be understood," wrote Mrs. Trollope. But her "six hundred pages of *griffonage*"—as she called them—are devoted mainly to domestic unmannerliness, tobacco-chewing and spitting, the impertinence of strangers and servants, with a few kind words for slaves, Indians, and misguided immigrants. She also described in some detail and with similar distaste the religious beliefs and rites which fascinated more sympathetic visitors, especially those from countries where there was no liberty of faith [321]. Hers were, indeed, the themes on which most subsequent travel writers dilated. Dickens added little, apart from some angry comments on the freedom of American publishers to pirate his books. His account of swampy Cairo in *American Notes* and *Martin Chuzzlewit* could have been derived from earlier sources as easily as from personal observation [328, 329]. Heine's poem "Jetzt wohin?" suggests that these jaundiced accounts of the United States had some influence outside the British Isles: "Sometimes I think of sailing to America, to the great freedom-stable inhabited by egalitarian boors, but I am put off by a country where the men chew tobacco, where they play skittles without a king, where they spit without spittoons."

That other visions of the United States were current in nineteenth-century Europe is partly because of American writers, who now, for the first time, made a serious impact abroad. First of all Washington Irving was popular both as an essayist and an historian—the forerunner, as Wilkie portrayed him, of thousands of American scholars later to be seen in European libraries [324]. "The best thing I yet know of America is that it should have produced so good a writer," Henry Crabb Robinson remarked of him in 1821. Fenimore Cooper enjoyed wider success both for the *Leatherstocking Tales* and for his sea stories, one of which inspired Hector Berlioz's overture *Le corsair*, and, from the later 1840s, Herman Melville, whose genius was recognised in France almost immediately.[4] All these writers seem to have been read by Europeans partly if not mainly for their subject matter—for the light they shed on their native land and its people and for the already recognisably American ideals they expressed. Edgar Allan Poe was different [331]. The tortured, hypersensitive opponent and victim of the cult of progress on both sides of the Atlantic, he revealed a previously unknown aspect of the American character. But, paradoxically, his life story as recounted by Baudelaire only strengthened the belief that materialism ruled the United States.

Nineteenth-century attitudes toward America were often paradoxical. In the 1850s Karl Marx viewed the prosperity of its workers askance, because it seduced emigrants from the class struggle in Europe and converted them into contented bourgeois. A similar view was expressed in psychological rather than economic terms by Dostoevsky in *The Brothers Karamazov*. When Dimitri is advised to flee to the "Promised Land" of America, he replies: "But on the other hand, what about my conscience? I should have run away from suffering … What is America? America is nothing but a vain preoccupation with material gain." The still greater boom in American industry after the Civil War gave Marx reason to hope that a revolutionary situation was being created. Engels also had hopes of revolution on the "more favoured soil of America, where no mediaeval castles bar the way."[5] His words recall, perhaps intentionally, Goethe's famous poem written half a century earlier — with very different ideas in mind:

Amerika, du hast es besser	America, you are better off
Als unser Kontinent, das alte	Than our old continent
Hast keine verfallene Schlösser	You have no ruined castles
Und keine Basalte.	And no volcanic rock.
Dich stort nich im Innern	Your soul is not disturbed
Zu lebendiger Zeit	At the vital moment
Unnützes Erinnern	By useless memories
Und vergeblicher Streit.	And fruitless strife.

1. D. Echeverria: *Mirage in the West* (1957), Princeton, 1965, p. 186.

2. Henrietta-Lucy, marquise de La Tour du Pin: *Memoirs*, ed. and tr. F. Harcourt, London, 1970, p. 247.

3. See J. L. Mesick: *The English Traveller in America 1785-1835*, New York, 1922.

4. An interesting account of Melville's work and that of earlier American writers is in P. Chasles: *Etudes sur la littérature et les moeurs des Anglo-Américains au XIXᵉ siecle*, Paris, 1851.

5. For both Marx and Engels on America, see R. L. Moore: *European Socialists and the American Promised Land*, New York, 1970, pp. 1-24.

Pavel Petrovich Svinin

Russian, 1787-1839.

321 *A Philadelphia Anabaptist
Immersion During a Storm*

Watercolours on paper. 1811-1813.
7 x 9¾ inches (17.8 x 24.8 cm.). Provenance: R. T. H. Halsey, New York.
New York, The Metropolitan Museum of Art, Rogers Fund.

Svinin, like nearly all European travellers in America, was amazed by the
number and variety of different religious sects and studied their beliefs and
customs.

Literature: A. Yarmolinsky: *Picturesque
United States of America, 1811, 1812, 1813,
being a Memoir on Paul Svinyn, Russian
Diplomatic Officer, Artist, and Author*,
New York, 1930, pl. XIX; M. Jeffery: "As
Russia Saw Us in 1812" in *The Metro-
politan Museum of Art Bulletin*, Novem-
ber 1942, vol. I, no. 3, p. 136.

Charles-Alexandre Lesueur

French, 1778-1846.
Lesueur joined, at first in a humble
capacity, Nicolas Baudin's scientific
expedition to the South Seas in 1800.
He and François Peron made notable
zoological discoveries during the expedition and were entrusted with publishing the voyage. He returned to
France in 1804 and in 1815 went to
America with the Scottish geologist
William McClure. They explored the
geography, geology, and everyday life
in New England, New York, and the
Great Lakes region. Lesueur collected
material for a projected work on
North American fish. From ca. 1818
until 1826 he lived in Philadelphia. He
then joined Robert Owen's utopian
settlement at New Harmony, Indiana,
where he spent ten years. He returned
to France in 1835.

Charles-Alexandre Lesueur

322 *River Boat: Philanthropiste*
Pencil. 1816-1837. 5⅞ x 8¹⁵⁄₁₆ inches
(15 x 22.7 cm.). Inscription: *1826 Jᵉʳ 10*
mardy au soir / avant d'arriver a Cap-
tain Island. beau ciel sur le 3 heures.
Le Havre, Museum d'Histoire Naturelle du Havre.

This is one of many drawings made by
Lesueur on his several journeys up and
down the Mississippi. Like many other
Europeans, he seems to have been
fascinated by the river boats, which
provided the most popular means of
long-distance travel before the development of the railroad system. The
craft were unlike any to be seen in
Europe. Dickens wrote of them in
1842: "they have no mast, cordage,
tackle, or other such boat-like gear;
nor have they anything in their shape
at all calculated to remind one of a
boat's head, stern, sides, or keel.
Except that they are in the water, and
display a couple of paddle boxes, they
might be intended, for anything that
appears to the contrary, to perform
some unknown service, high and dry,
upon a mountain top."

Literature: R. W. G. Vail: "American
Sketchbooks of Charles Alexandre Le-
sueur, 1816-1837" in *Proceedings of the
American Antiquarian Society*, April 1938.

323 *Champ d'Asile*
France. Aquatint. ca. 1819. Signed:
Dessiné et gravé par Yerenrag. 12⁵⁄₁₆ x
15¾ inches (31.3 x 40 cm.). Inscription: *1ere vue d'Aigleville, colonie du
Texas ou Champ d'Asile. Occupations
des nouveaux colons, Fort Henri,
chemin couvert qui mène au fort et
habitation d'un colon.*
Washington, D.C., Library of Congress, Prints and Photographs Division.

Champ d'Asile was the name given to
a tract of land in Texas very briefly
settled by a group of some four hundred French Bonapartist refugees
under General Charles Lallemand in
1818. It was on the banks of the Trin-
ity River, some thirty miles north of
Galveston. One of the settlers described the site as being on the edge of
"an immense uninhabited plain, several leagues in extent and surrounded
by a belt of wood down to the river.
A fruitful soil, an abundance of tropical plants and flowers, a river as wide
as the Seine, but full of alligators, a sky
as pure and a climate as temperate as
that of Naples—such were the advantages of the place we had chosen and
which is now christened Champ
d'Asile." The settlers had obtained
some encouragement from the United
States government, but unfortunately
for them the land was so close to the
border of Mexico, that it was also
claimed by Spain. No sooner had they
begun to build forts, than a Spanish
force advanced on them, and they beat
a retreat to Galveston. (For the history
of the colony, see Jesse S. Reeves: *The
Napoleonic Exiles in America. A Study
in American Diplomatic History 1815-
1819*, Johns Hopkins University
Studies in Historical and Political
Science, ser. XXIII, no. 9-10, Baltimore,
1905, pp. 80-92.)

News of the beginning of the Champ d'Asile venture was published in France in the liberal newspaper *La Minerve,* which opened a subscription to support the refugees. The popular poet Pierre Jean de Béranger wrote a song, "Le Champ d'Asile." Another song was printed with a cover by the painter Horace Vernet. And several prints fancifully illustrating the site of the colony and the work of the settlers were issued. Many years later it was more memorably commemorated by Balzac in *La rabouilleuse,* where the venture is inaccurately interpreted as a Machiavellian scheme of the Restauration government to rid France of Bonapartists by luring them to Texas.

The print exhibited is one of a pair issued (as the inscription of the other reveals) after the settlers had been obliged to abandon Champ d'Asile. But the inscriptions on both are somewhat confusing, as Aigleville was not an alternative name for Champ d'Asile but a town which another group of Bonapartist refugees, associated with Lallemand, attempted to found in Alabama, also in 1818. (The name was maintained when a town was later built on the same site, and the county in which it is located is called Marengo in memory of the Bonapartists.) The authorship of the prints is hard to establish, for, although *Yerenrag* is a back-to-front spelling of Garnerey, several artists of this name were active in Paris under the Restauration, and all were printmakers as well as painters and draughtsmen: François-Jean Garnerey (1755-1837) and his three sons, Ambroise-Louis (1783-1857), Auguste (1785-1824), and Hippolyte (1787-1858). The best known, Ambroise-Louis, who was a marine painter, is the least probable candidate, as he seems to have differed from his father and brothers in spelling his name *Garneray.*

David Wilkie
Scottish, 1785-1841.

324 *Washington Irving in the Archives of Seville*

Oil on canvas. 1828. 48¼ x 48¼ inches (123 x 123 cm.). Provenance: Sir William Wentworth Knighton, sold Christie's 23 May 1885, lot 437. Leicester, Leicestershire Museums and Art Galleries.

When sold in 1885 by Sir William Wentworth Knighton, whose father was a friend of Wilkie, the painting was entitled *Washington Irving in the Convent of La Rabida, Searching the Archives for the Life of Columbus.* However, this is spurious, for the subject and genesis of the painting are described in a letter of 30 January 1829 from Wilkie in London to Irving in Seville (see below). Irving had met Wilkie in London, probably through C. R. Leslie, by 1823, and they became close friends. They were together in Paris in the summer of 1825 and again in Madrid in the fall of 1827. Irving had just finished writing his *Life and Voyages of Christopher Columbus,* and on 13 October 1827 in Madrid Wilkie made a drawing of Columbus at the Convent of La Rabida (Leicestershire Museums and Art Galleries), which he later worked up into a painting (North Carolina Museum of Art, Raleigh). On 2 April 1828 Wilkie went to Seville and was joined there by Irving a few days later. Wilkie left for London on 24 April.

In the letter mentioned above, Wilkie wrote:

One day at Seville when you were examining the Boo[k] which a monk was showing you in an old Library, I remarked t[he] striking effect your two figures made together—on my way to Madrid I made a drawing of this effect in colours which is here thought so strong and simple that I

have been induced to begin a picture of it on a half-length canvas—I call it the Archives of Seville—you are looking down upon the Book [at this point the text is broken by a small sketch of Irving's head] in this position—If you were here I would take some pains to make it like—the drawing at Mr. Murrays will scarcely serve me—could you get a drawing made in this view in a letter—or what would be still better, are you likely to be in London within a reasonable time yourself?—perhaps to you as to me it would be a pleasing recollection of our visit to Seville.

Irving apparently had a portrait made of himself by J. M. Escacena (ca. 1800-1858) and sent it to Wilkie. It is now lost, as is the coloured drawing he mentions. (The latter may have been that included in lot. 386 in the Knighton Sale, 1885, as *Washington Irving at the Convent.*) Wilkie's drawing of Irving is still in the John Murray Collection, London; it is dated 23 April 1828. In his diary for 22 April, Irving noted: "Sit to Wilkie this morning for a sketch of my portrait. Go with him and Sy^m to the library of the city. Small collection—old friar very kind and attentive." Irving remembered the incident some years later and in a letter of 1853 recalled being "seated in a dusky chamber at a table looking over a folio volume which a monk who was standing by had just handed down to me. Wilkie thought the whole had a Rembrandt effect."

Literature: H. Miles: "Aduotatiunculae Leicestriensis: Wilkie and Washington Irving in Spain" in *Scottish Arts Review,* vol. XII, no. 1, pp. 21-25.

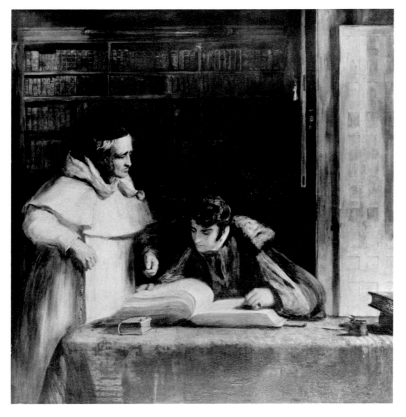

August Hervieu

French, 1794-1858.
Born in Paris, Hervieu went to London during the Restoration and studied briefly under Sir Thomas Lawrence before leaving for America in 1827 with Mrs. Trollope, presumably to be drawing-master at the Utopian colony recently organised at Nashoba, near Memphis, Tennessee, by Frances Wright, a close friend of Mrs. Trollope. He soon left it, however, and settled in Cincinnati, where he decorated Mrs. Trollope's ill-fated bazaar. He also collaborated with Hiram Powers in a show entitled "The Infernal Regions" at the Western Museum, Cincinnati. He returned to France in 1831.

August Hervieu

325 *Cupid at a Rout at Cincinnati*
Watercolours. Signed and dated: *Augte Hervieu / 1830.* 6½ x 11 inches (16.5 x 27.9 cm.).
Cincinnati, Cincinnati Art Museum, gift of Mrs. George H. Warrington.

Unlike his satirical illustrations to Mrs. Trollope's *Domestic Manners of the Americans* [326], this presents an attractive and sensitive depiction of fashionable life in the new city.

Literature: *The French in America: 1520-1880,* exhibition catalogue, Detroit Institute of Arts, Detroit, 1951, pp. 178-179; R. Fastnedge: "Furniture of the Young United States" in *Country Life,* 11 June 1964, p. 1494.

August Hervieu

326 *Ancient and Modern Republics, frontispiece to Mrs. (Frances) Trollope:* Domestic Manners of the Americans

Lithograph. 1832. Page size 8¾ x 4¾ inches (20 x 12 cm.). Provenance: Part of the Gansevoort-Lansing Collection given to the Library, 1919.
New York, The New York Public Library, Astor, Lenox and Tilden Foundations, American History Division.

The frontispiece to Mrs. Trollope's notorious account of her travels in America contrasts the elegant republics of ancient Greece with what she regarded as the slovenly democracy of the United States. "Both as a woman, and as a stranger, it might be unseemly for me to say that I do not like their government, and therefore I will not say so," she wrote in her concluding chapter. Of the population, however, "as seen in town and country, among the rich and the poor, in the slave states, and the free states," she did not mince her words. "I do not like them. I do not like their principles. I do not like their manners. I do not like their opinions."

Frances Trollope, née Milton (1780-1863), went to America in 1827 with two of her children in the hope of restoring the family fortunes lost by her reckless husband. After briefly visiting the Utopian settlement which her friend Frances Wright had established for the education and emancipation of slaves at Nashoba, near Memphis, Tennessee, she settled in Cincinnati. Here she built a bazaar as a store for fancy goods and a kind of cultural centre, but the venture was a disaster, and she lost what little money she had. She then travelled for a short time, visiting Niagara and Washington, and sailed back to England in 1830 from New York. *Domestic Manners of the Americans*, published in London and New York in 1832, was more than a little disingenuous. She made no reference in it either to her commercial activities or to her relations with August Hervieu (which may well account for the cold-shouldering she received from society in Cincinnati). Accounts of her personal experiences are liberally interwoven with clichés which hark back to the time-worn comments of Buffon and de Pauw. But her book was widely read in both England and the United States and launched her on a successful literary career. As her son, the novelist Anthony Trollope, who had not been with her in America, later wrote: "Her volumes were very bitter; but they were very clever, and they saved the family from ruin."

Literature: F. Trollope: *Domestic Manners of the Americans,* ed. D. Smalley, New York, 1949; E. Bigland: *The Indomitable Mrs. Trollope*, London, 1953.

C. J. Grant
English, fl. 1832-1833.

327 *Emigration: Detailing the Progress and Vicissitudes of an Emigrant!!*

Lithograph. 1833. 18 x 14 inches (45.6 x 35.5 cm.).
Washington, D.C., Library of Congress, Prints and Photographs Division.

A sheet with almost identical illustrations was published in Germany, entitled *Der Auswanderer,* with German text. It is undated and unsigned (example in the Bibliothèque Nationale, Paris).

EMIGRATION.

Detailing the Progress and Vicissitudes of an Emigrant !!

Dedicated to all those, who would leave their native Country to seek a better condition in a distant Foreign Land.

Embarking with your Family for America —
taking leave of Albion's white Cliffs —
No more Taxes

"On the wide and boundless Sea" — Rolling
mountains high, a month on the Atlantic Provisions
nearly exhausted or spoild, but no lack of hard Junk
and Putrid Water —

Landing at an American Port more dead than
alive — the Cholera raging — Coffins as common
as packing cases — half a mind to go back again.

Sailing up the S.t Lawrence in an American Boiler —
stow'd in a hold very like the Black hole of Calcutta —
all got a Fit of the American Ague —
Thermometer at 100.

Arrived at your allotment on the borders of a
huge Canadian Forest under the guidance of a knowing
agent — and which must be cut, clear'd, spaded &
till'd, before you can settle (no work at all)

Strolling in the Woods — and having
an interview with the Natives —

A view of your Log Hut — digging under
a burning Sun — Thermometer at 90 in
the shade — infested by Musquitoes
with stings like Stocking needles —

In exploring the neighbouring land, you tumble over an Alligator —
makes him run — the devil catch the hindmost !

Visited by a Cobbler
not the Tax gatherer —

A Twelve month's residence — having an addition to your
family already too many — sitting after a day's toil at your
door — drop a tear for deserted England yet "England with
all thy faults I love thee still" — a Spider as big as a crab
spins a web on your hat, & a Scorpion creeps into your Hut
unobserved, takes a lodging under the Bed & gives birth
to a numerous brood.

Sleeping under Buffalo skins lined with fleas as big as
blue bottles — alarmed in the night by a colony of Rats
in your room — where Ferocity almost bids fair to
take final possession —

A melancholy prospect — after 2 years toil of your Farm
can turn it to no account — Visited by a neighbour the
nearest by 5 miles, who see no reason why you & your
Farmer with a large family should not be like him in
about 40 or 50 years by dint of perseverance & asks to
openly condoles with you in laughing in his sleeve at you
quitting the land of Prayers Taxes & Petitions.

Your Hut on Fire for the 3.d time — goods & chattels included — no engines no water nor Neighbourly assistance
not incurred — & no prospect of Subscription or Parish
relief — this scene unable to do any thing to witness the
destruction of your little all — untill the dry grass catches
Fire & compels you to run off your own estate.

Fall into the hands of the Cannibals — you & your
family's lives at stake — being roasted for a Feast
yourself escapes by a miracle.

The Finale or wind up — Poor Friendless & Broken
down — and like Robinson Crusoe on an uninhabited Island
looking out for a Ship to convey you back to Old England
works your passage back to land — sans Money
sans Friends & sans every thing !

C.J Grant invent. Del & Lith.

Pub by J. Pattie, Bookseller, 16 High St. Bloomsbury opposite S.t Giles Church, London.

Hablôt Knight Browne, known as Phiz
English, 1815-1882.
Browne was born in London and trained as an engraver under William Finden and as a painter under William Etty. After making some engravings of English mediaeval architecture, he succeeded Robert Seymour as illustrator to the novels of Dickens, adopting the name "Phiz." He illustrated *The Pickwick Papers* (1836), *Nicholas Nickleby* (1839), *Martin Chuzzlewit* (1844; see below), *Dombey and Son* (1848), *David Copperfield* (1850),

Bleak House (1853), *Little Dorrit* (1855), and *A Tale of Two Cities* (1859). The result of close collaboration with the author, his illustrations often add, as Angus Wilson has recently remarked "a dimension (and an imaginatively valid one) to Dicken's fictional world." He also illustrated many other novels and some books of poetry, but with less success.

Hablôt Knight Browne, known as Phiz (after)

328 *The Thriving City of Eden as it appeared on Paper, illustration to Charles Dickens:* Martin Chuzzlewit, *part IX, chapter 21*

Lithograph made by transfer of etching on steel. 1843. Page size 8⅞ x 5½ inches (22.5 x 14 cm.).
Cleveland, Cleveland Public Library, Literature Department, Rare Books.

Hablôt Knight Browne, known as Phiz (after)

329 *The Thriving City of Eden as it appeared in Fact, illustration to Charles Dickens:* Martin Chuzzlewit, *part IX, chapter 23*
Lithograph made by transfer of etching on steel. 1843. Page size 8⅞ x 5½ inches (22.5 x 14 cm.).
Cleveland, Case Western Reserve University, Freiberger Library.

The Life and Adventures of Martin Chuzzlewit, his Relations and Enemies, contains what is probably both the most famous and the most hostile fictional account of society in the United States written in the nineteenth century. In the first of the two illustrations exhibited here, Martin and his faithful companion Mark Tapley inspect the plan of Eden described to them as a city, "A flourishing city too! An architectural city! There were banks, churches, cathedrals, market-places, factories, hotels, stores, mansions, wharves: an exchange, a theatre; public buildings of all kinds, down to the office of the Eden Stinger, a daily journal; all faithfully depicted in the view before them."

The true appearance of Eden, where Martin had foolishly bought a plot of land, is shown in the other illustration: "The waters of the Deluge might have left it but a week before: so choked with slime and matted growth was the hideous swamp which bore that name. . . . There were a few log-houses visible among the dark trees: the best, a cow-shed or a rude stable. But for the wharves, the market-place, the public buildings!" The illustrator, Phiz, had never been to America, and his visualization of the second scene is derived from Dicken's text, aided, perhaps, by anti-emigration prints, of which several were published during the previous decade [327]. Dickens's account is based on Cairo, at the junction of the

Ohio and Mississippi, which he visited in 1842, and the fraudulent Cairo City and Canal Company, established in 1837 by Darius B. Holbrook, who sold shares in it through a London banking house. In *American Notes for General Circulation* (1842) he wrote:

At the junction of the two rivers, on ground so flat and low and marshy, that at certain seasons of the year it is inundated to the house-tops, lies a breeding place of fever, ague, and death; vaunted in England as a mine of Golden Hope, and speculated in, on the faith of monstrous representations, to many people's ruin. A dismal swamp, on which the half-built houses rot away: cleared here and there for the space of a few yards; and teeming, then, with rank unwholesome vegetation, in whose baleful shade the wanderers who are tempted hither, droop, and die, and lay their bones; the hateful Mississippi circling and eddying before it, and turning off upon its southern course a slimy monster hideous to behold; a hot bed of disease, an ugly sepulchre, a grave uncheered by any gleam of promise: a place without a single quality, in earth or air or water, to commend it: such is this dismal Cairo.

No doubt Cairo was, at that time, an insalubrious place, and Dickens's account is based on personal observation, but he was also aware, if only at second hand, of earlier literature in which America was described as a new world which had emerged from the Deluge later than the other continents.

Dickens spent some five months in America, from late January to late June 1842, and immediately after returning to London wrote *American Notes for General Circulation,* which was published and reprinted three times before the end of the year. In January 1843 he began to publish *Martin Chuzzlewit* in monthly instalments. It was initially less successful

than his previous novels, and he may well have inserted the account of Martin's adventures in America as a topical afterthought. Martin forms "a desperate resolution" of emigrating at the end of part V; his Atlantic crossing and his misadventures in the United States are the subject of chapters in parts VI, VII, IX, and XIII. These chapters give a far more uniformly hostile account of America than his travel book (only one sympathetic American appears in them) and caused still greater and more justifiable offence in the United States. They are also an artistic failure, comprised largely of unconvincing character sketches and conversations. But, as part of the novel which contains two of Dickens's most memorable creations, Pecksniff and Mrs. Gamp, they were widely read, and his account of Eden gave a new lease of life to the vision of America as the wet continent.

Literature: W. G. Wilkins: *Charles Dickens in America,* New York, 1911; U. Pope-Hennessy: *Charles Dickens,* London, 1945, pp. 152-173; A. Gerbi: *La Disputa del nuovo mondo,* Milan, 1955, pp. 546-559; Albert Johannsen: *Phiz Illustrations from the Novels of Charles Dickens,* Chicago, 1956, pp. 173, 201-203.

Johann Friedrich Hesse

German, 1792-after 1853.
Born in Magdeburg and trained at the Dresden Academy, Hesse worked in Hamburg from 1818 and in Berlin from 1838. He was first known as a portrait painter but made lithographs from 1819 onwards.

Johann Friedrich Hesse

330 *The Emigrants' Hope—
Sacramento in California*
Lithograph coloured by hand. ca. 1850. 14⅛ x 19⅜ inches (35.9 x 49.2 cm.). Inscription: *Druck v.J Hesse in Berlin.*
Washington, D.C., Library of Congress, Prints and Photographs Division.

In 1841 John Augustus Sutter (1803-1880), a Swiss military officer who joined the Mexican army, obtained land on the Mexican-Californian frontier on which to build a fort, known as "Sutter's Fort" or "New Helvetia." When gold was discovered there in 1848, several towns and settlements sprang up, Sacramento grew very rapidly—from a population of 2,000 in 1849 to 20,000 in 1850 and so on. In 1854 it became the state capital.

Edouard Manet

French, 1832-1883.
One of the greatest French painters of the nineteenth century, Manet was often associated with the Impressionists, though he denied the connection and never showed his pictures in their exhibitions. He first became notorious with *Déjeuner sur l'herbe*, shown at the Salon des Refusés in 1863, and *Olympia*, which was included in the official Salon in 1865. Both works aroused a furor of critical abuse, against which he was defended by Emile Zola. He had great influence on the avant garde artists of the younger generation (Degas, Monet, Sisley, and Renoir) but hankered after official recognition, which he began to win in his last years (he was awarded the Légion d'Honneur in 1882). Apart from his early portrait of Poe (see below), his only works which refer to America are *The Execution of the Emperor Maximilian* in Mexico (1867) and *The Battle of the Kearsarge and Alabama* (1872), recording an incident in the Civil War—the sea-fight in which the Confederate cruiser Kearsarge was destroyed off Cherbourg.

335
Frank Buchser,
*William H. Seward
in His Garden*.
Kunstmuseum
Basel.

Edouard Manet

331 *Edgar Allan Poe*
Pen, ink, and watercolour. 1858-1859.
Signed: *E. Manet.* 11⅞ x 8⅞ inches
(30.2 x 22.6 cm.).
Paris, Bibliothèque Nationale, Cabinet
des Estampes.

Apart from James Fenimore Cooper
[293], Edgar Allan Poe (1809-1849)
was the first American writer to be
recognised as such in Europe and,
moreover, to exert considerable influence on European, not merely English, writers. Stories by him were first
translated into French in 1847 by Isa-
belle Meunier, but he owed his reputation in France mainly to Baudelaire's
advocacy and translations, the first of
which appeared in *La Liberté de pen-
ser* in 1848. Baudelaire sensed an un-
canny bond of affinity with him. "Do
you know why I have translated Poe so
patiently?" he asked Théophile Thoré
in 1864. "Because he is like me. The
first time I opened one of his books, I
saw with terror and delight not only
the subjects I had dreamed of, but the
phrases I had thought out, written by
him twenty years earlier." From him
Poe's influence was transmitted to the
next generation of French writers. He
published an essay on Poe—largely a
word-for-word translation of an
American review, without acknowl-
edgement—in the *Revue de Paris* in
1852 (reprinted as the introduction to
his translation of a selection of the
Tales as *Histoires extraordinaires,*
1856) and another as an introduction
to a second selection, *Nouvelles Histoires extraordinaires,* in 1857. In 1858
he planned to reprint these essays with
a third (which seems never to have
been written) and in connection with
this project wrote to the publisher
Malassis in 1858, sending a sketch of a
portrait of Poe, from which a frontispiece might be engraved. Manet's
drawing, exhibited here, and his
etched portrait of Poe of 1859 (his
earliest work in this medium; cf. M.
Guérin: *L'Oeuvre gravé de Manet,*
Paris, 1944, no. 55) were both done
from a daguerreotype, probably for
this projected publication.

Literature: *Baudelaire,* exhibition catalogue, Petit Palais, Paris, 1968-69, no. 237.

Franky Magniada

French, fl. 1848-1865.
In 1848 Magniada unsuccessfully submitted designs for the French Republican coinage. His name appears on medals of the composer Jean-François Le Sueur (1852), the poet Jean-Pierre Béranger (1856), Garibaldi (1859), and Abraham Lincoln (see below). Nothing else is known about him; but the subjects of his medals suggest republican sympathies.

Franky Magniada

332 *Medal Commemorating the Death of Abraham Lincoln*

Bronze. 1866. Signed: *Franky Magniada.* Diameter 3¼ inches (83 mm.). Inscriptions: Obverse, *Dédié par la démocratie française a Lincoln Président deux fois élu des Etats-Unis;* reverse, *Lincoln l'honnête homme / abolit l'esclavage rétablit l'Union / sauva la République / sans voiler la statue de la liberté / il fut assassiné le 14 avril 1865* and *Liberté . Egalité . Fraternité.*
New York, private collection.

This is a bronze version of the gold medal struck to commemorate the death of Abraham Lincoln and sent to his widow. The obverse shows Lincoln's head surrounded by an inscription stating that the medal was dedicated to him by "French Democracy." On the reverse a sarcophagus is inscribed: "Lincoln, the honest man, abolished slavery, re-established the Union, saved the Republic without veiling the statue of liberty, he was assassinated 14th April 1865." Above it there is the eagle and shield of the United States, below, the motto of the first French Republic—liberty, equality, fraternity. A winged figure of Hope with an anchor and laurel wreath stands on one side of the sarcophagus, a steam-ship in the background behind her. On the right side a black youth

holds a book in one hand and a quill in the other, while a black man with a rifle points to the American emblem: beside them there is a ballot box marked *vote* and in the distance a railroad steam engine. The design thus refers to the achievements of Lincoln, the new dawn of liberty for the former slaves, and material progress. But it had an additional significance in France, where, under Napoleon III, democracy was curbed, and liberty, equality, and fraternity were no more than memories of the past. Thus the figure of hope seems to refer to the future of France as well as the United States.

Soon after Lincoln's death a proposal to strike a gold medal in his honour, for presentation to his widow, was announced in a French newspaper, *Phare de la Loire.* A public subscription was opened, but the funds were confiscated and the list of supporters destroyed by the agents of Napoleon III, who recognised the sub-

versive ulterior motive of the scheme. The gold medal was finally struck in Switzerland, smuggled into France, and transmitted to Mrs. Lincoln by way of the American Embassy in 1866. With it went a letter signed by twenty-six leading French Republicans, including Jules Michelet, Louis Blanc, and Victor Hugo. It is no coincidence that also in 1865 a group of French Republicans first mooted the idea of erecting a Franco-American monument to the independence of the United States, to be realised in the Statue of Liberty, set up in New York harbour in 1886. The Lincoln medal was, indeed, the forerunner of this vast monument to French and American ideals of liberty.

Literature: L. M. Case and W. F. Spencer: *The U.S. and France: Civil War Diplomacy,* Philadelphia, 1970, pp. 575-576; M. Trachtenberg: *The Statue of Liberty,* London and New York, 1976, pp. 27-28.

Frank Buchser
Swiss, 1828-1890.

333 *Landscape near Fort Laramie*
Oil on canvas. 1866 (4 September). 6¾ x 17¹⁄₁₆ inches (17 x 43.3 cm.). Inscription: In artist's hand—*4 Sept. from fort big Laramie.* Provenance: Inherited by the artist's brother Dr. Josef Buchser, who gave it to the Museum, 1896.
Basel, Offentliche Kunstmuseum.

This is one of the several sketches made by Buchser on his tour of the Great Plains [303, 304]. Two days later he made a drawing inscribed: *On Laramie Plaines 6 Sept. 66. The rocky mountains in the distance.* (Offentliche Kupferstichkabinett, Basel. BU.48.1866 f. 18.) On other drawings made in the same months, he wrote notes describing the brilliant colouring of the landscape at this time of year.

Literature: H. Lüdeke: *Frank Buchsers amerikanische Sendung,* Basel, 1941, p. 31.

Frank Buchser

334 *A Sacred Nook in Virginia*
Oil on canvas. 1867. Signed: *F.B.*
21 x 30¹³⁄₁₆ inches (53 x 78 cm.).
Provenance: Prof. K. Kottmann, 1941.
Selzach, Collection of Josef B. Gisiger.

This is one of a group of paintings of
woodland scenes near Laurel Creek
made by Buchser in July 1867, while
he and a female friend were staying at
Piedmont, West Virginia. They include
a *plein air* oil sketch of a woman
seated with a book by a woodland
stream (Offentliche Kupferstichkabinett, Basel, 1896.66.163) and two
highly finished views of streams similar to that in the painting exhibited,
one with a fisherman (Kunsthaus,
Zurich), the other with a nude black
girl (Museum der Stadt, Solothurn).

Literature: H. Lüdeke: *Frank Buchsers
amerikanische Sendung*, pp. 50-52; *Frank
Buchser 1828-1890*, exhibition catalogue,
Kunstsammlung der Stadt Thun, Thunerhof, 1967, no. 76.

Frank Buchser

335 *William H. Seward in His Garden*
Oil on canvas. 1869. 17⅛ x 13⁵⁄₁₆
inches (43.5 x 34 cm.). Provenance:
Inherited by the artist's brother Dr.
Josef Buchser, who gave it to the
Museum, 1896.
Basel, Offentliche Kunstmuseum.
Colorplate 8.

William H. Seward, who had been
made secretary of state by Lincoln in
1861 and confirmed in the office by
Andrew Johnson, was one of the first
leading political figures Buchser met
on his arrival in Washington in 1869.
After he had retired from public life
early in 1869, Seward invited Buchser
to stay at his home in Auburn, in order
to paint portraits of him and members
of his family. Buchser described him
as "a cunning old fox; politician that
he is, and one of the greatest in the
land, he is also small in many respects"
—especially so far as paying for works
of art was concerned. In addition to

the sketch exhibited—one of the works
in which he came closest to the French
Impressionists—Buchser painted a formal portrait of Seward (also in the
Basel museum) "für la patrie at
home," as he wrote in his diary. He
also portrayed Seward's wife, son, and
daughter-in-law.

Literature: H. Lüdeke: *Frank Buchsers
amerikanische Sendung*, Basel, 1941, pp.
77-78; Frank Buchser: *Mein Leben und
Streben in Amerika*, ed. G. Wälchli,
Zurich-Leipzig, 1942, p. 61; *Frank Buchser
1828-1890*, exhibition catalogue, Kunstsammlung der Stadt Thun, Thunerhof,
1967, no. 84.

Frank Buchser

336 *Robert E. Lee*
Oil on canvas. Signed and dated:
*Frank Buchser / Lexington Va. / Oct.
18. 1869.* 54⅜ x 40½ inches (137.8 x
102.7 cm.). Provenance: Given by the
artist to the Swiss Federal Council,
May 1870 and deposited at the Museum, 1924.
Bern, Schweizerische Eigenossenschaft,
on loan to the Kunstmuseum.

This is the best of Buchser's formal
portraits and one of the most memorable likenesses of the Confederate general. Buchser had gone to America in
1866 with the intention of painting a
large picture celebrating the end of the
Civil War, but he seems gradually to
have abandoned this project and substituted for it a series of portraits.
Early in 1869 he painted that of William Sherman, and on 25 September
1869 he went to Lexington to paint
that of Robert E. Lee, which he completed on 18 October. (Several of his
preliminary pencil sketches for it are
in the Offentliche Kupferstichkabinett,
Basel, BU.60.1869.) Although Buchser's sympathies were with the Union,
he developed great admiration for Lee,
who spoke to him of the war while he

was sitting for the portrait. "Lee never uttered one spiteful word against anybody," Buchser wrote in his diary. "One cannot see and know this great soldier without loving him." It was Lee's wish that he should be painted in civilian clothes. "I am no longer a soldier and it is time to put the pomp and circumstance of war aside," he remarked to Buchser. Thus, the uniform is symbolically laid on the table, and the portrait makes a striking contrast with that of Sherman, who is shown in action at Atlanta.

The portrait of Lee was exhibited in November 1869 at Smith and Strong's art gallery in F. Street, Washington, and praised by a writer in the *National Republican* of 22 November 1869 for its "calm, imposing dignified expression." (From the artist's collection of press cuttings, Museum der Stadt, Solothurn.) In May next year Buchser sent it and the portrait of Sherman to

Bern, expressing the hope that they would be hung in the parliament house as a "symbol of our friendship with the people of America"—and implying that he would appreciate some financial compensation to defray the cost of his journey. In his letter to the Bundesrat he remarked that the portrait of Sherman needed no comment; "his name will never be forgotten." But he explained that sending that of Lee as a pendant "should not surprise you, he

is a greater character and now that the hatred against the South has declined he may soon sit in the Senate, and he is furthermore the ideal of American democracy."

Literature: Jules Coulin: *Der Maler Frank Buchser*, Basel, 1912, p. 43; *Frank Buchser*, exhibition catalogue, Kunsthalle, Bern, 1928, no. 47; W. Uberwasser: *Frank Buchser. Der Maler*, Basel and Olten, 1940, p. 41; G. Wälchli: *Frank Buchser, Leben und Werk*, Zurich and Leipzig, 1941, p. 146; H. Lüdeke: *Frank Buchsers amerikanische Sendung*, pp. 82-90; Frank Buchser: *Mein Leben und Streben in Amerika*, ed. G. Wälchli, Zurich-Leipzig, 1942, pp. 64-68; *Frank Buchser 1828-1890*, exhibition catalogue, Kunstsammlung der Stadt Thun, Thunerhof, 1967, no. 86; *This New Man, A Discourse in Portraits*, exhibition catalogue, National Portrait Gallery, Washington, D.C., 1968, p. 93.

Jean-Julien Deltil

French, 1791-1863.
Deltil was born in Paris, trained at the Ecole des Beaux Arts under Jean-Baptiste Debret, and began to exhibit at the Salon in 1812. His paintings included landscapes, portraits, and religious subjects. But he is best known for the scenic wallpapers printed after his designs, notably *Vues de la Grèce moderne*, with incidents from the War of Independence (1817), *Les Grandes Chasses* (1831), and *Vues de L'Amérique du Nord* or *Scenic America* (1834; see below).

Jean-Julien Deltil (after)

337 Boston Harbour
Wallpaper printed in distemper colours from wood blocks. 1834. 144 x 162 inches (366 x 411.5 cm.) as printed (reduced in height for exhibition). Purchased for *The European Vision of America* from A. L. Diament and Company, New York, Philadelphia, Chicago.

This view of Boston Harbour and an Indian calumet dance forms part of the set of scenic wallpapers *Vues de L'Amérique du Nord* first printed at Rixheim, near Mulhouse in Alsaca, in 1834 by the firm of Jean Zuber et Cie. The publisher's description declared: "Thanks to its beautiful buildings, and, above all, to its most recent importance in trade, Boston is now the second city in the Union. Its harbour, frequented by vessels from all over the world bristles with steam-boats; the landing scene in the foreground and the bustle on the wharfs give an idea of the maritime activity of the city, whose ships ply the oceans of the world." When all the sheets of paper are assembled to form a panorama, the group of Winnebago Indians performing a calumet dance on the right is associated with a view of the natural bridge in Virginia, which merges into a prospect of Niagara, followed by New York harbour and West Point, with a military parade in progress. The paper seems to have been printed mainly for export to America, where such scenic wallpapers were very popular. Another series issued by Zuber in 1836 illustrated incidents from the American Revolution.

The wood blocks from which *Vues de l'Amérique du Nord* were printed are still being used by Zuber, for the hand-printed production of this paper. The scene exhibited here was recently produced in this manner and acquired from A. L. Diament and Company of New York, Philadelphia, and Chicago.

Charles Meryon

French, 1821-1868.
Born in Paris, the son of an English doctor and a ballet dancer at the Opéra, Meryon served in the French navy from 1839 to 1847 and went round the world (1842-46), though without touching North America. He then studied painting and later etching and from 1850 began to make prints of views of Paris. In 1858 he was admitted to the asylum at Charenton and was finally confined there from 1866 until his death.

Charles Meryon

338 San Francisco
Etching and drypoint. Signed and dated: *C. Meryon del sculp. Paris, 1856* and, lower right margin, *A. Delatre imp. Rue Fbg Poissonière 145.* 13 5/16 x 40¾ inches (33.7 x 103.5 cm.). Provenance: Mrs. Albert H. Wolf. Chicago, The Art Institute of Chicago, The Albert H. Wolf Memorial Collection.

This panoramic view of San Francisco was commissioned by François-Alfred Pioche and Jules B. Bayerque, two French real estate speculators there. Their portraits are in medallions, with allegorical figures of Abundance and Work, above the title. Meryon never went to San Francisco. He worked from photographs (daguerreotypes), as he explained to his father:

> The materials on which I had to work consisted of *un panorama Daguerre* on plates, composed of five little square views, made successively, possibly on the same day, at different hours in any case, since one end-piece was lighted from one side, whereas the other was lighted from the opposite side. Thus, to avoid the fatigue that results from the glare on the plates, they had the kindness to give me also some partial views recorded on paper.

The original daguerreotypes are lost, but paper albumen prints from collodion negatives made from them belong to The Art Institute of Chicago. They show a view from Russian Hill to Rincon Hill, with Alcatraz Island on the left and Yerba Buena Island in the centre. Meryon spent over a year on this etching and made many sketches and other preliminary drawings, some of which survive, including the final master drawing from which the print was made (The Art Institute of Chicago and The Sterling and Francine Clark Art Institute, Williamstown, Mass.).

During the year Meryon worked on this etching, he suffered the initial bout of serious mental illness which culminated in his admission to the Asylum at Charenton in May 1858. He had intended to introduce some disturbing imagery into the print, as he wrote in 1863: "At the time when I executed this print, I had the idea, to avoid the break in continuity that exists in the center, to represent there fire, with flames and smoke reaching toward the sky, and birds of prey whirling above; but rushed as I was, I was not able to carry out this idea."

Literature: Lloyd L. Rollins: "Charles Meryon and His 'Vue de San Francisco' " in the *Quarterly of the Society of California Pioneers*, IX, no. 2 (1932), pp. 97-107; O. J. Rothrock: "The San Francisco of Alfred Pioche and Charles Meryon" in the *Princeton University Library Chronicle* (1973), pp. 1-25; James D. Burke: *Charles Meryon. Prints and Drawings,* exhibition catalogue, Toledo Museum of Art and elsewhere, 1974-1975, pp. 100-103.

Ernest Narjot

French-American, 1826-1898.
Narjot was born in Brittany and is said to have left France to go to America at the time of the Gold Rush. His earliest American painting, a mining scene, is dated 1851 (formerly with Messrs. Edward Eberstadt & Sons). He also painted Indian subjects. But very little is known of his career.

Ernest Narjot

339 Gold Rush Camp
Oil on canvas. Signed and dated: *L. E. Narjot 1882.* 41 x 51 inches (104.1 x 129.5 cm.). Provenance: Hirschl & Adler Gallery, 1966.
Los Angeles, The Los Angeles Athletic Club.

This highly idealised view of life among the gold miners in California was painted long after the Gold Rush had reached its peak. It began in 1848, but subsequent discoveries of gold in South Dakota and Idaho in the 1870s and in Canada (the Yukon) in 1898 kept the Gold Rush mythology alive. It was most notably commemorated in David Belasco's play *The Girl of the Golden West* and the opera made from it by Giacomo Puccini in 1910.

Literature: P. Hills: *The American Frontier: Images and Myths,* exhibition catalogue, Whitney Museum of American Art, New York, 1973, no. 47.

Photograph Credits

Fratelli Alinari, Florence—124; Kenneth Berry Studios, Hull—316; E^{ts} J. E. Bulloz, Paris—311; Barney Burstein, Boston—300; Ellebé, Rouen—8; Fico and Winograd, Cranston, R.I.—215; Hans Hinz, Basel—333, 335; Scott Hyde, New York—113, 120, 146, 176; F. La Haye, Maastricht—6; E. Le Grand, Quimper—139; Studio Meusy, Besançon—265, 290, 291; Tom Scott, Edinburgh—314; Service de documentation photographique de la Réunion des musées nationaux, Paris—51, 76, 114-117, 130, 133, 175, 182, 209-212, 217, 226, 267, 268, 271, 272, 275, 279, 280, 302, 307, 317, 319; Walter Steinkopf, Berlin—71-73; Toso, Venice—152; Nigel Trow, Willington, Derbyshire—184; Liselotte Witzel, Essen—284.

With the exception of the items listed above, photographs were supplied by the lender.

List of Lenders

Rijksmuseum, Amsterdam—83
Dr. Willem J. Russell, Amsterdam—77
William L. Clements Library, University of Michigan, Ann Arbor—57, 58
The University of Michigan Museum of Art—89
Museum Plantin-Moretus, Antwerp—35
Stedelijk Prentenkabinet, Antwerp—88
Städtische Kunstsammlungen Augsburg-Deutsche Barockgalerie—137
The Walters Art Gallery, Baltimore—127
Kunstmuseum Basel—303, 320, 333, 335
Ibero-Amerikanisches Institut Preussischer Kulturbesitz, Berlin—252, 255
Staatliche Museen Preussischer Kulturbesitz, Berlin—71-73
Kunstmuseum Bern—336
Musée de Besançon—265, 290, 291
Musée National de la Coopération Franco-Américaine, Château de Blérancourt—182, 209, 217, 226, 271, 302, 319
The Trustees of the Public Library of the City of Boston—159, 230, 237
R. M. Light & Co., Inc., Boston—300
Museum of Fine Arts, Boston—191, 315
The Brooklyn Museum—118, 147, 246
Artemis S.A., Brussels—195-199
The Harvard College Library (The Houghton Library), Cambridge—25, 69
Peabody Museum of Archaeology and Ethnology, Harvard University, Cambridge—169, 173, 178, 179
Mr. A. Ledyard Smith Collection, Cambridge—260
Middleton Place, Charleston—42, 43
Devonshire Collection, Chatsworth, Derbyshire—99
The Art Institute of Chicago—155, 338
The John Crerar Library, Chicago—243
The Newberry Library, Chicago—158
The Cincinnati Art Museum, Cincinnati—325
Public Library of Cincinnati and Hamilton County—276
Case Western Reserve University, Cleveland—329
Cleveland Medical Library Association—27-29, 36-38
The Cleveland Museum of Art—204
Cleveland Museum of Natural History Library—242
Cleveland Public Library—62, 310, 328
The Western Reserve Historical Society, Cleveland—70
Ohio State University Libraries, Columbus—247, 248, 257
Danish National Museum, Copenhagen—74, 75
Royal Museum of Fine Arts, Copenhagen—84, 308
Derby Museums and Art Gallery, Derbyshire—184
The Detroit Institute of Arts—80, 193
Grünes Gewölbe Dresden—110
Edinburgh University Library—15
Museum Volkwang Essen—284
The Lewis Walpole Library, Farmington—227, 228, 238, 239
Biblioteca Marucelliana, Florence—97
Galleria d'Arte Moderna, Florence—282
Amon Carter Museum of Western Art, Fort Worth—295, 297A-E
Jean-Pierre Durand, Geneva—298

379

Index

Italicized numerals refer to the catalog entries; numerals in roman type refer to page numbers for the division essays.